Scott Foresman - Addison Wesley

Practice Masters

Grade 3

Scott Foresman - Addison Wesley

Editorial Offices: Menlo Park, California • Glenview, Illinois
Sales Offices: Reading, Massachusetts • Atlanta, Georgia • Glenview, Illinois
Carrollton, Texas • Menlo Park, California

http://www.sf.aw.com

Overview

Practice Masters provide additional practice on the concept or concepts taught in each core lesson.

For Learn and Explore lessons, the masters provide additional exercises that reflect those in the Connect section and/or the Skills and Reasoning section of the student edition Practice sets.

For Problem Solving lessons, the masters closely mirror the Problem Solving Practice sets in the student edition.

The *Practice Masters* also include Section Reviews that supplement the Section Review pages in the student edition. These Section Review masters also provide Mixed Review problems (from previous sections of the student edition). Cumulative Review masters are included at the end of each chapter to provide a comprehensive review of skills covered up through that chapter.

ISBN 0-201-31235-2

Printed in the United States of America

4 5 6 7 8 9 10 – BW – 02 01 00 99 98

Contents

Name ______________________________

Reading Pictographs

Use the pictograph to answer each question.

Sleepy Animals

Animal	Average Hours of Sleep a Day
Armadillo	
Cat	
Hamster	
Koala	
Lemur	
Opossum	
Pig	
Sloth	
Spiny anteater	
Squirrel	

= 2 hours of sleep

1. Which animal sleeps the most? ______________
2. Which two animals get the same amount of sleep each day.

   ____
3. Which animal sleeps 16 hours per day? ______________
4. How many more hours per day does a koala sleep than a pig? ______________
5. How many animals sleep more than 12 hours? ______________
6. Which animal sleeps exactly 12 hours? ______________
7. Which animal sleeps the least? ______________
8. Suppose a dog sleeps 6 hours per day. How many symbols would the dog have? ______________

Name ________________________________

Practice 1-2

Reading Bar Graphs

Use the bar graph to answer each question.

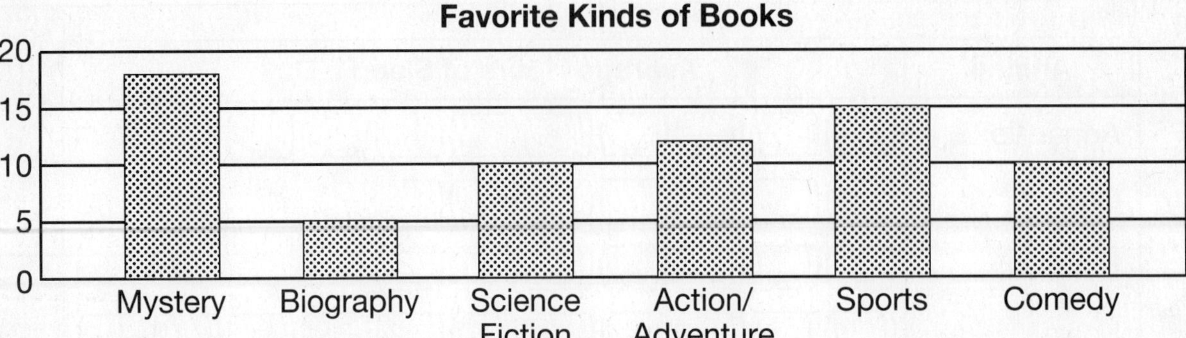

1. How many people chose sports books as their favorite? ____________

2. Which kind of book is the favorite of all? ____________

3. Which kind of book is the least favorite? ____________

4. Do more people like sports books or science fiction books? Explain.

____

____

5. Which kind of book has 12 votes? ____________

6. Which two kinds of books have the same number of votes?

____

7. Which kinds of book have over 13 votes?

____

8. Which kinds of books have less then 12 votes?

____

9. If 5 more people chose comedies as their favorite books, which kind of book would be the favorite of all?

____

10. If you voted, which kind of book would you vote for?

____

Name ______________________

Practice 1-3

Reading Line Graphs

Use the line graph to answer each question.

A hot tub holds many gallons of water. Cold water is put into the tub and warmed slowly. This graph shows how long it will take for water to reach 100 degrees. You don't want the water in a hot tub much warmer than 100 degrees or it would be too hot.

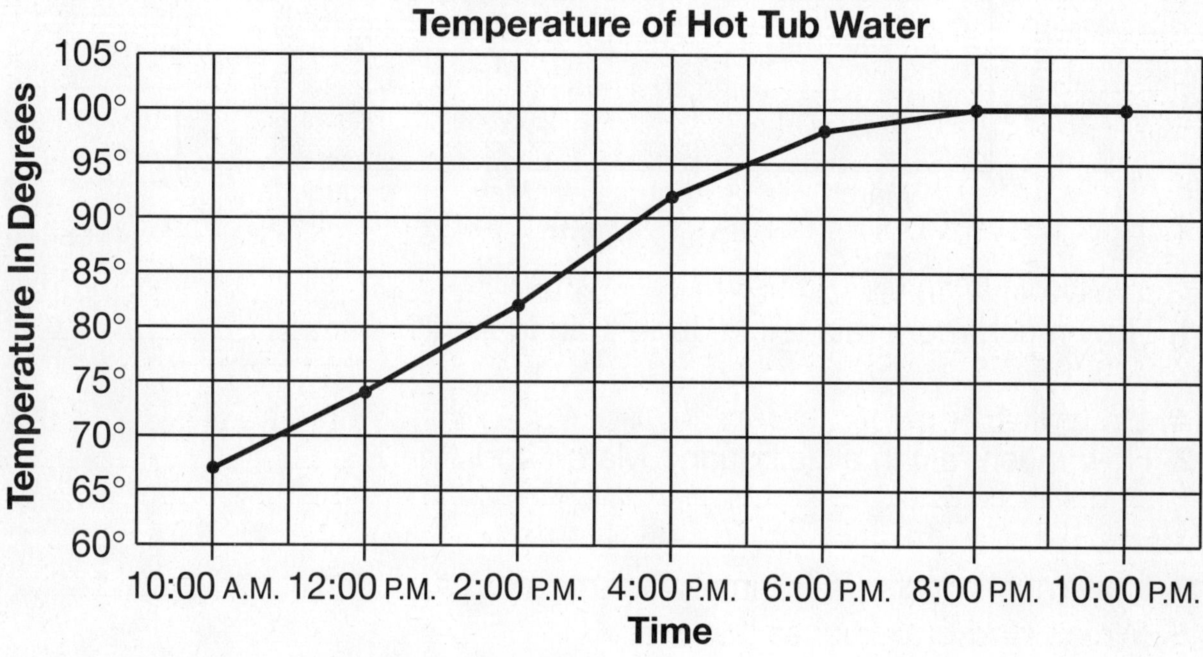

1. How hot was the water at 10:00 A.M.? ______
2. At what time was the water about 74°? ______
3. How many degrees did the water change between 10:00 A.M. and 12:00 P.M.? ______
4. How many degrees did the water change between 12:00 P.M. and 2:00 P.M.? ______
5. At what time was the water about 92°? ______
6. When did the water reach 100°? ______
7. What happened to the temperature of the water between 8:00 P.M. and 10:00 P.M.? ______

Name ______________________

Practice 1-4

Analyze Word Problems: Introduction to Problem Solving

Plan how you will solve each problem. Then solve.

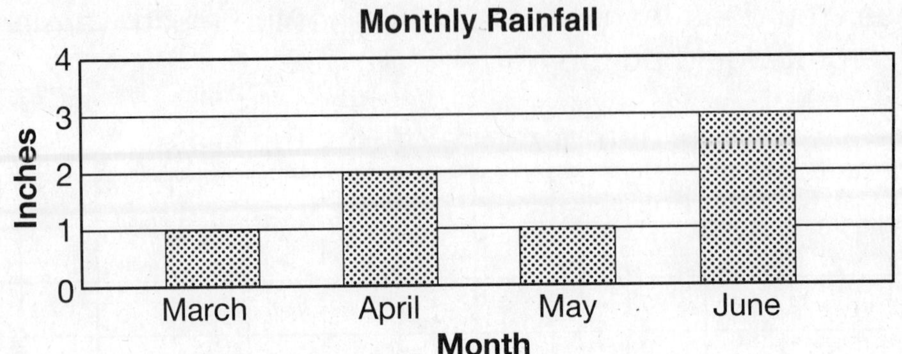

1. How much more rain fell in June than in April? ______

2. How much rain in all fell during March and April? ______

3. How much total rain fell in all four months? ______

4. If there was 2 inches more rain in July than there was in April, how much rain was there in July? ______

5. Which 2 months combined had the same amount of rainfall as there was in April? ______

6. Which month had twice as much rain as March? ______

7. Which month had three times as much rain as March? ______

Name ______________________

Practice 1-5

Analyze Word Problems: Choose an Operation

Choose the number sentence you would use to solve. Explain.

1. Sam owns 3 lizards and 2 cats. How many pets does Sam own?

a. $3 + 2 = 5$ **b.** $3 - 2 = 1$

____

____

2. Lisa moved 9 boxes. On Monday, she unpacked 5 boxes. How many more boxes are left to unpack?

a. $9 + 5 = 14$ **b.** $9 - 5 = 4$

____

3. Tony baked 4 dozen muffins in the morning and 3 dozen more in the afternoon. How many dozen muffins did he bake in one day?

a. $4 + 3 = 7$ **b.** $4 - 3 = 1$

____

Write which operation you would use. Then solve.

4. Sarah bought 10 cherries on Saturday. On Sunday, she ate 5. How many cherries does she have now?

____

5. Francis bought 7 cans of beans and 6 cans of corn. How many cans did he buy?

____

6. Judy is in a 10-kilometer road race. She has run 6 kilometers already. How many more kilometers will she run?

____

Name ______________________________

Practice
1-6

Exploring Algebra: What's the Rule?

1. A rule describes what to do to the **In** number to get the **Out** number. What is the rule? ____________

In	8	9	10	11	12	13
Out	5	6	7	8	9	10

Complete each table. Write the rule for each.

2.

In	4	6	2	5	10	8
Out	8	10	6			

Rule: ______________________

3.

In	8	4	3	5	11	6
Out	6	2	1			

Rule: ______________________

4.

In	10	7	6	4	12	3
Out	15	12	11			

Rule: ______________________

5.

In	9	11	8	4	6	7
Out	5	7	4			

Rule: ______________________

Name ___________________________

Review and Practice

(Lesson 1) Use the pictograph to answer each question.

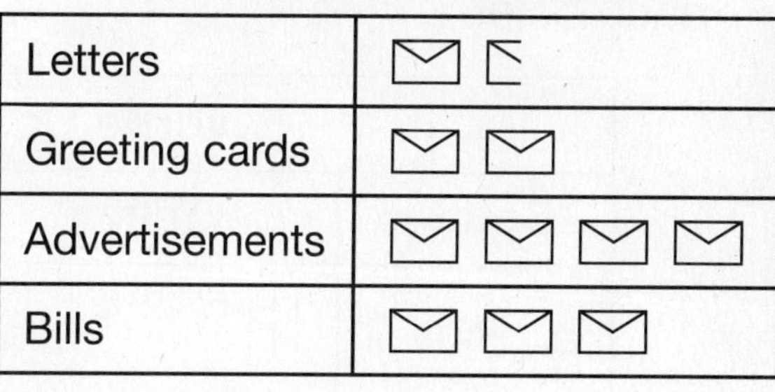

Mail Received This Month
Letters
Greeting cards
Advertisements
Bills
= 4 items of mail

1. How many letters were received?

____

2. Which type of mail was received the most? ___________________

3. How many symbols would there be if 20 greeting cards were received? ___________________

(Lesson 2) Use the bar graph to answer each question.

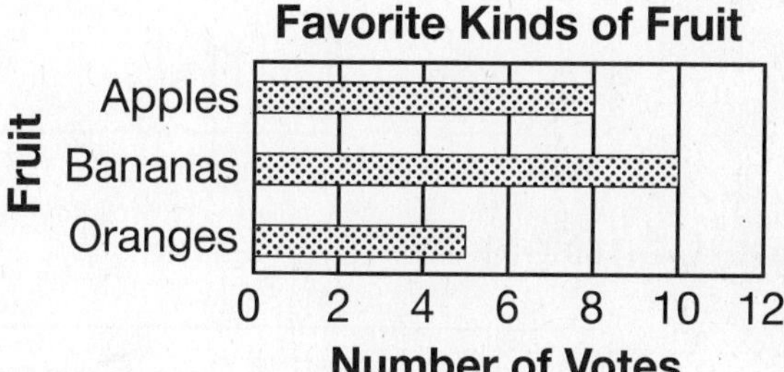

4. Which fruit was the least favorite?

____

5. Which fruit did 10 people vote for?

____

6. How many more voted for apples than oranges? _____________

(Lesson 3) Use the line graph to answer each question.

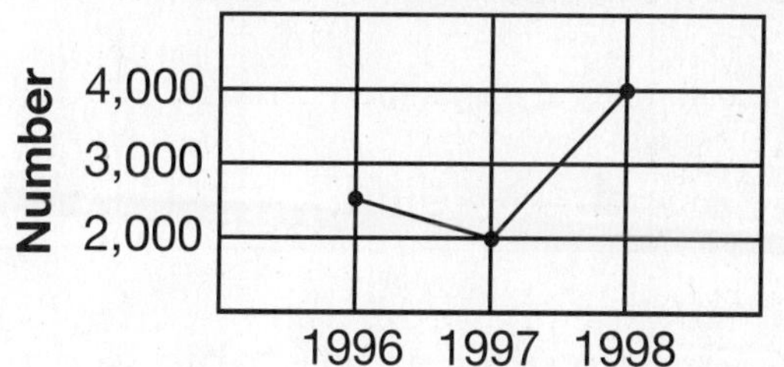

7. In what year were the most books checked out? _________

8. In what year were only 2,000 books checked out? _________

(Lesson 5) Tell which operation you would use. Then solve.

9. There are 12 boys in the class. 8 have brown eyes. How many do not have brown eyes? ___________________

(Mixed Review) Add or subtract.

10. 6 + 9 = _______ **11.** 8 − 6 = _______ **12.** 7 + 7 = _______

Name ______________________________

Exploring Organizing Data

1. This tally table shows students' votes for their favorite colors. Write the number of students who voted for each color.

Favorite Colors		
Color	**Tally**	**Number**
a. Blue	卌	
b. Purple	卌 ||||	
c. Red	|	
d. Green	卌	
e. Yellow	卌 |	

2. Complete the tally table.

Our Favorite After-School Activities		
Activity	**Tally**	**Number**
a. Bike Riding	|||	
b. Crafts	卌	
c. Sports	卌 ||	
d. Reading	||||	

3. Explain why a tally table is a useful way to present survey results.

____

____

Name ______________________________

Practice 1-8

Exploring Making Pictographs

Here are two different ways to show data using a pictograph.

Francie's Way

Foods We Like to Eat

Tacos	✻ ✻ ✻ ✻ ✻
Hot dogs	✻ ✻ ✻ (half ✻)
Salad	✻ ✻
Pasta	✻

✻ = 10 votes

Chuck's Way

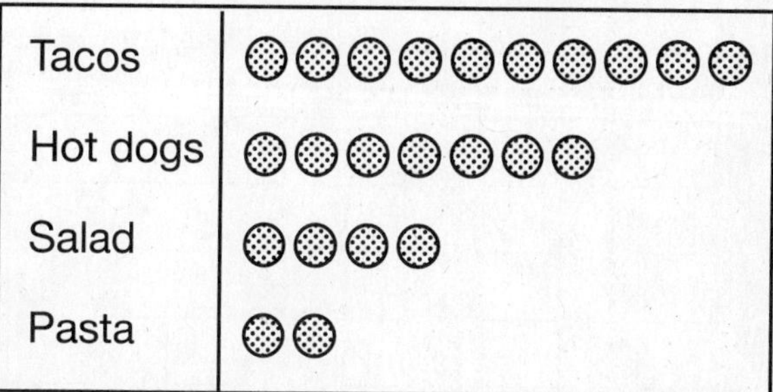

◍ = 5 votes

1. Describe one difference between the 2 pictographs.

____

2. Students like to study in different places. Complete the pictograph. Use the data in the table.

Where Students Like to Study

Library	𝍸 I
At a desk	𝍸 𝍸 𝍸 I
On the bed	𝍸 III
On the floor	𝍸 𝍸
Other	𝍸 𝍸 II

Where Students Like to Study

Library	■ ■ ■
At a desk	
On the bed	
On the floor	
Other	

■ = 2 students

3. Suppose each symbol in the pictograph above represented 3 students. How many symbols would there be for "Other"? ____________

Name ________________________

Practice 1-9

Exploring Making Bar Graphs

Here are two bar graphs that show the same data.

Brianna's Way

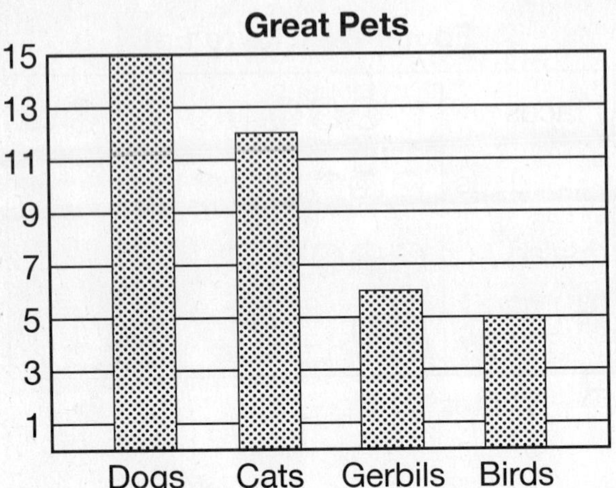

Elijah's Way

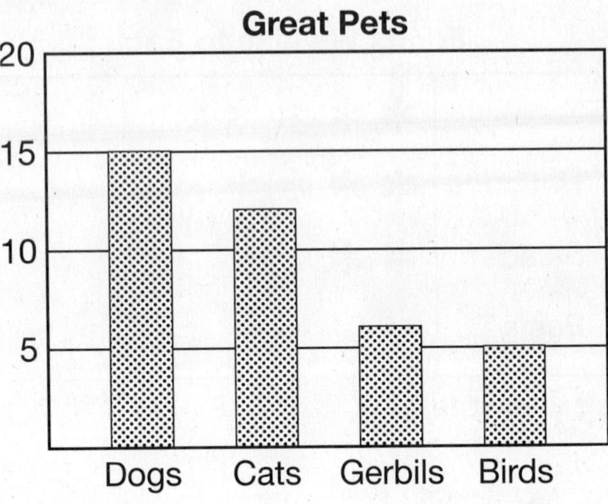

1. Describe how the bar graphs are different.

____

Use the data in the table to complete the bar graph.

Day	Number of Books Sold
Monday	6
Tuesday	9
Wednesday	3
Thursday	12
Friday	9

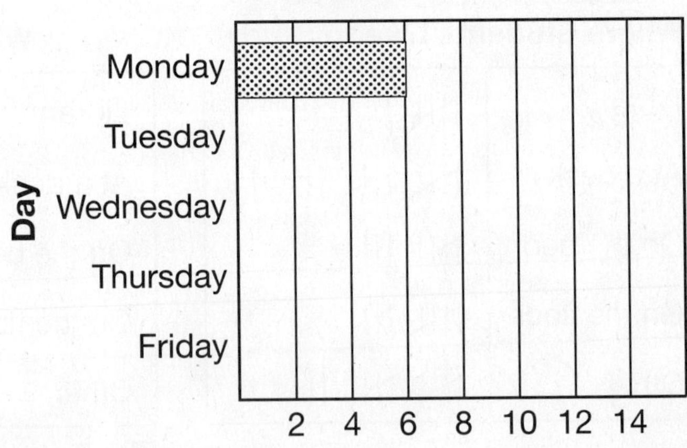

2. Complete the bar graph.

3. How many more books were sold on Tuesday than Monday? ________

4. On what days were the same number of books sold?

____

5. How would you display this data in a pictograph?

____

Name ______________________________

Practice
1-10

Decision Making

Suppose the members of your class are collecting containers for recycling. The table shows the kind and number of containers collected.

Items Collected	
Aluminum cans	80
Milk containers	45
Soft drinks	65
Large glass	50
Small glass	15

1. Look at the data. Is the information best suited for a bar graph or a pictograph? Explain.

____

____

2. What would you title the graph?

____

3. Use the space provided to make a graph. If you make a pictograph, let each symbol show 10 containers. If you make a bar graph, make a scale by counting by 10s.

4. What if each symbol in your pictograph showed 5 containers? Or, what if you made your scale in your bar graph by counting by 5s? How would your graph be different?

____

____

____

____

Name ____________________

Practice 1-11

Analyze Strategies: Look for a Pattern

Look for a pattern to help you solve each problem.

1. If the pattern continues, which shape should come next? ________

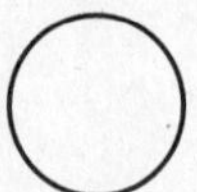 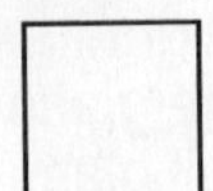 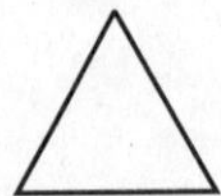 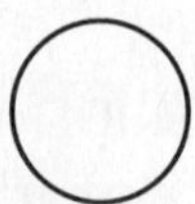 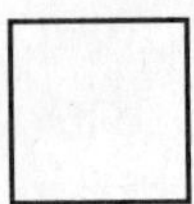 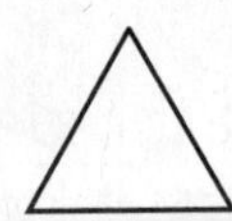 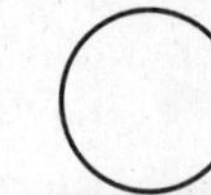

2. If the pattern continues, which shape should come next? ________

 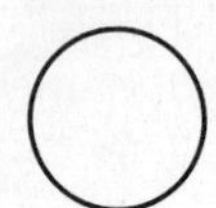 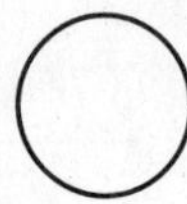  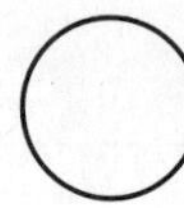 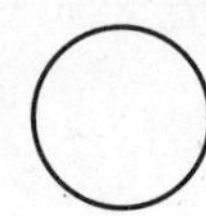 

3. What are the next 3 numbers?

2, 6, 10, 14, ______, ______, ______

4. What are the next 3 numbers?

10, 20, 30, 40, ______, ______, ______

5. Andrea says, "The next picture in this pattern should be a spoon." Do you agree or disagree? Explain.

____

Look for a pattern or use any strategy to help you solve each problem.

6. Members of the Sal Pal Club receive member cards with their member I.D. number. The first member's number is 111. The second member's number is 121. The third and fourth members' numbers are 131 and 141.

a. What I.D. numbers should be given to the next 2 members? ________

b. What two I.D. numbers could the tenth member receive that would still fit the pattern? Explain.

____

____

Name ______________________

Review and Practice

(Lesson 7) Complete the tally table.

1. Number of pets in the homes of Mr. Gregory's third grade class:

2, 1, 0, 2, 2, 0, 0, 1, 2, 1, 0, 0, 2, 1,

1, 2, 0, 0, 1, 1, 1, 1, 0

Pets	Tally	Number
0		
1		
2		

(Lesson 8) Use the data in the table. Complete the pictograph.

2.

My Favorite Flavor	
Peppermint	5
Chocolate	15
Butterscotch	7

My Favorite Flavor

Peppermint	
Chocolate	
Butterscotch	

Key = 2

(Lesson 9) Use the data in the table. Complete the bar graph.

3.

Warren's Reading Time	
Day of Week	**Minutes**
Monday	30
Tuesday	20
Wednesday	15
Thursday	35

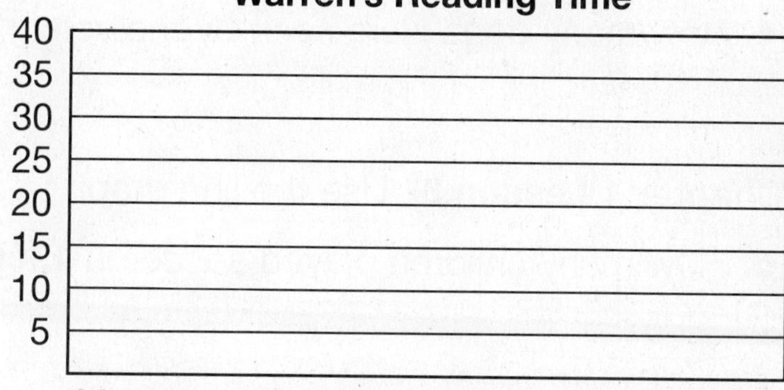

(Lesson 11) Solve. Use any strategy.

4. Leandra is learning to play the trombone. She increases her practice time by 3 minutes each day. Monday she practiced 8 minutes. How many minutes will she practice on Friday? ________

(Mixed Review) Add or subtract.

5. 6 + 9 = ________ **6.** 16 − 9 = ________ **7.** 5 + 8 = ________

Name ______________________________

Practice
Chapter 1

Cumulative Review

(Chapter 1 Lessons 1 and 8) Use the data to complete the pictograph.

1.

Number of Rooms in Home	
Marlene	5
Patrick	4
Lois	6

Number of Rooms in Home

Marlene	
Patrick	
Lois	

Key:
= 2 rooms

2. How many symbols would you use to represent 11 rooms? ______________

(Chapter 1 Lessons 2 and 9) Use the data to complete the bar graph.

3.

Dogs at Veterinarian's Office	
Day of Week	**Number of Dogs**
Monday	3
Tuesday	1
Wednesday	5

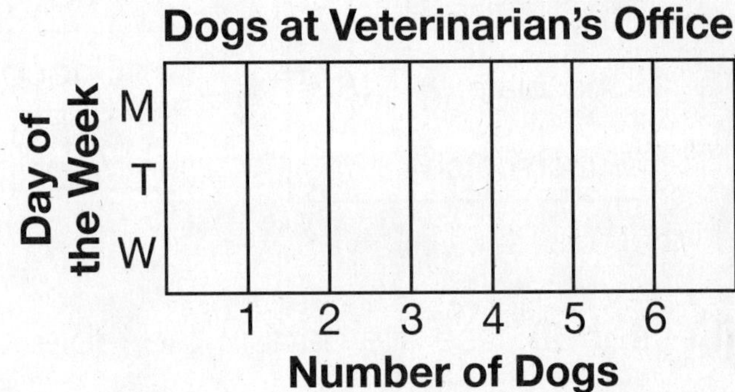

4. How many dogs were seen by the veterinarian on all three days?

____

(Chapter 1 Lesson 3) Use the line graph to answer the questions.

5. How many children played soccer in 1996?

____

6. Do you think the number of children playing soccer in 1999 will be greater than in 1998? Explain.

____

____

(Facts Review) Add or subtract.

7. $13 - 7 =$ __________

8. $6 + 8 =$ __________

9. $7 + 5 =$ __________

10. $7 - 4 =$ __________

Name ____________________

Place Value Through Hundreds

Write each number in standard form.

1. ________

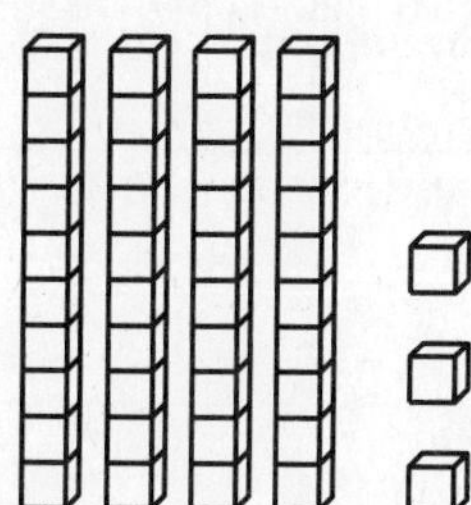

2. ________

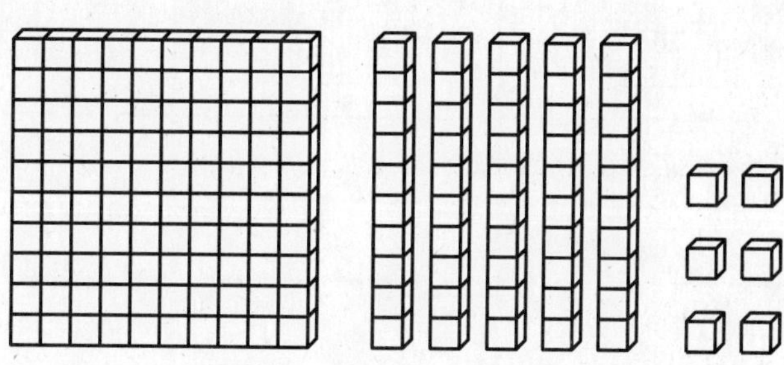

3. forty-nine ________
4. thirteen ________
5. 200 + 70 + 8 ________
6. 100 + 30 + 2 ________
7. 300 + 30 ________
8. sixty-five ________
9. 200 + 2 ________
10. 500 + 40 + 5 ________
11. two hundred sixty-two ________
12. three hundred forty-seven ________

Write the word name for each number.

13. 93 ____________________
14. 348 ____________________
15. 102 ____________________
16. 56 ____________________
17. 210 ____________________
18. 312 ____________________
19. 452 ____________________
20. 205 ____________________

21. In the number 349, which digit has the least value? Explain.

____

22. To write the number three hundred ten, do you need a 0? Explain.

____

23. Write the numbers five hundred ten and five hundred one.

____

Name ________________________________

Practice
2-2

Exploring Place-Value Relationships

Complete.

1.	standard form ____ , 000			
2.	word form ______ thousand			
3.	3 thousands = ____ hundreds	4 hundreds = ____ tens	16 tens = ____ hundred, ____ tens	17 ones = ____ ten, ____ ones

Write each number in standard form.

4. __________

5. __________

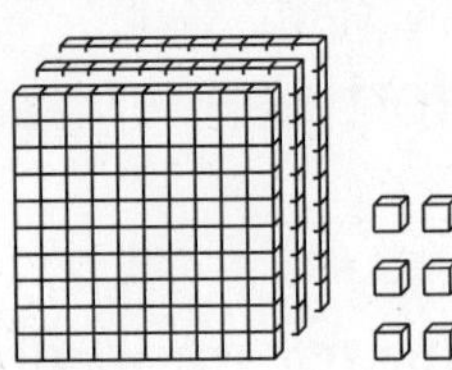

Complete the table.

	Number	Number of Ones	Number of Tens	Number of Hundreds
6.	100	100		
7.	700			7
8.	400		40	
9.	1,000	1,000		

10. How many ways can you write 600? Write them.

____

11. How many ways can you write 5,000? Write them.

____

Name ______________________________

Practice
2-3

Place Value Through Thousands

Write each number in standard form.

1. __________

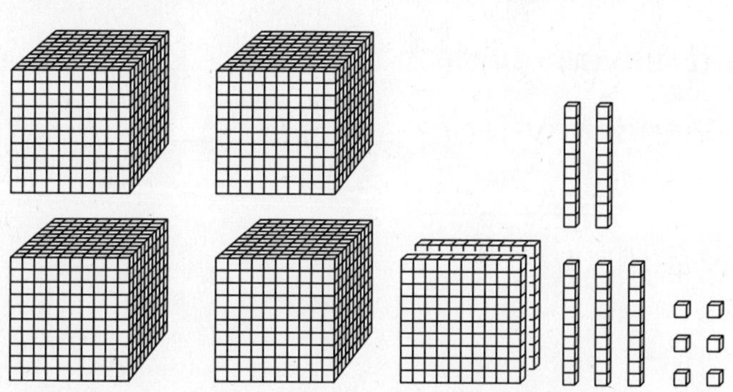

2. __________

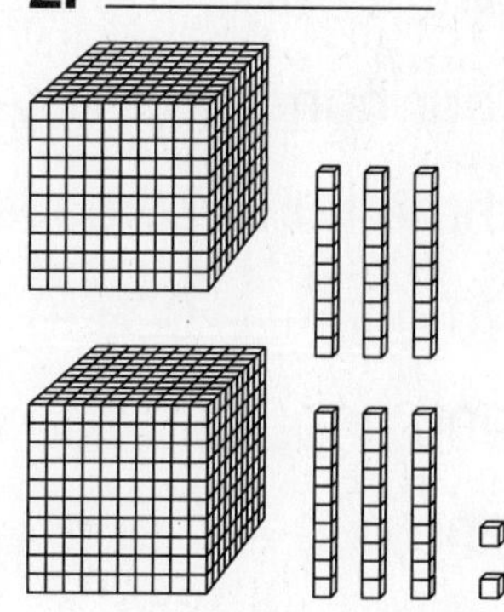

3. three thousand, four hundred seventeen __________

4. six thousand, seven hundred thirty-eight __________

5. 2,000 + 60 + 8 __________

6. 7,000 + 100 + 40 + 5 __________

Write the word name for each number.

7. 393 ______________________________

8. 9,463 ______________________________

9. 6,795 ______________________________

Complete the table.

	Number	100 More	100 Less
10.	2,612		
11.	3,911		
12.	6,208		

13. Is 27 hundreds the same as 27 tens? Explain.

____

14. Is 100 the same as 10 ones or 10 tens? __________

15. Choose a number greater than 1,000 and write it 3 ways.

____

Name ______________________

Practice 2-4

Place Value Through Hundred Thousands

Write each number in standard form.

1. twenty-nine thousand, five hundred sixteen ____________

2. four hundred thirty-five thousand, seven hundred eight ____________

3. three hundred seventy-two thousand, fifty-four ____________

4. 20,000 + 9,000 + 700 + 80 + 1 ____________

5. 900,000 + 50,000 + 1,000 + 70 + 5 ____________

6. 700,000 + 2,000 + 400 + 80 + 2 ____________

Write the value of each underlined digit.

7. $\underline{2}$3,045 ____________

8. 5$\underline{6}$2,021 ____________

9. $\underline{8}$03,096 ____________

10. 451,3$\underline{8}$2 ____________

11. 12,$\underline{5}$38 ____________

12. 837,03$\underline{6}$ ____________

13. 34,$\underline{7}$89 ____________

14. 8$\underline{9}$,123 ____________

15. $\underline{3}$24,598 ____________

16. 4$\underline{7}$8,654 ____________

17. Which digit has the least value in 34,187? Explain.

____

____

18. How many thousands is 100,000? How many ten thousands?

____

19. Using the digits 2, 4, and 6, write a number with a 4 in the hundred thousands place and a 2 in the hundreds place.

____

20. Using the digits 1, 3, and 5 only once, write the greatest and least three-digit numbers you can.

____

Name ______________________________

Analyze Strategies: Make an Organized List

Make a list or use any strategy to help solve each.

1. Suppose Carlos wants to order 40 light bulbs for the factory. He can buy light bulbs in boxes of 4 or 8. How many ways could he order exactly 40 bulbs?

a. List all possible ways he could order 40 light bulbs.

boxes of 8						
boxes of 4						

b. How many ways are there? ____________

2. Suppose Susan wants 49 boxes of light bulbs. She can order them in packs of 10 boxes or 1 box at a time. How many ways can she order 49 boxes?

____

____

____

3. Pamela has a red shirt and a white shirt, black pants and a yellow skirt. How many different outfits can she make?

____

4. Three students are waiting in line to buy a venus fly trap. Barb is behind Jan. Mike is first in line. In what order are the students standing? ____________________

5. Don and Carrie had 13 orders for plants in the last two days. If they had 5 orders yesterday, how many orders did they have today? ____________

6. When would you make a list to solve a problem?

____

____

Name ______________________________

Practice
Chapter 2
Section A

Review and Practice

Vocabulary Choose the best number for each description.

_______ **1.** Standard form **a.** 240

_______ **2.** Expanded form **b.** 0, 1, 2, 3, 4, 5, 6, 7, 8, and 9

_______ **3.** Digits **c.** 300 + 50 + 2

(Lesson 1) Write the word name for each number.

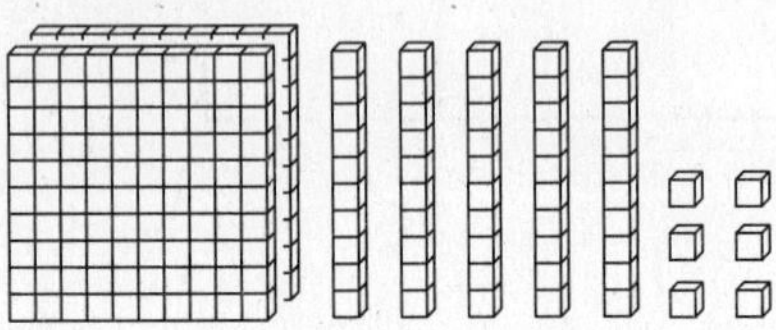

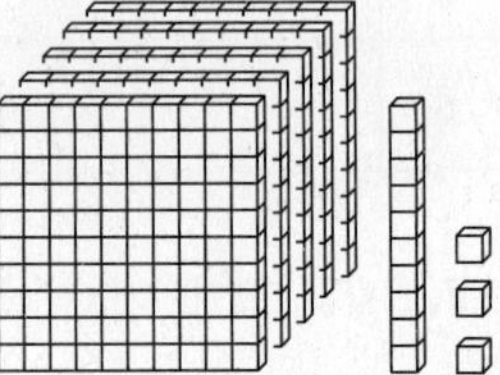

4. ______________________ **5.** ______________________

6. 246 ______________________ **7.** 80 + 2 ______________________

(Lesson 2) Write each missing value.

8. 60 ones = _______ tens **9.** _______ ones = 3 hundreds

10. 70 tens = _______ hundreds **11.** _______ tens = 600 ones

(Lesson 3) Write each number in standard form.

12. seven thousand three _______ **13.** 5,000 + 700 + 7 _______

(Lesson 4) Write the value of each underlined digit.

14. 23<u>5</u>,641 _______ **15.** <u>8</u>99,002 _______

(Lesson 5) Make a list to help solve.

16. Kara needs $35 for an aquarium for 6 fish. How can she pay with the least ten and one dollar bills?

____

(Mixed Review) Add or subtract.

17. 7 + 3 = _______ **18.** 16 − 7 = _______ **19.** 9 + 9 = _______

Name ______________________________

Practice
2-6

Comparing Numbers

Compare. Use <, >, or =.

1. 27 ◯ 24

2. 416 ◯ 925

3. 2,197 ◯ 3,208

4. 2,450 ◯ 450

5. 20 ◯ 311

6. 1,717 ◯ 7,171

7. 624 ◯ 620

8. 329 ◯ 923

Write "is less than," "is greater than," or "equals."

9. 47 ____________________ 74

10. 1,444 ____________________ 1,399

11. 919 ____________________ 919

12. 436 ____________________ 4,360

13. 426 and 264 have the same digits, but in a different order. Do they have the same value? Explain.

____

____

14. Can you compare the 4 in 934 with the 4 in 647 to find how 934 and 647 compare? Explain.

____

____

Complete.

15. To compare 2,457 and 2,464 you should look at the digits in the ______________ place.

16. To compare 1,830 and 1,799 you should look at the digits in the ______________ place.

Name ______________________________

Practice
2-7

Ordering Numbers

Order from least to greatest.

1. 649, 469, 964 ______________________

2. 215, 512, 255 ______________________

3. 375, 752, 527 ______________________

4. 823, 838, 282 ______________________

5. 439, 394, 934 ______________________

Order from greatest to least.

6. 315, 153, 453 ______________________

7. 8,042; 4,028; 2,408 ______________________

8. 3,962; 2,396; 9,632 ______________________

9. 484, 884, 448 ______________________

10. 1,256; 1,652; 2,165 ______________________

11. Circle the number that comes between 3,010 and 3,325.

3,001 3,332 3,125 3,521

12. Circle the greatest number.

2,909 2,999 2,990 2,900

13. Write a number between 2,458 and 3,002.

____

14. Write a number between 2,999 and 3,008.

____

Name ______________________________

Practice
2-8

Rounding to Tens

Round to the nearest ten.

1. 47 ________	**2.** 14 ________	**3.** 25 ________
4. 42 ________	**5.** 38 ________	**6.** 16 ________
7. 111 ________	**8.** 105 ________	**9.** 674 ________
10. 417 ________	**11.** 326 ________	**12.** 575 ________
13. 233 ________	**14.** 620 ________	**15.** 337 ________
16. 517 ________	**17.** 224 ________	**18.** 889 ________
19. 28 ________	**20.** 620 ________	**21.** 55 ________
22. 155 ________	**23.** 8 ________	**24.** 404 ________

25. Joanne's bus was 27 minutes late tonight. She called to say she would be about a half hour late for dinner. Explain why this was correct.

____

26. The library in Frank's town is 16 blocks from his house. When he asked to walk there alone, he told his mother that it was about 10 blocks away. Is this correct? Explain.

____

27. Beth has read 218 pages of her new book. She tells a friend that to the nearest 10 she has read 210 pages. Is this correct?

____

28. Name 3 two-digit numbers that round to 60 when rounded to the nearest ten.

____

29. Name 3 three-digit numbers that round to 250 when rounded to the nearest ten.

____

Name ______________________

Practice 2-9

Rounding to Hundreds

Round to the nearest hundred.

1. 427 ______	**2.** 453 ______	**3.** $178 ______
4. 211 ______	**5.** $319 ______	**6.** 296 ______
7. 871 ______	**8.** $531 ______	**9.** 497 ______
10. 902 ______	**11.** 890 ______	**12.** 711 ______
13. 623 ______	**14.** 451 ______	**15.** 366 ______
16. $350 ______	**17.** 95 ______	**18.** $329 ______

19. Round 79 to the nearest hundred. ______

20. Round 152 to the nearest hundred. ______

21. Round 242 to the nearest hundred. ______

22. What is the greatest number that rounds to 700 when you round to the nearest hundred? ______

23. What is the least number that rounds to 700 when you round to the nearest hundred? ______

24. Write any 5 numbers less than 400 that round to 400 when you round to the nearest hundred.

____

25. Write any 5 numbers greater than 400 that round to 400 when you round to the nearest hundred.

____

26. Give the greatest and least numbers that round to 500 when rounded to the nearest 100.

____

Name ______________________________

Review and Practice

Vocabulary Match each with its definition.

_____ **1.** compare **a.** one way to estimate

_____ **2.** round **b.** to place a set of numbers from least to greatest or greatest to least

_____ **3.** order **c.** a way to decide which of two numbers is greater

(Lesson 6) Compare. Use $<$, $>$, or $=$.

4. 623 ◯ 632 **5.** 2,300 ◯ 320 **6.** 556 ◯ 655

7. 8,900 ◯ 8,900 **8.** 367 ◯ 1,240 **9.** 459 ◯ 459

(Lesson 7) Order from least to greatest.

10. 308, 299, 315 ______________________

11. 2,453; 2,053; 998 ______________________

12. 1,245; 1,425; 542 ______________________

Order from greatest to least.

13. 5,180; 5,108; 5,810 ______________________

14. 606; 6,006; 6,600 ______________________

(Lesson 8) Round to the nearest ten.

15. 71 __________ **16.** 38 __________ **17.** $45 __________

(Lesson 9) Round to the nearest hundred.

18. 651 __________ **19.** $439 __________ **20.** $860 __________

21. Clara found pictures of her mother dated 1978, 1971, 1983, and 1973. Clara wants to put them in order from oldest to newest. Write the dates in order. ______________________

(Mixed Review) Compare. Write $<$, $>$, or $=$.

22. $6 + 9$ ◯ $9 + 6$ **23.** $8 - 5$ ◯ $7 - 2$ **24.** $9 + 3$ ◯ $15 - 4$

Name ________________________________

Practice
2-10

Time to the Nearest Five Minutes

Write each time two ways.

1. 

____

____

2. 

____

____

3. 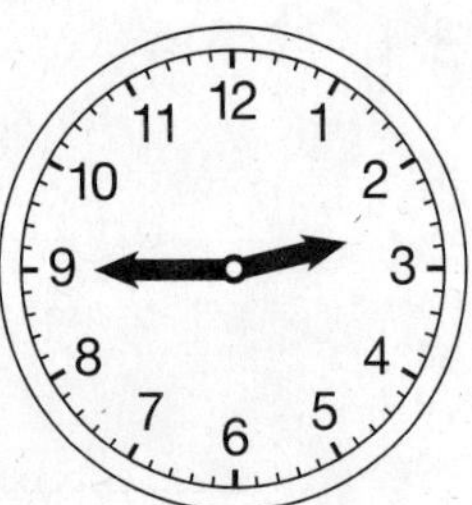

____

____

4. 

____

____

5. 

____

____

6. 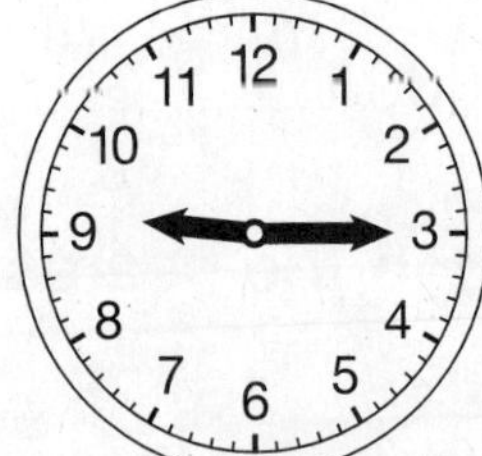

____

____

7. How many minutes are between 8:20 and 8:35? __________

8. What's another way to write 10 minutes before five? __________

9. Suppose it's 8:45. What time will it be 15 minutes later? __________

Name ______________________

Practice
2-11

Exploring Time to the Nearest Minute

Write each time two ways.

1.

____

2.

____

3.

____

4.

____

5.

____

6.

____

7. Duke's vet appointment is at 4:30. You arrive at 4:17. Are you early or late?

____

8. If it is 3:22, in how many minutes will it be 3:30?

____

9. Suppose you waited 12 minutes for your school bus. About how many minutes did you wait? Round to the nearest ten minutes.

____

Name ______________________________

Practice 2-12

Time to the Half Hour and Quarter Hour

Write each time two ways. Write A.M. or P.M.

1. 

go to a Saturday afternoon movie

____

____

2. 

sunrise

____

____

3. 

school's out

____

____

4. 

sleep time

____

____

5. 

dinner time

____

____

6. 

lunch time

____

____

7. Write a time that is between noon and half past twelve in the afternoon. ______________________

8. Write a time that is between quarter to three and quarter after three in the morning. ______________________

9. How many times in one day will the clock show 6:30? Explain. ______________________

Name ______________________________

Practice
2-13

Elapsed Time

1. Sam wants to let his dog run for twenty minutes. If he starts at 12:15 P.M., what time should he call the dog in? ______________

2. "I tried to call you an hour ago!" says Sheila. If it is 8:45 P.M. now, what time did she call before? ______________

3. "This movie lasts for 2 hours and 45 minutes," says Marc. If it begins at 7:00 P.M., what time will the movie end? ______________

4. Kai started his homework at 4:35 P.M. and finished at 7:00 P.M. How much time did he spend doing homework? ______________

5. Carla's karate class lasts for 45 minutes. If it begins at 4:15 P.M., what time will it end? ______________

6. Suppose it is 6:20 A.M. What time will it be in half an hour? ______________

7. The school bus arrives at 7:15 A.M. It is now 6:35 A.M. How much time does Amir have to get ready? ______________

Three cars left school at 2:30 P.M. Each traveled for the amount of time shown. When did each car arrive at its destination?

Car	Driving Time	Arrival Time
8. Juan's car	35 minutes	______
9. Hannah's car	60 minutes	______
10. Beryl's car	1 hour and 5 minutes	______

Name ______________________________

Practice
2-14

Ordinal Numbers and the Calendar

Use the calendar to answer **1–6**.

February						
Sun.	**Mon.**	**Tues.**	**Wed.**	**Thur.**	**Fri.**	**Sat.**
				1	2	3
4	5	6	7	8	9	10
11	12	13	14	15	16	17
18	19	20	21	22	23	24
25	26	27	28			

1. How many Tuesdays are in this month? ____________

2. Abraham Lincoln was born on February 12th.

What day of the week is that? ____________

Mark it on the calendar above.

3. George Washington was born on the twenty-second of February.

What day of the week is that? ____________

Mark it on the calendar above.

4. What day of the week is February 3rd? ____________

5. What is the date of the third Saturday in February?

____

6. What are the dates of the last weekend in February?

____

7. February is the second month of the year. What is the first month?

____

8. Name the fourth month. ____________

Name ____________________

Practice 2-15

Decision Making

1. Part of making a schedule is knowing how much time you have to get everything done. Figure out how much time you have available for each activity on this list and write it down.

Activity	Total time
a. The meeting begins at 3:15 P.M. and lasts until 4:00 P.M.	______
b. You have from 6:00 P.M. until 8:20 P.M. to do your homework.	______
c. Practice begins at 3:45 P.M. and ends at 5:15 P.M.	______
d. You begin your chores at 8:30 A.M. and must be done by noon.	______

2. Another step in making a schedule is estimating—or guessing—how long something will take. Give it a try. Estimate how long it would take you to:

a. brush your teeth ______

b. clean your room ______

c. read 10 pages ______

d. play a game of checkers ______

e. walk to the nearest store ______

f. make a sandwich ______

g. change your clothes ______

h. take a bath ______

Name ______________________________

Practice
Chapter 2
Section C

Review and Practice

Vocabulary Match each word with its definition.

______ **1.** A.M. **a.** times from noon to midnight

______ **2.** P.M. **b.** numbers used for ordering

______ **3.** ordinal numbers **c.** times from midnight to noon

(Lessons 10, 11, and 12) Write each time two ways. Write A.M. or P.M.

4. 
after lunch
____
____

5. 
prepare dinner
____
____

6. 
get dressed
____
____

(Lesson 13) Write each time.

7. Daniela ate lunch at 12:30 P.M. and went fishing 2 hours and 15 minutes later. What time did she go fishing? ______________

8. Justin began his chores at 9 A.M. and ended at 11:15 A.M. How long was he doing his chores? ______________

(Lesson 14) Use the calendar to answer **9** and **10.**

9. What day of the week is the 23rd?

____

10. How many Mondays are in the month shown?

____

October

Sun.	Mon.	Tues.	Wed.	Thur.	Fri.	Sat.
				1	2	3
4	5	6	7	8	9	10
11	12	13	14	15	16	17
18	19	20	21	22	23	24
25	26	27	28	29	30	31

(Mixed Review) Write the value of each digit in 473,826.

11. 8 ______________ **12.** 4 ______________

13. 7 ______________

Name ________________________

Practice
Chapters 1–2

Cumulative Review

(Chapter 1 Lesson 2) Use the data from the graph to answer each question.

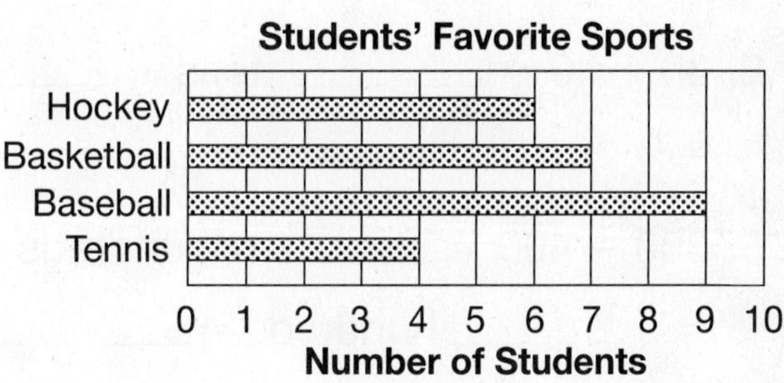

1. How many sports are the favorite of more than 5 students? ____________

2. What sport is the favorite of 9 students? ____________

(Chapter 1 Lesson 5) Write a number sentence and use it to solve the problem.

3. Liz read 10 books. 6 were mysteries. The rest were biographies. How many were biographies? ____________

(Chapter 1 Lesson 11) Write the next four numbers.

4. 10, 20, 30, 40, ______, ______, ______, ______

5. 29, 26, 23, 20, ______, ______, ______, ______

(Chapter 2 Lesson 4) Write the value of each underlined digit.

6. 64<u>5</u>,861 ________

7. 293,<u>8</u>62 ________

(Chapter 2 Lesson 7) Order from least to greatest.

8. 455, 450, 530, 545 ____________

9. 4,670, 5,839, 4,668, 5,355 ____________

(Chapter 2 Lesson 10) Write each time in two ways.

10.

____

11.

____

Name ______________________________

Practice
3-1

Exploring Addition Patterns

Use basic facts and place value to complete each problem.

1. 3 + 4 = ________

2. 30 + 40 = ________ tens + ________ tens

= ________ tens = ________

3. 300 + 400 = ________ hundreds + ________ hundreds

= ________ hundreds = ________

4. 3 + 5 = ________

30 + ________ = 80

________ + 500 = 800

5. 4 + 9 = ________

________ + 90 = 130

400 + ________ = 1,300

6. 8 + 1 = ________

80 + ________ = 90

________ + 100 = 900

7. 8 + 7 = ________

________ + 70 = 150

800 + ________ = 1,500

Find each sum using mental math.

8. \$20 + \$50 = __________

9. 100 + 700 = __________

10. 600 + 400 = __________

11. \$30 + \$80 = __________

12. 20 + 90 = __________

13. \$60 + \$70 = __________

14. There are 30 students on one school bus and 70 on another school bus. How many students are there altogether? ________

15. Can you use the basic fact 3 + 2 to add 30 + 200? Explain.

____

____

Name ________________________________

Practice
3-2

Exploring Adding on a Hundred Chart

You can think about adding numbers in different ways.

1. 50 + 36 = 50 + 30 + ________ = ________

Show how you can use the hundred chart to add 48 and 37.

2. 48 + 37 = ________

1	2	3	4	5	6	7	8	9	10
11	12	13	14	15	16	17	18	19	20
21	22	23	24	25	26	27	28	29	30
31	32	33	34	35	36	37	38	39	40
41	42	43	44	45	46	47	48	49	50
51	52	53	54	55	56	57	58	59	60
61	62	63	64	65	66	67	68	69	70
71	72	73	74	75	76	77	78	79	80
81	82	83	84	85	86	87	88	89	90
91	92	93	94	95	96	97	98	99	100

Find each sum. You may use the hundred chart to help.

3. 43 + 20 = ________

4. 52 + 18 = ________

5. 27 + 6 = ________

6. 6 + 27 = ________

7. \$78 + \$21 = ________

8. 40 + 45 = ________

9. 37 + 14 = ________

10. \$13 + \$29 = ________

11. Find the sum of 14 and 67. ________

12. Add 54 and 39. ________

13. If you know the sum of 24 + 37, how can you find the sum of 37 + 24? Explain.

____

____

14. Explain how you would add 39 + 22 using mental math.

____

Name ______________________

Practice 3-3

Exploring Algebra: Missing Numbers

There are two ways to find the missing number in ☐ + 4 = 21.

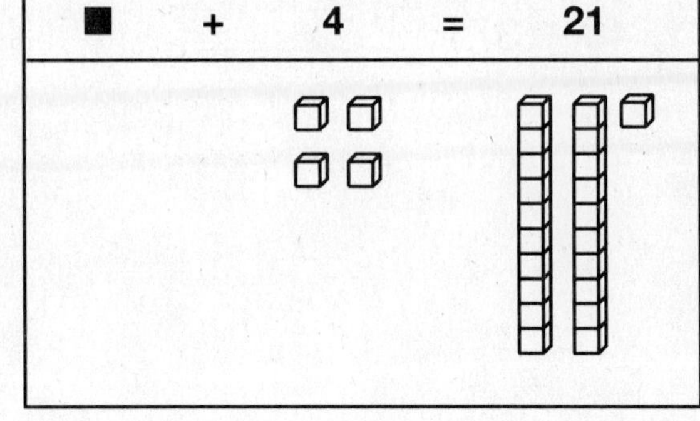

1. Match 4 cubes on one side with 4 on the other. How many more cubes do you need to make 21?

   ________ + 4 = 21.

2. You already have 4 on one side, so you can count on from 4 until you have 21.

   You count on ________ more cubes.

Find each missing number. You may use color cubes to help.

3. ________ + 7 = 23
4. ________ + 8 = 14
5. ________ + 5 = 12
6. ________ + 6 = 21
7. 4 + ________ = 10
8. 9 + ________ = 28
9. 11 + ________ = 19
10. ________ + 13 = 22
11. ________ + 19 = 23
12. Is the missing number in ☐ + 4 = 16 the same as the missing number in 4 + ☐ = 16? Explain.

    ____

    ____

Use patterns to find each missing number.

13. ________ + 7 = 13
14. 6 + ________ = 13
15. ________ + 5 = 11
16. 6 + ________ = 11
17. 3 + ________ = 12
18. ________ + 9 = 12

Name ______________________________

Practice
3-4

Estimating Sums

Estimate each sum.

1. 48 + 39 __________ **2.** 713 + 224 __________

3. $354 + $239 __________ **4.** $77 + $62 __________

5. 85 + 41 __________ **6.** 528 + 867 __________

7. 91 + 26 __________ **8.** 333 + 690 __________

9. Estimate the sum of 915 and 166. __________

10. Estimate the sum of 43 and 25. __________

11. Estimate the sum of $67 and $62. __________

12. Two addends have a sum of about 800. What are two possible addends?

____

13. Two addends have a sum of about 70. What are two possible addends?

____

14. Round to find which two pairs of numbers have a sum of about 700.

412 355 268 508 149

____

15. Round to estimate the sum of all the numbers in **14**.

____

Name ____________________

Review and Practice

Vocabulary Match each with its definition.

______ **1.** estimate — **a.** the answer obtained when adding numbers

______ **2.** sum — **b.** to find an answer that is close to an exact answer

(Lesson 1) Complete.

3. 8 + 8 = ______

80 + ______ = 160

______ + 800 = 1,600

4. \$3 + \$______ = \$12

\$______ + \$90 = \$120

\$300 + \$900 = \$______

5. What basic fact can you use to find 300 + 800? ______

(Lesson 2) Find each sum. You may use a hundred chart to help.

6. 36 + 8 = ______

7. 82 + 12 = ______

8. 25 + 30 = ______

9. \$64 + \$27 = ______

(Lesson 3) Find each missing number. You may use color cubes to help.

10. ______ + 7 = 32

11. 8 + ______ = 30

12. I am a 2-digit number. If you add me to 6 you will get a sum of 38. What number am I? ______

(Lesson 4) Circle the letter that shows the best estimate of each sum.

13. 34 + 55 **a.** 80 **b.** 100 **c.** 90

14. 522 + 131 **a.** 600 **b.** 700 **c.** 800

(Mixed Review) Use the pictograph to answer each question.

15. How many students does each [cat] represent? ______

16. How many boys have cats? ______

17. How many more girls than boys have cats? ______

Name ______________________________

Practice
3-5

Exploring Adding with Regrouping

Find each sum. You may use place-value blocks to help.

1. 24 + 47

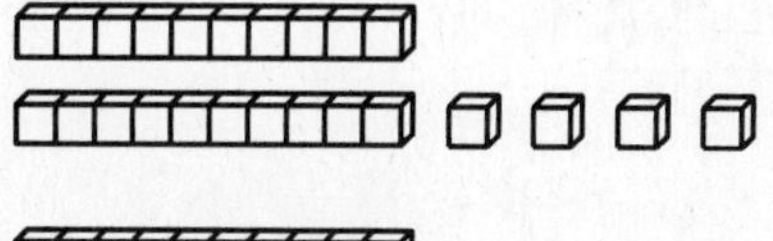

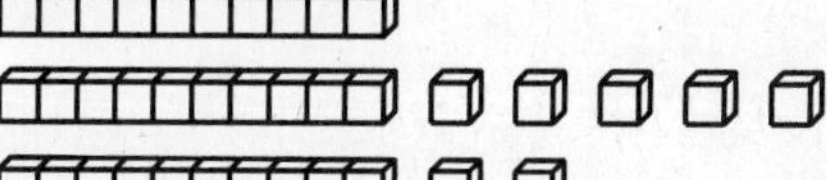

a. How many ones? ________

b. Do you need to regroup? ________

c. How many tens? ________

d. Do you need to regroup? ________

e. 24 + 47 = ________

2. 18 + 55 = ________

3. 34 + 28 = ________

4. 62 + 43 = ________

5. 59 + 21 = ________

6. 77 + 69 = ________

7. 45 + 86 = ________

8. 32 + 39 = ________

9. 29 + 99 = ________

10. 33 + 57 = ________

11. 62 + 39 = ________

12. 58 + 46 = ________

13. 16 + 86 = ________

14. 89 + 75 = ________

15. 57 + 24 = ________

16. 35 + 97 = ________

17. 59 + 79 = ________

18. Do you need to regroup 10 ones for 1 ten when you add 56 + 37? Explain.

____

19. Do you need to regroup 10 ones for 1 ten when you add 56 + 42? Explain.

____

Name ______________________

Practice
3-6

Adding 2-Digit Numbers

Add. Estimate to check.

1. $43 + 16$

2. $26 + 72$

3. $\$39 + 41$

4. $52 + 9$

5. $85 + 67$

6. $64 + 89$

7. $96 + 6$

8. $\$58 + 15$

9. $22 + 81$

10. $\$54 + 7$

11. $88 + 99$

12. $16 + 77$

13. $91 + 79$

14. $76 + 37$

15. $55 + 86$

16. $47 + 65$

17. 28 + 54 = ________

18. \$37 + \$78 = ________

19. 63 + 87 = ________

20. 92 + 21 = ________

21. Find the sum of 45 and 37. ________

22. Add 38 and 19. ________

23. Write two numbers that add to 70 without regrouping.

____

24. When you add 27 + 5 do you start by adding 2 + 5? Explain.

____

Name ______________________________

Practice
3-7

Adding 3-Digit Numbers

Complete.

1. $\begin{array}{r} {}^{1}\,{}^{1} \\ 217 \\ +\ 384 \\ \hline \square 01 \end{array}$

2. $\begin{array}{r} {}^{1} \\ 583 \\ +\ \ 74 \\ \hline 6\square\square \end{array}$

3. $\begin{array}{r} {}^{1}\,{}^{1} \\ \$357 \\ +\ \ 66 \\ \hline \square 2\square \end{array}$

4. $\begin{array}{r} {}^{1} \\ 445 \\ +\ 208 \\ \hline \square\square\square \end{array}$

Add. Estimate to check.

5. $\begin{array}{r} \$826 \\ +\ 151 \\ \hline \end{array}$

6. $\begin{array}{r} 737 \\ +217 \\ \hline \end{array}$

7. $\begin{array}{r} \$42 \\ +\ 59 \\ \hline \end{array}$

8. $\begin{array}{r} 431 \\ +\ \ 94 \\ \hline \end{array}$

9. $\begin{array}{r} 621 \\ +377 \\ \hline \end{array}$

10. $\begin{array}{r} 456 \\ +255 \\ \hline \end{array}$

11. $\begin{array}{r} 388 \\ +\ \ 94 \\ \hline \end{array}$

12. $\begin{array}{r} \$982 \\ +\ 635 \\ \hline \end{array}$

13. 97 + 42 = __________

14. 358 + 715 = __________

15. $39 + $75 = __________

16. 118 + 647 = __________

17. Find the sum of 380 and 442.

____

18. Find the sum of 832 and 79.

____

19. Write two addends with a sum of 258.

____

20. Estimate to decide which sum is greater than 1,000:
590 + 462 or 311 + 628.

____

____

Name ______________________

Practice
3-8

Adding 4-Digit Numbers: Choose a Calculation Method

Add.

1. 5,347 + 2,491

2. 6,200 + 3,500

3. 4,619 + 1,592

4. 7,416 + 2,347

5. $2,400 + 5,500

6. 1,348 + 721

7. 4,827 + 3,164

8. 6,038 + 831

9. 6,371 + 2,293

10. 3,849 + 5,163

11. 7,345 + 1,681

12. 4,691 + 5,366

13. 1,495 + 5,622 = ______

14. 6,400 + 3,500 = ______

15. 9,046 + 716 = ______

16. $5,807 + $2,164 = ______

17. Find the sum of 648 and 2,115.

______

18. Find the sum of 2,800 and 5,000.

______

19. Estimate to decide if the sum of 6,701 and 2,399 is greater than or less than 10,000.

______

______

20. Which two numbers have a sum of 6,000?

1,500 5,000 3,000
2,000 4,500 3,500

______

Name ______________________

Practice
3-9

Column Addition

Add.

1. $\begin{array}{r} 78 \\ 94 \\ +\ \ 5 \\ \hline \end{array}$ **2.** $\begin{array}{r} 416 \\ 172 \\ +\ \ 21 \\ \hline \end{array}$ **3.** $\begin{array}{r} 660 \\ 218 \\ +\ \ 34 \\ \hline \end{array}$ **4.** $\begin{array}{r} 54 \\ 793 \\ +415 \\ \hline \end{array}$

5. $\begin{array}{r} 348 \\ 506 \\ +270 \\ \hline \end{array}$ **6.** $\begin{array}{r} 529 \\ 32 \\ +410 \\ \hline \end{array}$ **7.** $\begin{array}{r} 481 \\ 9 \\ +573 \\ \hline \end{array}$ **8.** $\begin{array}{r} 855 \\ 26 \\ +\ \ 91 \\ \hline \end{array}$

9. 84 + 394 + 250 = ________ **10.** 15 + 7 + 989 = ________

11. What is the sum of 23, 462, and 117?

____

12. Add 851, 756, and 922.

____

13. What is the greatest possible sum using three of these numbers?

97	541	472	149	608

____

14. To add 67 + 45 + 821, would you start by adding 6 + 4 + 2? Why or why not?

____

____

15. Does it matter in which order you write 549, 192, 420 and 37 to add?

____

Name ______________________

Practice 3-10

Analyze Strategies: Guess and Check

Guess and check to solve.

1. The Hawks beat the Jays in a baseball game. The scores were 6 runs apart and there were 22 runs scored in the game. How many runs did each team score?

____

2. The Hawks lost to the Orioles by 4 runs. There were 18 runs scored in the game. How many runs did the Orioles score?

____

Use any strategy to solve.

3. The Jays beat the Orioles by 8 runs. There were 16 runs scored in the game. How many runs did the Jays score?

____

4. The sum of two numbers is 65. The numbers are 3 apart. What are they?

____

5. The sum of two numbers is 92. The numbers are 12 apart. What are they?

____

6. Tim bought three items at the school bookstore. He spent $23. What did Tim buy? Use the prices in the table to solve.

____

____

____

Item	Cost
Backpack	$14
Calculator	$ 9
Dictionary	$ 5
Notebook	$ 3
Set of Markers	$ 4

Name ______________________________

Practice
Chapter 3
Section B

Review and Practice

(Lesson 5) Find each sum. You may use place-value blocks to help.

1. 68 + 35 = ________ **2.** 237 + 125 = ________

3. 56 + 39 = ________ **4.** 53 + 34 = ________

(Lessons 6 and 7) Add. Estimate to check.

5. $\begin{array}{r} 43 \\ +24 \\ \hline \end{array}$ **6.** $\begin{array}{r} 651 \\ +\ 86 \\ \hline \end{array}$ **7.** $\begin{array}{r} 738 \\ +339 \\ \hline \end{array}$ **8.** $\begin{array}{r} 49 \\ +71 \\ \hline \end{array}$

9. 823 + 119 = ________ **10.** 545 + 126 = ________

11. Do you need to regroup 10 tens for 1 hundred when you add 241 + 387? ________

(Lessons 8 and 9) Add.

12. $\begin{array}{r} 2,568 \\ +\ 812 \\ \hline \end{array}$ **13.** $\begin{array}{r} 355 \\ 51 \\ +\ 19 \\ \hline \end{array}$ **14.** $\begin{array}{r} 402 \\ 313 \\ +\ 66 \\ \hline \end{array}$ **15.** $\begin{array}{r} 7,220 \\ +\ 867 \\ \hline \end{array}$

(Lesson 10) Guess and check to solve.

16. The Jays beat the Tigers by 5 runs. There were 17 runs scored. How many runs did the Jays score? ________

(Mixed Review) Circle the letter that answers each question.

17. Which does not tell the correct time?

A. half after 5 **B.** 15 minutes before 5

C. 4:45 **D.** 45 minutes after 4

18. What time will it be in 1 and a half hours?

A. 4:15 **B.** 6:00 **C.** 6:15 **D.** 7:30

19. Sal's soccer practice began at 2:45 P.M. and finished at 4:00 P.M. How long was practice?

____

Use with page 122.

Name ____________________

Practice 3-11

Mental Math

Use mental math to find each sum.

1. 80 + 55 = ________
2. 62 + 9 = ________
3. 18 + 40 = ________
4. 45 + 35 = ________
5. 59 + 36 = ________
6. 21 + 18 = ________
7. 99 + 5 = ________
8. 73 + 9 = ________
9. 47 + 29 = ________
10. 25 + 60 = ________
11. 88 + 4 = ________
12. 7 + 43 = ________
13. 81 +
14. 27 + 62 = ________
15. 7 +
16. 32 + 21 = ________
17. 55 +
18. 28 + 83 = ________
19. 46 + 52 = ________
20. 67 + 9 = ________
21. 34 + 28 = ________
22. 35 + 17 = ________
23. 8 + 37 = ________
24. 42 + 17 = ________

25. Find the sum of 475 and 15.

____

26. Find the sum of 133 and 7.

____

27. Add 389 + 4.

____

28. Add 225 + 25.

____

29. How does knowing 7 + 3 = 10 help you to add 37 + 13 mentally?

____

____

30. How can finding digits that add up to 10 help you to add 64 + 26?

____

____

Name ______________________________

Practice
3-12

Counting Coins

Write the total value in cents.

1. ______________

2. ______________

3. ______________

4. ______________

5. ______________

6. ______________

7. Find three ways to make 67 cents.

____

____

____

8. Find a way to make 56 cents.

____

9. Use the fewest coins to make 37 cents.

____

Name ______________________________

Practice 3-13

Using Dollars and Cents

Write the total value in dollars and cents.

1. 

____

2. 

____

3. Give at least two ways to show $2.65.

____

____

____

____

4. Give at least three ways to show $8.57.

____

____

____

____

____

5. Alicia said, "I lost a coin! I had $6.96. Now I only have 1 five-dollar bill, 1 one-dollar bill, 3 quarters, 1 dime, 1 nickel, and 1 penny." What coin did Alicia lose?

____

Name ______________________________

Practice
3-14

Exploring Making Change

Your class is having an art sale to make money for new supplies. You are the cashier.

1. Andy buys a papier-maché mask worth $3.24. He pays with $5.00. How much change will you give him?

a. Count on by circling the coins and bills you will use to make change. Write the amount.

__________ __________ __________ __________ __________

b. How much change is that? __________

2. June buys a painting worth $3.31. She pays with $5.00. List which coins and bills you would use to make change. Then write the change in dollars and cents.

____

____

3. Sheila's purchases total $2.09. She pays with $3.00.

a. Write three ways you could make change.

____

____

____

b. Which way uses the fewest coins?

____

Name ______________________________

Practice
3-15

Adding Money

Add. Estimate to check.

1. $5.17 + 4.39

2. $8.89 + 3.14

3. $0.52 + 7.93

4. $2.22 + 3.33

5. $4.87 + 5.14

6. $2.06 + 7.34

7. $9.40 + 1.61

8. $6.73 + 2.99

9. $4.34 + $3.71 = __________

10. $9.49 + $8.84 = __________

11. $3.25 + $2.96 = __________

12. $7.69 + $5.91 = __________

13. Find the sum of $2.41 and $5.57. __________

14. Add $8.12 + $8.69. __________

Athletic Equipment	
baseball bat	$7.07
basketball	$6.49
volleyball	$3.34
softball	$2.98
soccer ball	$4.63

15. Will $10.00 be enough to buy a softball and a baseball bat? Explain.

____

16. Which two pieces of equipment together will cost about $11.00?

____

17. What two items together would cost less than $7.00? How much would they cost?

____

Name ______________________________

Practice 3-16

Front-End Estimation

Use front-end estimation to estimate each sum.

1. $\begin{array}{r} \$6.12 \\ +\ 3.77 \\ \hline \end{array}$

2. $\begin{array}{r} 334 \\ 865 \\ +202 \\ \hline \end{array}$

3. $\begin{array}{r} 789 \\ 122 \\ +960 \\ \hline \end{array}$

4. $\begin{array}{r} \$2.57 \\ 5.16 \\ +\ 8.45 \\ \hline \end{array}$

5. $\begin{array}{r} 691 \\ 423 \\ +606 \\ \hline \end{array}$

6. $\begin{array}{r} 928 \\ +890 \\ \hline \end{array}$

7. $\begin{array}{r} \$3.33 \\ 5.87 \\ +\ 6.63 \\ \hline \end{array}$

8. $\begin{array}{r} 478 \\ 150 \\ +822 \\ \hline \end{array}$

9. 345 + 312 + 637 ________

10. 841 + 797 + 141 ________

11. Use front-end estimation to estimate the sum of 263, 804, and 469.

    ____

12. Use front-end estimation to estimate the sum of $7.34, $3.69, and $9.51.

    ____

13. Is the sum of $4.32 + $6.90 + $7.86 greater than $17.00? Explain.

    ____

14. If you buy 2 items that cost $6.32 each, will $11.00 be enough to buy both items? Explain.

    ____

15. If you buy 3 items that cost $5.43 each, will $15.00 be enough to buy all 3 items? Explain.

    ____

16. If you buy 2 items for $6.29 and 1 item for $3.55, will $15.00 be enough? Explain.

    ____

Name ______________________________

Practice 3-17

Analyze Word Problems: Exact Answer or Estimate?

Ahmed is going shopping for art supplies.

Art Supplies	
crayons	$2.34
marker	$4.98
paintbrush	$1.86
construction paper	$3.15
watercolor paint set	$4.43
frame	$6.71

Write if you need an exact answer or an estimate. Then solve.

1. Ahmed has a $10 bill. Does he have enough money to buy construction paper and a frame? Explain.

____

2. How much would it cost to buy crayons, a marker, and construction paper?

____

3. If Ahmed has $8.00, and he buys 3 paint brushes, does he have enough money left to buy a watercolor paint set? Explain.

____

____

____

____

4. Ahmed wants to know if $9.00 is enough to buy 2 markers. Does he need to find the exact total? Explain.

____

5. Ahmed began shopping at 11:30 A.M. When he finished it was 12:15 P.M. How long did he spend shopping?

____

Name ______________________

Practice
Chapter 3
Section C

Review and Practice

(Lesson 11) Use mental math to find each sum.

1. 75 + 9 ________ **2.** 29 + 43 ________ **3.** 88 + 5 ________

(Lessons 12 and 13) Write the total value in cents or dollars and cents.

4. 

____

5. 

____

(Lesson 14) List which coins and bills you would use to make change. Then write the change in dollars and cents.

6. Metta buys a notebook that costs $1.19. She pays with $2.00.

____

(Lesson 15) Add. Estimate to check.

7. $9.15 + $4.82 ________ **8.** $3.56 + $6.89 ________

9. $1.75 + $9.10 ________ **10.** $7.29 + $0.54 ________

(Lesson 16) Use front-end estimation to estimate each sum.

11. 325 + 176 + 852 ________ **12.** 63 + 55 + 38 ________

(Lesson 17) Write if you need an exact answer or an estimate. Then solve.

13. Cheryl wants to buy three books that cost $5.95, $2.95, and $3.45. Will $10 be enough money? Explain.

____

____

(Mixed Review) Write the value of each underlined number.

14. <u>4</u>5,886 ________ **15.** 2,84<u>6</u> ________ **16.** <u>1</u>23,654 ________

Name ______________________

Practice
Chapters 1–3

Cumulative Review

(Chapter 1, Lesson 1)

1. Which of the following uses pictures to represent information in a graph?

A. line graph **B.** bar graph **C.** pictograph

____

(Chapter 1, Lesson 3)

2. Which of the following shows changes over time?

A. line graph **B.** bar graph **C.** pictograph

____

(Chapter 2, Lesson 4) Write the standard form of each number.

3. four hundred thousand, sixty-seven ______________

4. six hundred twenty-one thousand, one hundred ten ______________

5. one hundred thirty thousand, six ______________

(Chapter 2, Lesson 9) Round each to the nearest hundred.

6. 2,610 **7.** 987 **8.** 1,651 **9.** 705

(Chapter 3, Lessons 9 and 15) Add.

10.
$$\begin{array}{r} 456 \\ 238 \\ +\ 115 \\ \hline \end{array}$$

11.
$$\begin{array}{r} 321 \\ 56 \\ +\ 135 \\ \hline \end{array}$$

12.
$$\begin{array}{r} \$3.15 \\ +\ 1.49 \\ \hline \end{array}$$

13.
$$\begin{array}{r} \$5.11 \\ +\ 7.52 \\ \hline \end{array}$$

(Chapter 3, Lesson 12)

14. Dimitrios has a five-dollar bill, 2 one-dollar bills, 3 quarters, 1 dime and 2 nickels. How much money does he have?

____

Name ____________________

Practice
4-1

Reviewing the Meaning of Subtraction

Write a number sentence for each. Then solve.

1. A clown is juggling four bananas. He drops one of them. How many bananas are still in the air?

   ____

2. Karen invites eight friends to her home for a party. Three people cannot come. How many people are there for the party?

   ____

3. Josh had a spelling test today. There were fifteen questions on the test. Josh misspelled six words. How many did he spell correctly?

   ____

4. Twelve children attended Melissa's party. There were seven boys. How many girls were there?

   ____

5. The bus stops and six children get on. Now there are thirteen children on the bus. How many children were on the bus before this stop?

   ____

6. The cracker box contained eighteen crackers. Now there are only nine. How many crackers were taken?

   ____

7. Jennifer has read 4 chapters of her book. The book has 16 chapters. How many chapters does she have left to read?

   ____

8. Phil has $10. He buys a vase for $6. How much money does he have left?

   ____

Name ______________________________

Practice 4-2

Exploring Subtraction Patterns

Complete.

1. 8 − 3 = ______

______ − 30 = 50

800 − ______ = 500

2. 13 − ______ = 9

130 − 40 = ______

______ − 400 = 900

3. \$19 − \$7 = ______

\$190 − ______ = \$120

______ − \$700 = \$1,200

4. 12 − 6 = ______

______ − 60 = 60

______ − 600 = 600

Find each difference using mental math.

5. 90 − 50 = ______

6. \$100 − \$80 = ______

7. 1,800 − 400 = ______

8. \$1,200 − \$1,100 = ______

9. 1,700 − 500 = ______

10. \$1,100 − \$600 = ______

11. Karima and Rick are playing a game with play money. Rick has \$1,100. He lands on a space that makes him pay Karima \$400. How much money will he have left? ______

12. Marty and Dee live in the same town. Marty's grandparents live 30 miles away. Dee's grandparents live 80 miles away. How much farther away do Dee's grandparents live? ______

13. Continue the pattern. Then write the rule.

In	70	80	90	100	110	120
Out	40	50	60			

Rule: ______________________________

14. What basic fact could you use to find 1,300 − 500? Solve.

____

Name ______________________________

Practice 4-3

Exploring Subtracting on a Hundred Chart

Find each difference. You may use a hundred chart to help.

1. 92 − 27 = ________ **2.** 69 − 16 = ________

3. 29 − 12 = ________ **4.** $77 − $64 = ________

5. 44 − 11 = ________ **6.** 54 − 37 = ________

Use mental math to find each difference.

7. 71 − 51 = ________ **8.** $48 − $20 = ________

9. 80 − 40 = ________ **10.** $45 − $30 = ________

11. 42 − 22 = ________ **12.** 51 − 21 = ________

13. 31 − 8 = ________ **14.** 79 − 44 = ________

Find each missing number. You may use a hundred chart to help.

15. 56 − ________ = 21 **16.** 32 − ________ = 7

17. ________ − 12 = 49 **18.** ________ − 34 = 62

19. 88 − ________ = 71 **20.** 89 − ________ = 61

21. On a hundred chart, Lesley begins with her finger on 89. She moves back 5 rows and back 7 spaces.

a. On what number does she land? ________

b. What number did she subtract? ________

22. Victor has 40¢. He wants to buy 3 postcards. Each postcard costs 20¢. How much more money will he need to buy the postcards? ________

Name ______________________________

Practice
4-4

Estimating Differences

Estimate each difference.

1. 988 − 112 = __________
2. 992 − 400 = __________
3. 25 − 14 = __________
4. 98 − 22 = __________
5. 112 − 56 = __________
6. 506 − 210 = __________
7. 279 − 126 = __________
8. 767 − 547 = __________
9. $4.99 − $3.67 = __________
10. $8.22 − $4.83 = __________
11. $6.49 − $1.25 = __________
12. $5.81 − $2.84 = __________
13. 432 − 121= __________
14. 890 − 160 = __________
15. 62 − 19 = __________
16. 81 − 76 = __________

17. Suppose the length of a movie you plan to watch is 98 minutes. You have been watching it for 50 minutes. Would it make sense to say that you have watched about half of the movie? Explain.

____

____

18. Suppose the book that you're reading has 126 pages. You've read 62 pages. Would it make sense to say that you have read about half of the book? Explain.

____

19. The estimated difference of the cost of two games is $2.00. Give two examples of the exact amounts that would make the estimate reasonable.

____

____

20. The estimated difference of the weight of two elephants is 100 pounds. Give two examples of the exact amounts that would make the estimate reasonable.

____

 Use with pages 156–157.

Name ________________________

Practice 4-5

Exploring Regrouping

Regroup 1 ten for 10 ones. You may use place-value blocks or draw a picture to help.

1. 64 is the same as ________________________

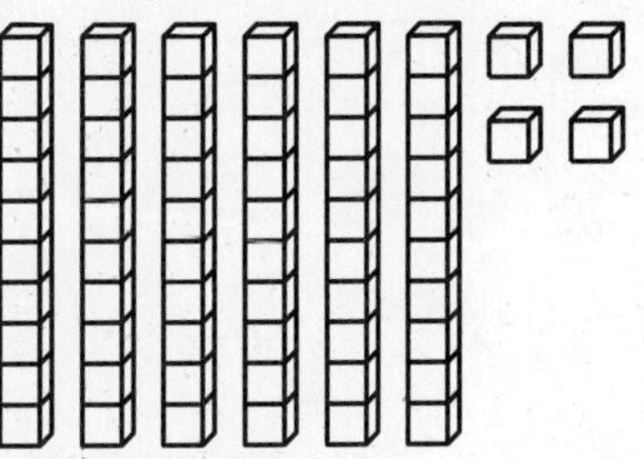

2. 42 = 3 tens, ________ ones

3. 95 = 8 tens, ________ ones

4. 63 = 5 tens, ________ ones

5. 57 = 4 tens, ________ ones

6. 53 = 4 tens, ________ ones

7. ________ = 5 tens, 17 ones

8. 32 = ________ tens, 12 ones

9. 90 = 8 tens, ________ ones

10. ________ = 3 tens, 11 ones

11. 88 = ________ tens, 18 ones

Regroup 1 hundred for 10 tens. You may use place-value blocks or draw a picture to help.

12. 215 = 1 hundred, ________ tens, 5 ones

13. 829 = 7 hundreds, ________ tens, 9 ones

14. 982 = 8 hundreds, ________ tens, 2 ones

15. 302 = 2 hundreds, ________ tens, 2 ones

16. 786 = 6 hundreds, ________ tens, 6 ones

17. 614 = 5 hundreds, ________ tens, 4 ones

18. Regroup 1 ten for 10 ones in the number 567.

____

19. Regroup 1 hundred for 10 tens in the number 412.

____

Name ______________________________

Practice
Chapter 4
Section A

Review and Practice

(Lesson 1) Write a number sentence for each. Then solve.

1. Harold bought 5 souvenirs in Maine and 3 in Massachusetts. How many more souvenirs did he buy in Maine than Massachusetts? ______

2. Phylis took 18 pictures. 9 are of the Grand Canyon. How many pictures are not of the Grand Canyon? ______

(Lesson 2) Look for a pattern. Complete.

3. 6 − 2 = ______
60 − ______ = 40
______ − 200 = 400

4. 13 − ______ = 4
130 − 90 = ______
______ − 900 = 400

5. 17 − 8 = ______
170 − ______ = 90
1,700 − 800 = ______

(Lesson 3) Solve. You may use a hundred chart to help.

6. 35 − 5 = ______

7. \$73 − \$30 = ______

8. 83 − 64 = ______

9. 59 − 17 = ______

10. ______ − 45 = 55

11. ______ − 28 = 16

(Lesson 4) Estimate each difference.

12. 623 − 455 ______

13. \$3.75 − \$2.29 ______

14. Suppose a movie lasts 100 minutes. Does it make sense to say you have about 30 minutes of the show to watch when you've been watching for 47 minutes? Explain.

____

(Lesson 5) Regroup 1 ten as 10 ones or 1 hundred as 10 tens. You may use place-value blocks or draw a picture to help.

15. 5 ☐ ☐
5 6̸ 4

16. ☐ ☐ 2
8̸ 8 2

17. ☐ ☐ 0
4̸ 9 0

(Mixed Review) Find each sum.

18. 30 + 60 = ______

19. 400 + 300 = ______

20. 90 + 20 = ______

Name ________________________

Practice 4-6

Exploring Subtracting 2-Digit Numbers

1. Find 86 − 48. You may use place-value blocks or draw a picture to help.

a. Regroup 1 ten for 10 ones in the number 86.

________ tens and ________ ones.

b. Subract the ones. ________ ones

c. Subtract the tens. ________ tens

d. The difference is ________.

Find each difference. You may use place-value blocks or draw a picture to help.

2. 28 − 17 = ________

3. 41 − 6 = ________

4. $97 − $16 = ________

5. 87 − 68 = ________

6. 33 − 25 = ________

7. $55 − $7 = ________

8. 19 − 11 = ________

9. 63 − 6 = ________

10. $77 − $48 = ________

11. 23 − 15 = ________

12. Subtract 23 from 81. ________

13. Find the difference of 63 and 47. ________

14. Find 91 − 52. ________

15. Your class needs to sell 50 tickets to the school show in order to win a prize. So far the class has sold 22 tickets. How many more tickets need to be sold? ________

16. Suppose you had a quarter, 2 dimes, and 7 pennies. If you lost 3 of your pennies, how much money would you have? ________

17. Genevieve has 60 minutes of homework to do. She has done 44 minutes. How many more minutes of homework does she have to do? ________

18. Yuki has read 14 pages of his 51-page book. How many more pages does he have left to read? ________

Name ______________________________

Practice 4-7

Subtracting 2-Digit Numbers

Subtract. Check each answer.

1. 76 − 42

2. 63 − 24

3. 34 − 7

4. $55 − 13

5. 82 − 54

6. 29 − 18

7. $21 − 9

8. 70 − 15

9. 32 − 8

10. 97 − 69

11. 60 − 31

12. 42 − 11

13. 37 − 28 = ________

14. 53 − 15 = ________

15. $24 − $6 = ________

16. 85 − 44 = ________

17. 66 − 39 = ________

18. 41 − 14 = ________

19. Find the difference of 50 and 18. ________

20. Subtract 27 from 42. ________

21. Write two numbers you could subtract from 25 with regrouping.

____

22. Write two numbers you could subtract from 83 without regrouping.

____

23. To subtract 22 from 74 do you need to regroup? Explain.

____

Name ______________________________

Practice
4-8

Exploring Subtracting 3-Digit Numbers

Use place-value blocks to help you subtract.

Find 236 − 141.

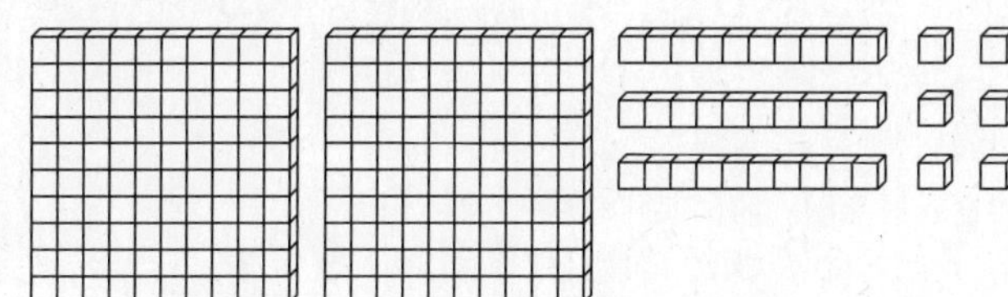

1. Do you need to regroup to subtract the ones? Explain.

____

2. Do you need to regroup to subtract the tens? Explain.

____

3. Find the difference.

$$\begin{array}{r} 236 \\ -\ 141 \\ \hline \end{array}$$

Find each difference. You may use place-value blocks or draw a picture to help.

4. 176 − 119 = ________

5. 218 − 54 = ________

6. 343 − 161 = ________

7. 135 − 72 = ________

8. 282 − 137 = ________

9. 329 − 258 = ________

10. 191 − 78 = ________

11. 245 − 195 = ________

12. Subtract 37 from 129. ________

13. Subtract 274 from 388. ________

14. Suppose you had 193 baseball cards and your brother had 249. How many more does your brother have? ________

Name ______________________________

Practice
4-9

Subtracting 3-Digit Numbers

Subtract. Check each answer.

1. $\begin{array}{r} 342 \\ -\ 138 \\ \hline \end{array}$

2. $\begin{array}{r} 184 \\ -\ 123 \\ \hline \end{array}$

3. $\begin{array}{r} 569 \\ -\ 298 \\ \hline \end{array}$

4. $\begin{array}{r} 257 \\ -\ \ 75 \\ \hline \end{array}$

5. $\begin{array}{r} 85 \\ -\ 29 \\ \hline \end{array}$

6. $\begin{array}{r} 614 \\ -\ 433 \\ \hline \end{array}$

7. $\begin{array}{r} \$232 \\ -\ \ 225 \\ \hline \end{array}$

8. $\begin{array}{r} 94 \\ -\ 38 \\ \hline \end{array}$

9. $\begin{array}{r} 427 \\ -\ 164 \\ \hline \end{array}$

10. $\begin{array}{r} \$394 \\ -\ \ 126 \\ \hline \end{array}$

11. $\begin{array}{r} 235 \\ -\ \ 81 \\ \hline \end{array}$

12. $\begin{array}{r} 522 \\ -\ 332 \\ \hline \end{array}$

13. 154 − 119 = __________

14. 244 − 51 = __________

15. 363 − 147 = __________

16. $878 − $56 = __________

17. 568 − 284 = __________

18. 216 − 162 = __________

19. Find the difference of 426 and 301. __________

20. Subtract 356 from 637. __________

21. Explain how to regroup to find 224 − 153.

____

____

22. Kim says, "To subtract 164 from 573, I began by subtracting 3 ones from 4 ones." What did she do wrong?

____

____

Name ______________________________

Practice
4-10

Subtracting with 2 Regroupings

Subtract. Check each answer.

1. 346 − 167 = ☐☐9

2. 182 − 95 = ☐7

3. 225 − 48 = 1☐☐

4. 814 − 526 = ☐8☐

5. 751 − 383

6. 427 − 148

7. $83 − 59

8. 520 − 451

9. 442 − 86

10. 653 − 275

11. 237 − 179

12. 866 − 77

13. 413 − 166 = ________

14. 243 − 59 = ________

15. $961 − $585 = ________

16. 92 − 36 = ________

17. 286 − 197 = ________

18. 354 − 188 = ________

19. Find the difference of 365 and 187. ________

20. Subtract 45 from 219. ________

21. Andrea subtracted 736 − 108 and found 628. She then added 736 and 108 to check her answer. Did she check her answer correctly? Explain.

____

____

22. To find 415 − 136, would you need to regroup hundreds? Explain.

____

____

Name ____________________

Practice 4-11

Subtracting Across 0

Subtract. Check each answer.

1. 207 − 82 = ____
2. \$403 − 235 = ____
3. 800 − 38 = ____
4. 520 − 359 = ____

5. 309 − 151 = ____
6. 705 − 467 = ____
7. 631 − 206 = ____
8. \$104 − 59 = ____

9. 240 − 198 = ____
10. 501 − 164 = ____
11. 408 − 311 = ____
12. 202 − 28 = ____

13. 306 − 147 = ____
14. 500 − 279 = ____
15. 940 − 458 = ____
16. 409 − 45 = ____
17. 604 − 335 = ____
18. 201 − 142 = ____
19. 703 − 497 = ____
20. 506 − 249 = ____
21. What is 703 minus 216? ____
22. Subtract 127 from 400. ____
23. Antonio said, "To solve 506 − 288, I can think of 5 hundreds as 50 tens." How might this help him subtract?

    ____

    ____

24. Write a number you could subtract from 202 without regrouping.

    ____

Name ______________________________

Practice
Chapter 4
Section B

Review and Practice

(Lessons 7 and 9) Subtract. Check each answer.

1. $\begin{array}{r} 87 \\ -38 \\ \hline \end{array}$ **2.** $\begin{array}{r} 56 \\ -27 \\ \hline \end{array}$ **3.** $\begin{array}{r} 95 \\ -54 \\ \hline \end{array}$ **4.** $\begin{array}{r} 73 \\ -9 \\ \hline \end{array}$

5. 371 − 369 = ________ **6.** 641 − 470 = ________

7. 974 − 58 = ________ **8.** 356 − 175 = ________

9. 342 − 159 = ________ **10.** 813 − 645 = ________

(Lessons 10 and 11) Subtract. Check each answer.

11. $\begin{array}{r} \$870 \\ -385 \\ \hline \end{array}$ **12.** $\begin{array}{r} 556 \\ -279 \\ \hline \end{array}$ **13.** $\begin{array}{r} 951 \\ -504 \\ \hline \end{array}$ **14.** $\begin{array}{r} 703 \\ -99 \\ \hline \end{array}$

15. 871 − 119 = ________ **16.** 601 − 473 = ________

17. 900 − 58 = ________ **18.** \$306 − \$177 = ________

19. 801 − 566 = ________ **20.** 709 − 23 = ________

21. Find the difference of 823 and 179. ________

22. Russia is 62 miles from Alaska. Washington is 500 miles from Alaska. How much farther from Alaska is Washington than Russia? ____________

(Mixed Review) Write each time two ways.

23. 

24. 

25. 

________________ ________________ ________________

________________ ________________ ________________

________________ ________________ ________________

Name ____________________

Practice
4-12

Subtracting 4-Digit Numbers: Choose a Calculation Method

Solve. Check each answer.

1. 4,282 − 1,718	**2.** \$6,359 − 3,342	**3.** 3,200 − 2,000	**4.** 7,650 − 5,365
5. 2,476 − 1,684	**6.** 5,699 − 3,940	**7.** 9,100 − 4,500	**8.** \$4,375 − 3,350
9. 1,671 − 400	**10.** \$6,500 − 999	**11.** 3,124 − 1,482	**12.** 8,146 − 7,938

13. 5,442 − 2,200 = ______ **14.** \$6,255 − \$1,391 = ______

15. \$1,450 − 650 = ______ **16.** 3,581 − 2,766 = ______

17. 4,733 − 3,627 = ______ **18.** 7,549 − 4,198 = ______

19. 5,555 − 3,472 = ______ **20.** 4,356 − 2,987 = ______

21. Subtract 1,234 from 4,321. ______

22. Subtract 6,487 from 7,486. ______

23. Subtract 8,322 from 9,323. ______

24. How could you use mental math to find 1,400 − 500?

____

25. Leo subtracted 232 from 1,345 on his calculator and found 113. Estimate to check. Is his answer reasonable?

____

Name ______________________

Practice
4-13

Analyze Word Problems: Multiple-Step Problems

Solve each problem.

Movie Admission Prices

Before 6 P.M.	
Children under 12	$2
Adults	$5
After 6 P.M.	
Children under 12	$3
Adults	$8

1. Mr. and Mrs. Riley want to take their 2 children to the movies. Their children are 5 and 9 years old.

a. How much will it cost for them to see a movie before 6:00 P.M.? ________

b. How much more will it cost for them to see a movie after 6:00 P.M.? ________

2. Mr. Ramirez told his 9-year old son that he could have $20 to take his friends to the movies. He wants to invite 4 friends from his class and his 14-year-old brother. How much more money does he need to take everyone to see a movie at 7:00 P.M.? ________

3. A scout troop leader is taking 14 scouts to the movies. Three scouts canceled and 5 more decided to go. How many scouts are going to the movies ? ________

4. The manager sold 55 adult tickets and 20 children's tickets for an afternoon movie. How many more adult tickets were sold than children's tickets? ________

Name ______________________

Mental Math

Write what number you would add to each in order to subtract mentally. Subtract.

1. 34 − 19 = ________

   I added ________.

2. 63 − 28 = ________

   I added ________.

3. 62 − 36 = ________

   I added ________.

4. 188 − 9 = ________

   I added ________.

5. 154 − 37 = ________

   I added ________.

6. 156 − 39 = ________

   I added ________.

7. 87 − 28 = ________

   I added ________.

8. 71 − 37 = ________

   I added ________.

9. 92 − 45 = ________

   I added ________.

10. 109 − 69 = ________

    I added ________.

11. 168 − 49 = ________

    I added ________.

12. 144 − 67 = ________

    I added ________.

13. What could you add to each number to find 730 − 260? Explain.

____

____

14. Would you add on to help you find 58 − 20? Explain.

____

____

Name ____________________

Practice 4-15

Subtracting Money

Subtract.

1. $\begin{array}{r} \$5.86 \\ -\ 2.55 \\ \hline \end{array}$

2. $\begin{array}{r} \$20.00 \\ -\ 7.05 \\ \hline \end{array}$

3. $\begin{array}{r} \$7.00 \\ -\ 5.76 \\ \hline \end{array}$

4. $\begin{array}{r} \$6.25 \\ -\ 2.98 \\ \hline \end{array}$

5. $\begin{array}{r} \$10.00 \\ -\ 5.87 \\ \hline \end{array}$

6. $\begin{array}{r} \$8.75 \\ -\ 4.35 \\ \hline \end{array}$

7. $\begin{array}{r} \$8.28 \\ -\ 4.99 \\ \hline \end{array}$

8. $\begin{array}{r} \$15.00 \\ -\ 3.89 \\ \hline \end{array}$

9. $\begin{array}{r} \$8.98 \\ -\ 2.79 \\ \hline \end{array}$

10. $\begin{array}{r} \$17.00 \\ -\ 6.72 \\ \hline \end{array}$

11. $\begin{array}{r} \$6.87 \\ -\ 1.98 \\ \hline \end{array}$

12. $\begin{array}{r} \$5.24 \\ -\ 4.25 \\ \hline \end{array}$

13. $6.50 – $2.17 = ____________

14. $11.50 – $6.75 = ____________

15. $13.85 – $5.98 = ____________

16. $20.00 – $8.88 = ____________

17. $9.89 – $3.57 = ____________

18. $15.00 – $7.99 = ____________

19. Rachel bought a puzzle for $4.89. She gave the clerk $10.00. How much change did she receive? ____________

20. Diego bought a toy and paid with $5.00. He received $3.29 in change. How much did the toy cost? ____________

21. Sophie is buying toothpaste. Superclean costs $4.89 and Sparkles cost $3.24. How much will Sophie save if she buys Sparkles? ____________

22. Sophie pays for Sparkles toothpaste with a $5 bill. How much change will she receive? ____________

Name ____________________

Practice
4-16

Analyze Strategies: Use Objects

Use objects to help solve each problem.

1. Kendra is going to a hockey game at the arena. She climbs 2 steps at a time to get to the door faster. Her little brother climbs 1 step at a time.

a. When Kendra has climbed 6 steps, how many steps has her brother taken? ________

b. When Kendra has climbed 12 steps, how many steps has her brother taken? ________

2. Keith is waiting in line to buy snacks. There are 8 people ahead of him. Two people leave the line without buying anything. Four people buy their snacks and go to their seats. How many people are ahead of him now? ________

3. Doug counts the pennies in his piggy bank. His sister has two pennies for every one penny Doug has. Doug has 9 pennies. How many pennies does his sister have? ________

4. Sheila lives 3 times as far from the school as Julia. If it takes Julia 5 minutes to walk to school, how long will it take Sheila? ________

5. From school, Kathy walks 2 blocks, then 1 block to mail a letter. She walks on 4 more blocks toward home. How many blocks does she walk in all? ________

Use any strategy to help you solve this problem.

6. Shandra rode her bike 1 mile to school. It took her 15 minutes. How long should it take Shandra to ride her bike 3 miles to the bookstore? ________

Name ____________________

Practice
Chapter 4
Section C

Review and Practice

(Lesson 12) Solve. Check each answer.

1. 5,738 − 2,667

2. 6,300 − 4,000

3. 7,856 − 2,133

4. 5,000 − 4,025

(Lesson 13) Solve.

5. It cost $3 for a child's ticket and $5 for an adult's ticket at the museum. Peter is going to the museum with his two sisters, Uncle Joe, and his mother. Peter and his 2 sisters can each get child's tickets. How much will it cost? ________

(Lesson 14) Write what number you would add to each in order to subtract mentally. Subtract.

6. 64 − 45 = ______ Add: ______

7. 372 − 68 = ______ Add: ______

8. 134 − 29 = ______ Add: ______

(Lesson 15) Subtract.

9. $4.56 − 1.38

10. $3.89 − 2.99

11. $9.00 − 3.46

12. $15.89 − 9.69

(Lesson 16) Use objects or any strategy to solve.

13. Tippy woke up at 7:00 A.M. She played for 1 hour. Then she napped. She woke up to play for another hour. Then she slept until Maggie came home from school at 3:00 P.M. How many hours did Tippy sleep? ________

(Mixed Review) Write each time.

14. Elizabeth did her homework at 4:30 P.M. and ate dinner 1 hour and 20 minutes later. What time did she eat? ________

15. Jerome got dressed for school at 7:15 A.M. Eight and a half hours later he returned home. What time was it when Jerome got home? ________

Name ________________________

Practice
Chapters 1–4

Cumulative Review

(Chapter 2 Lesson 13)

1. Brooke starts school at 8:10 A.M. School lets out at 3:25 P.M. How long is Brooke's school day? ________

A. 8 hours
B. 7 hours, 35 minutes
C. 7 hours, 15 minutes
D. 5 hours, 15 minutes

(Chapter 3 Lesson 14)

2. Clark bought a sandwich for a total of $2.35. He gave the sales person a $5 bill. What is the amount of change he should receive? ________

A. $3, 6 dimes, and 1 nickel
B. $2, 6 dimes, and 1 nickel
C. $2, 5 dimes, and 5 pennies

(Chapter 3 Lesson 15)

3. $2.19 + 1.97

4. $3.05 + 1.50

5. $6.89 + 3.27

6. Find the sum of $8.78 and $3.29. ________

7. What is the sum of $12.15 and $8.29? ________

A. $10.44 **B.** $20.14 **C.** $20.44 **D.** not here

(Chapter 4 Lessons 7–9)

Find each difference.

8. 56 − 12

9. 27 − 9

10. 342 − 116

11. 2,892 − 1,451

12. Find the difference of 517 and 230. ________

13. Subtract 338 from 522. ________

Name ______________________________

Practice 5-1

Exploring Equal Groups

Complete.

1.

a. _______ + _______ = _______

b. _______ rows of _______ equals _______.

2.

a. _______ + _______ + _______ = _______

b. _______ groups of _______ equals _______.

3.

a. _______ + _______ + _______ + _______ = _______

b. _______ rows of _______ equals _______.

4.

a. _______ + _______ + _______ = _______

b. _______ groups of _______ equals _______.

5. Do these counters show equal groups? Explain.

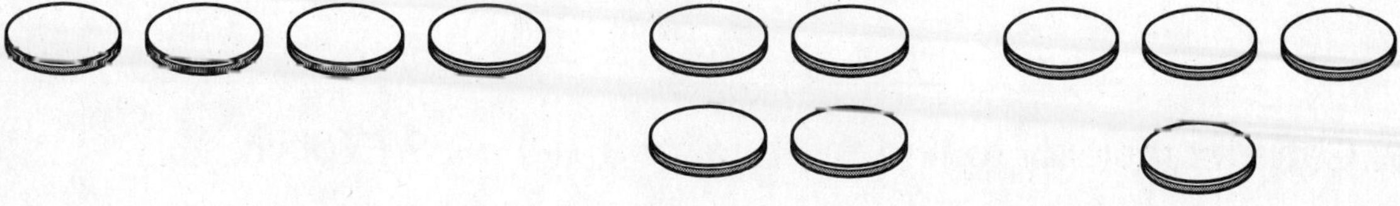

____

Name ______________________________

Practice 5-2

Writing Multiplication Sentences

Complete each number sentence.

1.

a. ______ + ______ + ______ = ______

b. ______ × ______ = ______

2.

a. ______ + ______ = ______

b. ______ × ______ = ______

3.

a. ______ + ______ + ______ + ______ = ______

b. ______ × ______ = ______

4. Draw a picture that shows 3 × 4. Find the product.

5. Can you multiply to find the total of 9 + 9 + 9? Explain.

____

6. Can you multiply to find the total of 3 + 4 + 5? Explain.

____

Name ______________________

Practice
5-3

Exploring Multiplication Stories

1. Is this a multiplication story? Explain.

Sam makes shirts. He sold 3 shirts one day, and 4 the next day. How many shirts did Sam sell?

____

Write a multiplication story for **2–6**.
You may use counters to solve.

2. 2×5

____

____

3. 3×6

____

____

4. 4×4

____

____

5. 6×2

____

____

6. 6×4

____

____

Solve.

7. There are 6 cars in the parking lot. Each car has 4 tires. How many tires are there?

____

Name ____________________

Practice
Chapter 5
Section A

Review and Practice

Vocabulary Match each with its definition.

____ **1.** product — **a.** one of the numbers multiplied

____ **2.** factor — **b.** an arrangement of rows and columns

____ **3.** array — **c.** the number obtained by multiplying numbers

(Lessons 1 and 2) Complete.

4.

a. □ + □ + □ + □ = □

b. □ groups of □ equals □.

c. □ × □ = □

5.

a. □ + □ = □

b. □ groups of □ equals □.

c. □ × □ = □

6. Idaho has 2 representatives in the House of Representatives. Minnesota has 4 times as many. How many representatives does Minnesota have?

____

7. Is the product of 7 × 3 the same as the product of 3 × 7? Explain.

____

____

(Lesson 3) Write a multiplication story for each. You may use counters to solve.

8. 4 × 5 = ________

____

9. 3 × 7 = ________

____

(Mixed Review) Add or subtract.

10. 23 + 17 = ________ **11.** 45 − 20 = ________ **12.** 58 + 26 = ________

Name ______________________

Practice 5-4

2 as a Factor

Find each product.

1. $3 \times 2 =$ ______ **2.** $5 \times 2 =$ ______

3. $2 \times 1 =$ ______ **4.** $2 \times 10 =$ ______

5. $2 \times 9 =$ ______ **6.** $8 \times 2 =$ ______

7. $4 \times 2 =$ ______ **8.** $6 \times 2 =$ ______

9. $2 \times 2 =$ ______ **10.** $2 \times 7 =$ ______

11. $\begin{array}{r} 4 \\ \times 2 \\ \hline \end{array}$ **12.** $\begin{array}{r} 2 \\ \times 5 \\ \hline \end{array}$ **13.** $\begin{array}{r} 6 \\ \times 2 \\ \hline \end{array}$ **14.** $\begin{array}{r} 8 \\ \times 2 \\ \hline \end{array}$ **15.** $\begin{array}{r} 9 \\ \times 2 \\ \hline \end{array}$

16. $\begin{array}{r} 10 \\ \times \ 2 \\ \hline \end{array}$ **17.** $\begin{array}{r} 7 \\ \times 2 \\ \hline \end{array}$ **18.** $\begin{array}{r} 2 \\ \times 1 \\ \hline \end{array}$ **19.** $\begin{array}{r} 2 \\ \times 3 \\ \hline \end{array}$ **20.** $\begin{array}{r} 10 \\ \times \ 2 \\ \hline \end{array}$

21. Find the product of 5 and 2. ______

22. Find the product of 2 and 8. ______

23. Find the product of 10 and 2. ______

24. Find the product of 6 and 2. ______

25. Find the product of 7 and 2. ______

26. Find the product of 3 and 2. ______

27. Is the product of 5 and 2 the same as the sum of 5 and 2? Explain.

____

28. Draw a picture to show that 7×2 is the same as 2×7.

Name ______________________

Practice 5-5

5 as a Factor

Find each product.

1. $2 \times 5 =$ ______ **2.** $5 \times 5 =$ ______

3. $5 \times 1 =$ ______ **4.** $5 \times 8 =$ ______

5. $2 \times 9 =$ ______ **6.** $3 \times 5 =$ ______

7. $5 \times 4 =$ ______ **8.** $5 \times 6 =$ ______

9. $5 \times 7 =$ ______ **10.** $2 \times 8 =$ ______

11. 4×5 **12.** 5×5 **13.** 6×2 **14.** 5×8 **15.** 9×5

16. 8×2 **17.** 7×2 **18.** 2×1 **19.** 2×3 **20.** 8×5

21. 5×2 **22.** 7×5 **23.** 8×5 **24.** 6×5 **25.** 3×5

26. Find the product of 5 and 7. ______

27. Multiply 8 by 5. ______

28. If you know the product of 8 and 5, how can you use it to find 9×5?

____

29. Is 7×5 greater or less than 8×5? Explain.

____

Name ______________________________

Practice
5-6

Exploring Patterns on a Hundred Chart: 2s and 5s

Finish these sentences.

1. a. Multiples of 2 always end in ______________________.

   b. Write some multiplication sentences to show the pattern:

   ____

2. a. Multiples of 5 always end in ______________________.

   b. Write some multiplication sentences to show the pattern:

   ____

Find each product.

3. $8 \times 2 =$ ______	**4.** $8 \times 5 =$ ______	**5.** $2 \times 2 =$ ______
6. $7 \times 5 =$ ______	**7.** $2 \times 7 =$ ______	**8.** $5 \times 4 =$ ______
9. $6 \times 5 =$ ______	**10.** $2 \times 9 =$ ______	**11.** $2 \times 10 =$ ______

12. $\begin{array}{r} 4 \\ \times\ 2 \\ \hline \end{array}$ **13.** $\begin{array}{r} 6 \\ \times\ 2 \\ \hline \end{array}$ **14.** $\begin{array}{r} 9 \\ \times\ 5 \\ \hline \end{array}$ **15.** $\begin{array}{r} 2 \\ \times\ 1 \\ \hline \end{array}$

16. $\begin{array}{r} 5 \\ \times\ 6 \\ \hline \end{array}$ **17.** $\begin{array}{r} 3 \\ \times\ 2 \\ \hline \end{array}$ **18.** $\begin{array}{r} 5 \\ \times\ 1 \\ \hline \end{array}$ **19.** $\begin{array}{r} 2 \\ \times\ 5 \\ \hline \end{array}$

20. Find the product of 5 and 3. ______

21. Multiply 6 by 2. ______

22. What numbers are shaded twice when you shade multiples of 2s and multiples of 5s on a hundred chart?

____

Name ________________________

Practice
5-7

Exploring 0 and 1 as Factors

Finish these sentences.

1. a. The product of any number and 1 is ____________.

b. Write a multiplication sentence to show this.

____

2. a. The product of any number and 0 is ____________.

b. Write a multiplication sentence to show this.

____

Find each product.

3. 8 × 0 = ______ **4.** 8 × 1 = ______ **5.** 0 × 2 = ______

6. 1 × 5 = ______ **7.** 2 × 1 = ______ **8.** 5 × 4 = ______

9. 5 × 5 = ______ **10.** 2 × 9 = ______

11. 4 × 2 **12.** 6 × 1 **13.** 9 × 0 **14.** 2 × 1

15. 1 × 6 **16.** 3 × 2 **17.** 5 × 1 **18.** 1 × 5

19. 0 × 3 **20.** 1 × 3 **21.** 0 × 1 **22.** 0 × 0

23. Find the product of 1 and 1. ______

24. Multiply 0 by 1. ______

Complete. Write × or +.

25. 8 ______ 1 = 9 **26.** 9 ______ 1 = 9 **27.** 0 ______ 5 = 5

28. 2 ______ 10 = 20 **29.** 2 ______ 0 = 0 **30.** 5 ______ 5 = 10

Name ______________________

Practice 5-8

9 as a Factor

Find each product.

1. $9 \times 8 =$ _____ **2.** $4 \times 9 =$ _____ **3.** $9 \times 7 =$ _____

4. $9 \times 6 =$ _____ **5.** $5 \times 9 =$ _____ **6.** $0 \times 5 =$ _____

7. $9 \times 3 =$ _____ **8.** $3 \times 5 =$ _____ **9.** $2 \times 6 =$ _____

10. $\begin{array}{r} 9 \\ \times\ 9 \\ \hline \end{array}$ **11.** $\begin{array}{r} 8 \\ \times\ 5 \\ \hline \end{array}$ **12.** $\begin{array}{r} 2 \\ \times\ 7 \\ \hline \end{array}$ **13.** $\begin{array}{r} 9 \\ \times\ 8 \\ \hline \end{array}$

14. $\begin{array}{r} 5 \\ \times\ 4 \\ \hline \end{array}$ **15.** $\begin{array}{r} 1 \\ \times\ 9 \\ \hline \end{array}$ **16.** $\begin{array}{r} 7 \\ \times\ 5 \\ \hline \end{array}$ **17.** $\begin{array}{r} 9 \\ \times\ 0 \\ \hline \end{array}$

18. Find the product of 8 and 9. _____

19. Multiply 9 by 2. _____

20. If you forget the product of 9 and 9, what can you do to figure it out?

____

____

21. Is 6×9 the same as 9×7? Explain.

____

22. Is 5×9 the same as 6×9? Explain.

____

23. Write a number sentence that shows the same product as the product of 9 and 2.

____

Name ______________________

Practice 5-9

Analyze Word Problems: Too Much or Too Little Information

Decide if the problem has too much or too little information. Then solve. If there is not enough information, tell what information is needed.

1. It takes about 3 months to grow tomatoes. The vines should be planted about 2 feet apart and get a lot of sun. If Taylor wants to plant 6 tomato vines in a row, how long should the row be?

   Too much or too little information? ______________

   How do you solve it? ______________________

   ____

2. Each tomato vine can grow about 25 tomatoes. Taylor wants to make 3 gallons of spaghetti sauce with his tomatoes. Will 6 vines be enough?

   Too much or too little information? ______________

   How do you solve it? ______________________

   ____

3. Kathryn is going to knit a sweater that is red and yellow. She needs 6 skeins of red yarn. If each skein is 100 meters long, how many meters of yarn will she need all together?

   Too much or too little information? ______________

   How do you solve it? ______________________

   ____

4. A piano keyboard has a total of 88 black and white keys. 36 of these are black. It takes 13 keys to play an octave. How many keys are white?

   Too much or too little information? ______________

   How do you solve it? ______________________

   ____

Name ____________________

Practice 5-10

Analyze Strategies: Draw a Picture

Draw a picture to help you solve.

1. How many bricks will Julia need to build a garden wall 9 bricks long and 8 bricks high? ________

2. Julia wants to build another garden wall, 10 bricks long and 3 bricks high. Can she build it with red and white bricks, so that no two bricks of the same color are next to each other? ________

Draw a picture or use any strategy to solve the problems.

3. Ray is setting the table for a birthday dinner. He needs to set 12 places at a round table. He has 3 different kinds of plates: white plates; blue plates; and gold plates. How can he set the table so that no two of the same kind of plates are next to each other?

____

4. Ray has 13 forks, 15 spoons, and 11 dinner knives. If 12 people are coming to dinner does he have enough silverware so that each person can have a fork, spoon and dinner knife?

____

Name ________________________________

Practice
Chapter 5
Section B

Review and Practice

(Lessons 4–8) Find each product.

1. 3×2 **2.** 5×8 **3.** 8×2 **4.** 4×9 **5.** 9×0

6. 5×7 **7.** 9×2 **8.** 1×5 **9.** 5×2 **10.** 7×2

11. $3 \times 5 =$ ______ **12.** $1 \times 2 =$ ______

13. $6 \times 2 =$ ______ **14.** $9 \times 5 =$ ______

15. $5 \times 4 =$ ______ **16.** $2 \times 2 =$ ______

17. List 5 multiples of 3. ______________________

(Lessons 9 and 10) Solve.

18. Harold gave each of his nine friends three stickers. Four of the stickers were red. How many stickers did he give away? ____________

19. Pamela has 2 boxes of crayons. Each box has 48 crayons in it. 8 of the crayons are sharpened. How many crayons does she have? ____________

20. Michele and 2 friends each live on a different floor of a three-story apartment building. Shaun lives above Barb and below Michele. Who lives on the first floor? ____________

(Mixed Review) Continue each pattern.

21. 7, 14, 21, 28, ______, ______, ______

22. 18, 27, 36, 45, ______, ______, ______

23. 10, 12, 14, 16, ______, ______, ______

Name ____________________

Practice
Chapters 1–5

Cumulative Review

(Chapter 3, Lesson 13) Solve.

1. Sue Ann has \$3.50 in quarters and \$1.15 in nickels. How many quarters does she have? How many nickels? How much money does she have in all?

____

(Chapter 2, Lesson 7) Write each set of numbers in order from greatest to least.

2. 470, 704, 740, 407 ____________________

3. 400,100; 410,000; 401,700; 407,100

____

(Chapter 3, Lesson 7) Find each sum.

4. $\begin{array}{r} 326 \\ +\,719 \\ \hline \end{array}$ **5.** $\begin{array}{r} 412 \\ +\,811 \\ \hline \end{array}$ **6.** $\begin{array}{r} 319 \\ +\,324 \\ \hline \end{array}$ **7.** $\begin{array}{r} 828 \\ +\,124 \\ \hline \end{array}$

(Chapter 4, Lesson 10) Find each difference.

8. $\begin{array}{r} 314 \\ -\,126 \\ \hline \end{array}$ **9.** $\begin{array}{r} 427 \\ -\,189 \\ \hline \end{array}$ **10.** $\begin{array}{r} 516 \\ -\,427 \\ \hline \end{array}$ **11.** $\begin{array}{r} 644 \\ -\,356 \\ \hline \end{array}$

12. 818 − 529 = ________ **13.** 745 − 266 = ________

(Chapter 5, Lessons 4 and 5) Find each product.

14. $\begin{array}{r} 3 \\ \times\,5 \\ \hline \end{array}$ **15.** $\begin{array}{r} 4 \\ \times\,2 \\ \hline \end{array}$ **16.** $\begin{array}{r} 5 \\ \times\,8 \\ \hline \end{array}$ **17.** $\begin{array}{r} 2 \\ \times\,9 \\ \hline \end{array}$ **18.** $\begin{array}{r} 6 \\ \times\,5 \\ \hline \end{array}$

19. 7 × 5 – ________ **20.** 2 × 6 = ________ **21.** 7 × 2 = ________

Name ______________________

Practice 6-1

3 as a Factor: Using Known Facts

Find each product.

1. 8×3 = ____ **2.** 3×1 = ____ **3.** 6×3 = ____ **4.** 7×3 = ____ **5.** 3×2 = ____

6. 3×3 = ____ **7.** 4×3 = ____ **8.** 9×3 = ____ **9.** 3×8 = ____ **10.** 5×3 = ____

11. 3×2 ____ **12.** 6×3 ____ **13.** 3×5 ____ **14.** 3×9 ____

15. 8×3 ____ **16.** 1×3 ____ **17.** 7×3 ____ **18.** 4×3 ____

19. What is the product of 9 and 3? ____

20. What is the product of 6 and 3? ____

21. Multiply 5 by 3. ____

22. Multiply 3 by 4. ____

23. If you know the product of 2×6, how can you find the product of 3×6? What is it?

____

24. Tim says, "To find 3×8, I can find 2×8 and add one more group of 3." What's wrong? Explain.

____

Name ______________________

Practice 6-2

4 as a Factor: Doubling

Find each product.

1. $\begin{array}{r} 4 \\ \times 5 \\ \hline \end{array}$

2. $\begin{array}{r} 6 \\ \times 4 \\ \hline \end{array}$

3. $\begin{array}{r} 9 \\ \times 4 \\ \hline \end{array}$

4. $\begin{array}{r} 4 \\ \times 3 \\ \hline \end{array}$

5. $\begin{array}{r} 1 \\ \times 4 \\ \hline \end{array}$

6. $\begin{array}{r} 8 \\ \times 2 \\ \hline \end{array}$

7. $\begin{array}{r} 4 \\ \times 8 \\ \hline \end{array}$

8. $\begin{array}{r} 4 \\ \times 4 \\ \hline \end{array}$

9. $\begin{array}{r} 2 \\ \times 4 \\ \hline \end{array}$

10. $\begin{array}{r} 4 \\ \times 7 \\ \hline \end{array}$

11. 5×4 ________

12. 4×9 ________

13. 4×2 ________

14. 4×4 ________

15. 1×4 ________

16. 6×4 ________

17. 3×4 ________

18. 7×4 ________

19. Multiply 8 by 4.

____

20. Multiply 4 by 7.

____

21. What is the product of 4 and 9? ________

22. What is the product of 4 and 5? ________

23. Draw arrays to show that 4×5 is the same as 5×4.

24. Could you use doubling to multiply 7×3? Explain.

____

____

Name ______________________________

Practice 6-3

6 as a Factor: Using Known Facts

Find each product.

1. $\begin{array}{r} 0 \\ \times\ 6 \\ \hline \end{array}$ **2.** $\begin{array}{r} 3 \\ \times\ 6 \\ \hline \end{array}$ **3.** $\begin{array}{r} 6 \\ \times\ 5 \\ \hline \end{array}$ **4.** $\begin{array}{r} 9 \\ \times\ 6 \\ \hline \end{array}$ **5.** $\begin{array}{r} 6 \\ \times\ 6 \\ \hline \end{array}$

6. $\begin{array}{r} 6 \\ \times\ 2 \\ \hline \end{array}$ **7.** $\begin{array}{r} 1 \\ \times\ 6 \\ \hline \end{array}$ **8.** $\begin{array}{r} 7 \\ \times\ 6 \\ \hline \end{array}$ **9.** $\begin{array}{r} 6 \\ \times\ 4 \\ \hline \end{array}$ **10.** $\begin{array}{r} 6 \\ \times\ 8 \\ \hline \end{array}$

11. 6×4 ______ **12.** 2×6 ______ **13.** 9×6 ______ **14.** 6×0 ______

15. 5×6 ______ **16.** 6×8 ______ **17.** 6×6 ______ **18.** 3×6 ______

19. Find the product of 6 and 7. ______

20. What is 9 multiplied by 6? ______

21. Find the product of 6 and 6. ______

22. What is 3 multiplied by 6? ______

23. Which is greater, 6×9 or 9×5? How can you tell without multiplying?

____

____

24. Can you think of a way to use doubling to multiply 6×7? Explain.

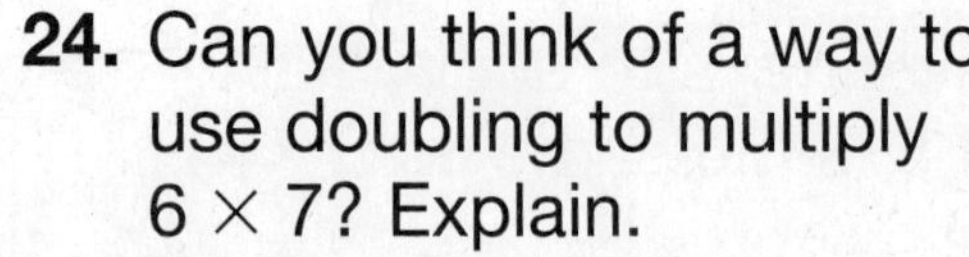

____

____

Name ______________________________

Practice
6-4

7 and 8 as Factors

Find each product.

1. $\begin{array}{r} 7 \\ \times 8 \\ \hline \end{array}$ **2.** $\begin{array}{r} 8 \\ \times 9 \\ \hline \end{array}$ **3.** $\begin{array}{r} 9 \\ \times 7 \\ \hline \end{array}$ **4.** $\begin{array}{r} 6 \\ \times 8 \\ \hline \end{array}$ **5.** $\begin{array}{r} 4 \\ \times 8 \\ \hline \end{array}$

6. $\begin{array}{r} 3 \\ \times 7 \\ \hline \end{array}$ **7.** $\begin{array}{r} 7 \\ \times 7 \\ \hline \end{array}$ **8.** $\begin{array}{r} 5 \\ \times 8 \\ \hline \end{array}$ **9.** $\begin{array}{r} 8 \\ \times 8 \\ \hline \end{array}$ **10.** $\begin{array}{r} 4 \\ \times 7 \\ \hline \end{array}$

11. 6×7 ______ **12.** 8×7 ______ **13.** 0×7 ______ **14.** 8×2 ______

15. 8×0 ______ **16.** 7×7 ______ **17.** 2×7 ______ **18.** 9×7 ______

19. Find the product of 8 and 9. ______

20. Find the product of 7 and 6. ______

21. Find the product of 7 and 8. ______

22. Find the product of 8 and 5. ______

23. How could you find the product of 7×8 if you know the product of 5×8?

____

____

24. How can you tell that 7×6 is greater than 6×5 without multiplying?

____

____

Name ______________________________

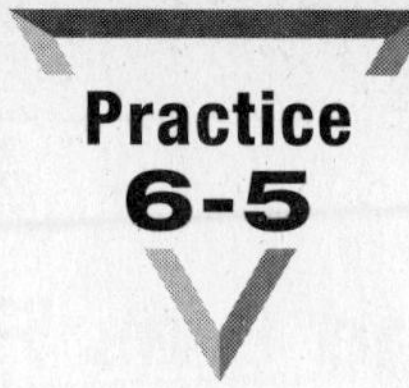

Decision Making

Annie is a party planner. She must plan the menu for 3 dinners; one for 4 people, one for 7 people, and one for 8 people. She needs to make a table to find out how many of each item will be needed for each dinner.

Complete the table.

Number per Serving	4-Person Dinner	7-Person Dinner	8-Person Dinner
6 snack crackers	24	42	48
4 potatoes			
2 chicken pieces			
7 baby carrots			
3 broccoli spears			
8 parsley sprigs			
7 strawberries			
1 mint			

1. How many baby carrots will Annie need for the 8-person dinner? ________

2. How many chicken pieces will she need for the 7-person dinner? ________

3. Annie decides she wants to serve cream with the strawberries. She needs 3 spoonfuls for each person. How many spoonfuls does she need for:

   a. the 4-person dinner? ________________

   b. the 7-person dinner? ________________

   c. the 8-person dinner? ________________

4. One of the people at the 7-person dinner can't go. How many chicken pieces will Annie need for that dinner now? ________

5. An extra person will be going to the 4-person dinner. How many strawberries will Annie need for that dinner now? ________

Name ______________________________

Practice
Chapter 6
Section A

Review and Practice

(Lesson 1) Find each product.

1. $5 \times 3 =$ ______ **2.** $3 \times 2 =$ ______

3. $6 \times 3 =$ ______ **4.** $7 \times 3 =$ ______

5. Leo wants to make 3 apple pies. The recipe calls for 4 apples per pie. How many apples will he need? ______________

(Lesson 2) Find each product.

6. $5 \times 4 =$ ______ **7.** $6 \times 4 =$ ______

8. $4 \times 4 =$ ______ **9.** $4 \times 9 =$ ______

10. Joel bought 4 boxes of note pads. Each box contained 8 note pads. How many notepads did Joel buy? ______________

(Lesson 3) Find each product.

11. $9 \times 6 =$ ______ **12.** $3 \times 6 =$ ______

13. $6 \times 8 =$ ______ **14.** $6 \times 0 =$ ______

15. Each actor receives 6 free passes to each show. There are 7 shows. How many free passes does each actor receive? ______________

(Lesson 4) Find each product.

16. $7 \times 6 =$ ______ **17.** $8 \times 3 =$ ______

18. $9 \times 8 =$ ______ **19.** $8 \times 7 =$ ______

20. $7 \times 7 =$ ______ **21.** $8 \times 8 =$ ______

(Mixed Review) Find each sum or difference.

22. $\begin{array}{r} 612 \\ +839 \\ \hline \end{array}$ **23.** $\begin{array}{r} 948 \\ -479 \\ \hline \end{array}$ **24.** $\begin{array}{r} 177 \\ -\ \ 91 \\ \hline \end{array}$ **25.** $\begin{array}{r} 608 \\ +\ \ 55 \\ \hline \end{array}$

Name ______________________

Practice 6-6

Exploring Patterns on a Hundred Chart: 3s and 6s

1	2	3	4	5	6	7	8	9	10
11	12	13	14	15	16	17	18	19	20
21	22	23	24	25	26	27	28	29	30
31	32	33	34	35	36	37	38	39	40
41	42	43	44	45	46	47	48	49	50
51	52	53	54	55	56	57	58	59	60

1	2	3	4	5	6	7	8	9	10
11	12	13	14	15	16	17	18	19	20
21	22	23	24	25	26	27	28	29	30
31	32	33	34	35	36	37	38	39	40
41	42	43	44	45	46	47	48	49	50
51	52	53	54	55	56	57	58	59	60

1. What is the sum of the digits in each multiple of 3?

____

2. How can you tell if a number is a multiple of 6?

____

____

Find each missing number. You may use a hundred chart to help.

3. $3 \times \square = 18$

4. $\square \times 3 = 9$

5. $6 \times \square = 36$

6. $\square \times 9 = 54$

7. $\square \times 8 = 48$

8. $3 \times \square = 18$

Write true or false. If the answer is false, explain why.

9. 34 is a multiple of 3.

____

10. 24 is a multiple of 3 and 6.

____

11. 16 is not a multiple of 6 or 3.

____

Name ______________________________

Practice 6-7

Exploring Patterns on a Fact Table

Look for patterns in multiples of greater numbers.

1. What is the pattern for multiples of 10?

____

2. What is the pattern for multiples of 11?

____

3. What is the pattern for multiples of 12?

____

Find each product.

4. 9×9 ________

5. 7×8 ________

6. 6×12 ________

7. 10×11 ________

8. 8×5 ________

9. 7×9 ________

10. 12×7 ________

11. 11×11 ________

12. 12×6 ________

13. 7×10 ________

14. 12×9 ________

15. 11×3 ________

Continue each pattern.

16. 33, 44, 55, ________, ________, ________

17. 72, 60, 48, ________, ________, ________

18. 0, 20, 40, ________, ________, ________

19. 132, 110, 88, ________, ________, ________

20. 48, 60, 72, ________, ________, ________

Name ______________________________

Practice 6-8

Multiplying with 3 Factors

Find each product.

1. $(4 \times 3) \times 2$ ______

2. $1 \times (6 \times 8)$ ______

3. $9 \times 1 \times 7$ ______

4. $5 \times (3 \times 3)$ ______

5. $2 \times 1 \times 5$ ______

6. $(0 \times 1) \times 8$ ______

7. $2 \times 0 \times 9$ ______

8. $3 \times (2 \times 5)$ ______

9. $6 \times (6 \times 1)$ ______

10. $(3 \times 2) \times 7$ ______

11. $1 \times 7 \times 4$ ______

12. $(2 \times 0) \times 8$ ______

13. $(3 \times 6) \times 0$ ______

14. $(2 \times 12) \times 1$ ______

15. $6 \times 3 \times 3$ ______

16. Find the product of 1, 7, and 6. ______

17. Find the product of 9, 4, and 0. ______

18. Does 6×4 have the same product as $3 \times 4 \times 2$? Explain.

____

____

19. If you know the product of $5 \times 2 \times 3$, do you also know the product of $3 \times 2 \times 5$? Explain.

____

____

Name ______________________________

Compare Strategies: Look for a Pattern and Draw a Picture

Use any strategy to solve each problem.

1. Suppose you are planning a picnic for 34 people. You must buy paper plates in packages of 8. How many packages of paper plates will you need? ____________

2. One package of rolls has enough rolls for 8 burgers. How many packages of rolls do you need for 25 burgers? ____________

3. Your softball team has a party. Everyone uses 4 napkins. If there are 13 people at the party, how many napkins were used? ____________

4. One loaf of bread makes 10 sandwiches. How many loaves do you need to make 54 sandwiches?

   ____

5. You are making pizza for a party. Each pizza has 8 slices.
   a. If 93 people will be at the party, how many pizzas should you make so that each person gets one slice?

   ____

   b. How many slices will be left over? ____________

6. Each jug of juice serves 12 people. How many jugs will you need for 60 people? ____________

Name ______________________

Review and Practice

(Lesson 6) Write true or false. You may use a hundred chart to help.

1. 42 is a multiple of 6. ________

2. 41 is a multiple of 3. ________

3. 83 is a multiple of 3 and 6. ________

4. All multiples of 6 are also multiples of 3. ________

(Lesson 7) Continue each pattern.

5. 18, 27, 36, ______, ______, ______

6. 36, 48, 60, ______, ______, ______

7. How can you tell without multiplying that 6×10 does not equal 66?

____

(Lesson 8) Find each product.

8. $5 \times 2 \times 8 =$ ______

9. $1 \times 9 \times 4 =$ ______

10. $0 \times 7 \times 1 =$ ______

11. $3 \times 2 \times 7 =$ ______

12. $2 \times (2 \times 3) =$ ______

13. $(6 \times 1) \times 5 =$ ______

(Lesson 9) Solve. Use any strategy.

14. You want to send cards to 37 people. The cards you want to send come in packages of 6. How many packages will you need? ________

15. While on vacation Marsha sent 35 postcards. She sent 7 postcards from each city she visited. How many cities did she visit? ________

(Mixed Review) Continue each pattern.

16. 48, 45, 42, ______, ______, ______

17. 6, 10, 14, 18, ______, ______, ______

18. 12, 24, 36, ______, ______, ______

Name ________________________________

Practice
Chapters 1–6

Cumulative Review

(Chapter 3 Lesson 9) Find each sum.

1. $\begin{array}{r} 35 \\ 66 \\ +\ 88 \\ \hline \end{array}$ **2.** $\begin{array}{r} 84 \\ 28 \\ +\ 53 \\ \hline \end{array}$ **3.** $\begin{array}{r} 679 \\ 44 \\ +\ 345 \\ \hline \end{array}$ **4.** $\begin{array}{r} 71 \\ 93 \\ +\ 309 \\ \hline \end{array}$

5. Patricia earned 96, 95, and 87 on three math tests. She needs a total of 279 points to get an A average. Does she have enough points for an A? Explain.

____

(Chapter 4 Lesson 11) Find each difference.

6. $\begin{array}{r} 800 \\ -\ 58 \\ \hline \end{array}$ **7.** $\begin{array}{r} 907 \\ -\ 628 \\ \hline \end{array}$ **8.** $\begin{array}{r} 600 \\ -\ 299 \\ \hline \end{array}$ **9.** $\begin{array}{r} 200 \\ -\ 184 \\ \hline \end{array}$

(Chapter 5 Lesson 4) Find each product.

10. $\begin{array}{r} 8 \\ \times\ 2 \\ \hline \end{array}$ **11.** $\begin{array}{r} 2 \\ \times\ 4 \\ \hline \end{array}$ **12.** $\begin{array}{r} 2 \\ \times\ 5 \\ \hline \end{array}$ **13.** $\begin{array}{r} 7 \\ \times\ 2 \\ \hline \end{array}$ **14.** $\begin{array}{r} 9 \\ \times\ 2 \\ \hline \end{array}$

(Chapter 6 Lessons 1–3) Find each product.

15. $\begin{array}{r} 3 \\ \times\ 2 \\ \hline \end{array}$ **16.** $\begin{array}{r} 4 \\ \times\ 3 \\ \hline \end{array}$ **17.** $\begin{array}{r} 4 \\ \times\ 5 \\ \hline \end{array}$ **18.** $\begin{array}{r} 7 \\ \times\ 4 \\ \hline \end{array}$ **19.** $\begin{array}{r} 9 \\ \times\ 6 \\ \hline \end{array}$

20. $\begin{array}{r} 8 \\ \times\ 3 \\ \hline \end{array}$ **21.** $\begin{array}{r} 6 \\ \times\ 4 \\ \hline \end{array}$ **22.** $\begin{array}{r} 3 \\ \times\ 6 \\ \hline \end{array}$ **23.** $\begin{array}{r} 7 \\ \times\ 6 \\ \hline \end{array}$ **24.** $\begin{array}{r} 9 \\ \times\ 3 \\ \hline \end{array}$

Use with page 271.

Name ______________________________

Practice 7-1

Exploring Division as Sharing

Mrs. Robbins and Mrs. Siani are making up flower baskets for a wedding celebration. They have to do 6 baskets in all. They decide to share the work equally. How many baskets will each prepare?

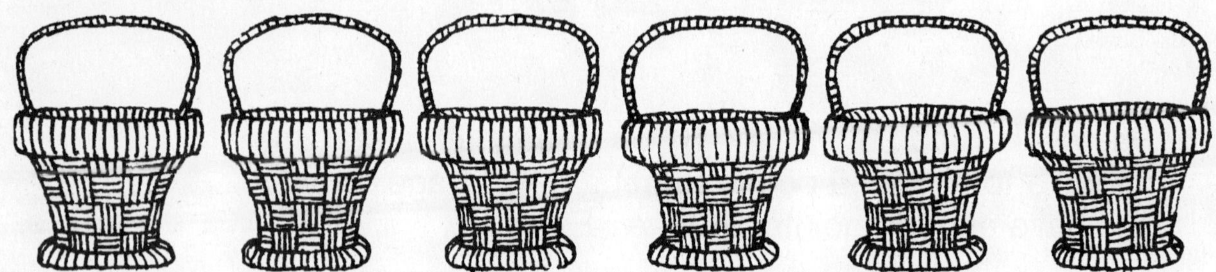

1. Draw a line to divide the baskets into 2 equal groups.
2. 6 flower baskets ÷ 2 women = ______ baskets each.

Complete. You may use counters or draw pictures to help.

3. 8 ÷ 2 = ______
4. 16 ÷ 4 = ______

Solve. You may use counters or draw pictures to help.

5. Misha and Angie have volunteered to call 10 people to raise money for their Girl Scout troop. If they divide the calls equally, how many calls will each girl make? ______________________
6. You are helping the school yearbook editor. There are 24 pictures that will go on 3 pages in the yearbook. How many photos will you put on each page if you divide them evenly? ______________________

Name ________________________________

Practice 7-2

Exploring Division as Repeated Subtraction

Maria is pouring glasses of iced tea. She has 18 ice cubes. If she wants to put 6 ice cubes in each glass, how many glasses can she fill?

1. Draw lines to show 6 ice cubes per glass.

2. 18 ice cubes ÷ 6 per glass = ______ glasses.

Complete. You may use counters or complete the pictures to help.

3. 10 letters

2 in each mailbox

10 ÷ 2 = ______

4. 12 flowers

3 in each pot

12 ÷ 3 = ______

5. Brenda puts 3 cookies on each plate. Can she make 5 plates with 15 cookies? Draw a picture and explain.

____

____

Name ______________________

Practice
7-3

Exploring Division Stories

1. Three friends share a 6-pack of juice equally. How many cans of juice does each one drink?

   6 ÷ 3 = ______ cans

2. Telia made 15 snowflake ornaments. If she gives 3 to each of her friends, how many friends will get ornaments?

   15 ÷ 3 = ______ friends

Write a division story for each. You may use counters to solve.

3. 8 ÷ 4 = ______

   ____

   ____

4. 21 ÷ 7 = ______

   ____

   ____

Complete each number sentence. You may use counters to solve.

5. 16 ÷ ______ = 2 6. 24 ÷ ______ = 8 7. 36 ÷ ______ = 4

Solve. You may use counters or draw pictures to help.

8. Dana has 10 free show tickets. He can give away 2 to each person in his family. How many people are in his family?

   ______

9. Beth's book has 28 pages. She reads 4 pages each day. How long will it take her to finish the book? ______

10. Michael used 12 slices of cheese to make 4 equal-sized sandwiches. How many slices of cheese did he put in each sandwich? ______

Name ______________________________

Practice
Chapter 7
Section A

Review and Practice

(Lessons 1 and 2) Use the pictures to help you complete each number sentence.

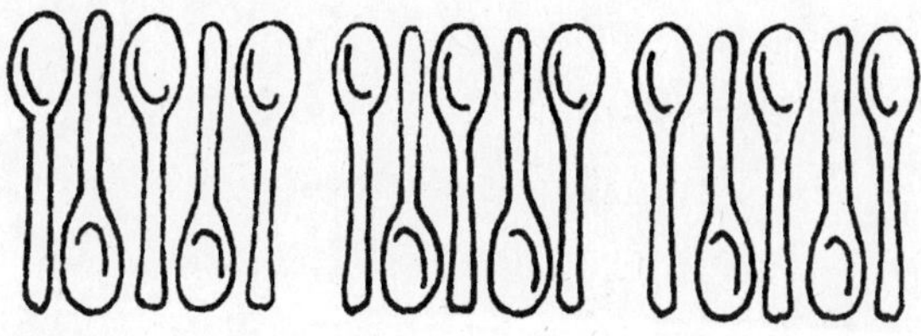

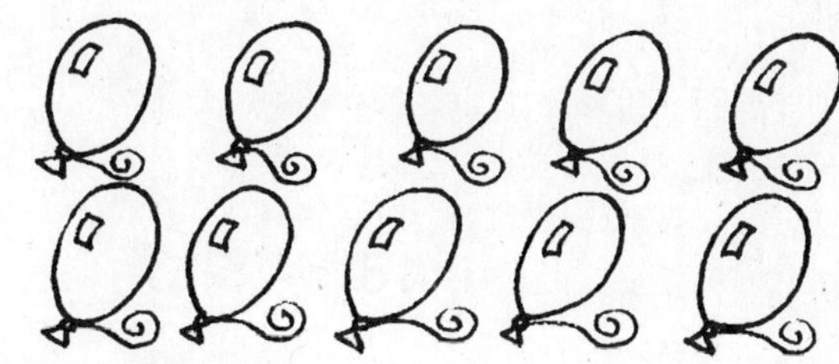

1. 15 ÷ 3 = ________

2. 10 ÷ 2 = ________

3. 14 ÷ 7 = ________

4. 8 ÷ 4 = ________

5. Natalie and her two brothers have $12 to spend on lunch. One Kid's Meal costs $3. Do they have enough money? Explain how you know.

____

(Lesson 3) Write a division story for each. You may use counters to solve.

6. 20 ÷ 4 = ________

____

____

7. 18 ÷ 9 = ________

____

____

(Mixed Review) Complete each number sentence.

8. ________ + 8 = 13

9. ________ − 9 = 5

10. 6 + ________ = 11

Name ______________________

Practice 7-4

Connecting Multiplication and Division

Complete. You may use counters to help.

1. $7 \times$ ______ $= 28$
$28 \div 7 =$ ______

2. $6 \times$ ______ $= 42$
$42 \div 6 =$ ______

3. $2 \times$ ______ $= 12$
$12 \div 2 =$ ______

4. $2 \times$ ______ $= 18$
$18 \div 2 =$ ______

5. $3 \times$ ______ $= 21$
$21 \div 3 =$ ______

6. $7 \times$ ______ $= 35$
$35 \div 7 =$ ______

7. $2 \times$ ______ $= 6$
$6 \div 2 =$ ______

8. $5 \times$ ______ $= 25$
$25 \div 5 =$ ______

9. $6 \times$ ______ $= 12$
$12 \div 6 =$ ______

10. $4 \times$ ______ $= 32$
$32 \div 4 =$ ______

11. $3 \times$ ______ $= 30$
$30 \div 3 =$ ______

12. $8 \times$ ______ $= 24$
$24 \div 8 =$ ______

13. What multiplication fact could you use to solve $24 \div 3$?

____

14. What are the number sentences in the fact family with $32 \div 4 = 8$?

____

15. What multiplication fact could you use to solve $20 \div 2$?

____

16. What are the number sentences in the fact family with $24 \div 4 = 6$?

____

Name ___________________________

Practice
7-5

Dividing by 2

Find each quotient.

1. $2\overline{)10}$ **2.** $2\overline{)4}$ **3.** $2\overline{)16}$ **4.** $2\overline{)18}$

5. 6 ÷ 2 = ______ **6.** 2 ÷ 2 = ______

7. 8 ÷ 2 = ______ **8.** 4 ÷ 2 = ______

9. Divide 12 by 2. ______ **10.** Divide 14 by 2. ______

11. How can you use multiplication to help you find 18 ÷ 2?

____

12. Nancy says, "I can solve 6 ÷ 2 using the fact 6 × 2 = 12." Do you agree or disagee? Explain.

____

13. Ben says, "I can solve 16 ÷ 2 by using the fact 2 × 8 = 16." Do you agree or disagree? Explain.

____

14. How can you use multiplication to help you find 8 ÷ 2?

____

15. How can you use multiplication to help you find 14 ÷ 7?

____

16. Use multiplication facts to help you find:

a. 20 ÷ 2 ______

b. 16 ÷ 2 ______

c. 12 ÷ 2 ______

Name ____________________

Practice 7-6

Dividing by 5

Find each quotient.

1. $5\overline{)15}$
2. $5\overline{)25}$
3. $5\overline{)10}$
4. $5\overline{)30}$
5. $2\overline{)8}$
6. $5\overline{)40}$
7. $5\overline{)35}$
8. $2\overline{)12}$
9. 45 ÷ 5 = ______
10. 20 ÷ 5 = ______
11. 25 ÷ 5 = ______
12. 30 ÷ 5 = ______
13. 16 ÷ 2 = ______
14. 10 ÷ 5 = ______
15. 15 ÷ 5 = ______
16. 45 ÷ 5 = ______
17. Divide 20 by 5. ______
18. What multiplication fact can help you find $5\overline{)40}$?

    ____

19. What multiplication fact can help you find $2\overline{)14}$?

    ____

20. What multiplication fact can help you find 45 ÷ 5?

    ____

21. What multiplication fact can help you find 10 ÷ 2?

    ____

22. How could you take away groups of 5 to find 25 ÷ 5?

    ____

    ____

Name ______________________________

Practice
7-7

Dividing by 3 and 4

Find each quotient.

1. $3\overline{)15}$ **2.** $4\overline{)8}$ **3.** $4\overline{)12}$

4. $5\overline{)30}$ **5.** $3\overline{)6}$ **6.** $3\overline{)21}$

7. $4\overline{)28}$ **8.** $4\overline{)20}$ **9.** $3\overline{)12}$

10. $2\overline{)10}$ **11.** $3\overline{)18}$ **12.** $4\overline{)32}$

13. $27 \div 3 =$ ______ **14.** $9 \div 3 =$ ______

15. $24 \div 4 =$ ______ **16.** $24 \div 3 =$ ______

17. $25 \div 5 =$ ______ **18.** $16 \div 4 =$ ______

19. $14 \div 2 =$ ______ **20.** $36 \div 4 =$ ______

21. Divide 18 by 3. ______

22. Divide 20 by 4. ______

23. How many 4s are in 28? ______

24. How many 3s are in 15? ______

25. How many 4s are in 40? ______

26. How many 3s are in 30? ______

27. How could you take away equal groups to find $4\overline{)12}$?

____

Name ______________________________

Practice 7-8

Exploring Dividing with 0 and 1

Find each quotient. Complete the division rule.

1. a. 3 ÷ 1 = ______

b. Rule: Any number divided by 1 equals ____________.

2. a. 5 ÷ 5 = ______

b. Rule: Any number (except 0) divided by itself equals ______.

3. a. 0 ÷ 2 = ______

b. Rule: Zero divided by any number (except 0) equals ______.

4. Can you divide by 0? ______

Find each quotient. Write the division rule that explains the answer.

5. 4 ÷ 4 = ______

Rule: ______________________________

6. 0 ÷ 7 = ______

Rule: ______________________________

7. 8 ÷ 1 = ______

Rule: ______________________________

Write >, <, or =.

8. 6 ÷ 6 ◯ 3 ÷ 3

9. 12 ÷ 4 ◯ 12 ÷ 3

10. 25 ÷ 5 ◯ 0 ÷ 5

11. 4 ÷ 1 ◯ 6 ÷ 1

12. 6 ÷ 2 ◯ 3 ÷ 1

13. 0 ÷ 4 ◯ 4 ÷ 2

14. 8 ÷ 4 ◯ 4 ÷ 2

15. 10 ÷ 5 ◯ 5 ÷ 5

Name ______________________

Practice 7-9

Analyze Word Problems: Choose an Operation

Which number sentence would you use to solve the problem? Explain.

1. Suppose Blair worked 6 hours a week for 3 weeks. How many hours did she work?

   A. $6 + 3 = 9$ **B.** $6 \times 3 = 18$ **C.** $6 - 3 = 3$ **D.** $18 + 6 = 24$

   ____

2. Marcie sold $8 worth of fruit tarts at a bake sale. Each tart cost $2. How many tarts did she sell?

   A. $8 - 2 = 6$ **B.** $8 \div 2 = 4$ **C.** $8 \times 2 = 16$ **D.** $8 + 2 = 10$

   ____

3. Arthur had 6 tickets to a concert. He gave 2 of them to Joe. How many tickets did he have left?

   A. $6 - 2 = 4$ **B.** $6 + 2 = 8$ **C.** $6 \times 2 = 12$ **D.** $6 \div 2 = 3$

   ____

Write which operation you would use. Then solve.

4. Zachary bought 4 bananas and 3 oranges. How many pieces of fruit did he buy?

   ____

5. Lars bought a 2-pound bag of dog food for $2.25 and a 1-pound bag of cat food for $1.54. How much money did he spend?

   ____

6. Isabella earns $4 per hour working at the pet store. If she works for 7 hours, how much money will she earn?

   ____

7. Nick had 16 marbles. He gave an equal number to each of 4 friends. How many marbles did each friend get?

   ____

Name ____________________

Practice
Chapter 7
Section B

Review and Practice

Vocabulary Write true or false for each statement.

1. In the problem 18 ÷ 2 = 9, the divisor is 9. ________
2. Fact families are groups of related facts using the same set of digits. ________
3. The dividend in the problem 24 ÷ 3 = 8 is 24. ________
4. The quotient in the problem 12 ÷ 4 = 3 is 12. ________

(Lessons 5–8) Find each quotient.

5. 2 ÷ 2 = ________
6. 16 ÷ 4 = ________
7. 20 ÷ 5 = ________
8. 8 ÷ 2 = ________
9. 12 ÷ 3 = ________
10. 40 ÷ 5 = ________
11. 20 ÷ 4 = ________
12. 18 ÷ 3 = ________
13. 14 ÷ 2 = ________
14. 45 ÷ 5 = ________
15. 54 ÷ 1 = ________
16. 0 ÷ 2 = ________
17. 27 ÷ 3 = ________
18. 36 ÷ 4 = ________
19. 0 ÷ 4 = ________
20. 16 ÷ 2 = ________

21. $2\overline{)18}$
22. $5\overline{)30}$
23. $3\overline{)21}$
24. $4\overline{)8}$

(Lesson 9) Write which operation you would use. Then solve.

25. Selma wants to build bird houses to give as gifts. It takes 4 boards to make one house. Selma has 24 boards. How many bird houses can she make?

____

26. Nu has to write 3 reports. Each report must be 2 pages. How many pages must he write?

____

(Mixed Review) Find each missing factor.

27. 1 × ________ × 8 = 0
28. 3 × ________ × 2 = 24
29. ________ × 5 × 2 = 20
30. 4 × 1 × ________ = 20

Name ______________________________

Practice
7-10

Dividing by 6 and 7

Find each quotient.

1. $6\overline{)18}$

2. $7\overline{)14}$

3. $6\overline{)24}$

4. $7\overline{)28}$

5. $6\overline{)6}$

6. $1\overline{)7}$

7. $6\overline{)54}$

8. $7\overline{)49}$

9. $7\overline{)42}$

10. $3\overline{)18}$

11. $6\overline{)12}$

12. $6\overline{)36}$

13. $42 \div 6 =$ ______

14. $7 \div 7 =$ ______

15. $56 \div 7 =$ ______

16. $12 \div 6 =$ ______

17. $63 \div 7 =$ ______

18. $21 \div 3 =$ ______

19. $0 \div 6 =$ ______

20. $30 \div 5 =$ ______

21. $35 \div 7 =$ ______

22. $48 \div 6 =$ ______

23. $24 \div 4 =$ ______

24. $21 \div 7 =$ ______

25. Divide 36 by 6. ______

26. Divide 30 by 6. ______

27. Divide 28 by 4. ______

28. Divide 0 by 7. ______

29. What multiplication fact can help you find $42 \div 7$?

____

30. What multiplication fact can help you find $24 \div 6$?

____

31. Is the quotient of $48 \div 6$ greater than or less than the quotient of $42 \div 7$? Explain.

____

32. Is the quotient of $63 \div 7$ greater than or less than the quotient of $54 \div 6$? Explain.

____

Name ______________________________

Practice 7-11

Dividing by 8 and 9

Find each quotient.

1. $8\overline{)16}$ **2.** $9\overline{)36}$ **3.** $8\overline{)40}$

4. $9\overline{)36}$ **5.** $7\overline{)21}$ **6.** $8\overline{)8}$

7. $9\overline{)45}$ **8.** $8\overline{)72}$ **9.** $9\overline{)0}$

10. $4\overline{)36}$ **11.** $9\overline{)63}$ **12.** $8\overline{)56}$

13. $81 \div 9 =$ ______ **14.** $32 \div 8 =$ ______

15. $27 \div 9 =$ ______ **16.** $9 \div 9 =$ ______

17. $64 \div 8 =$ ______ **18.** $54 \div 9 =$ ______

19. $72 \div 9 =$ ______ **20.** $24 \div 8 =$ ______

21. Divide 56 by 8. ______ **22.** Divide 18 by 9. ______

23. Divide 45 by 9. ______ **24.** Divide 56 by 7. ______

25. What multiplication fact can help you find $63 \div 9$?

____

26. What multiplication fact can help you find $48 \div 8$?

____

27. How does knowing $4 \times 9 = 36$ help you solve $36 \div 9$?

____

28. Which is greater, $48 \div 6$ or $48 \div 8$? Explain.

____

29. Which is greater, $81 \div 9$ or $36 \div 4$?

____

Name ______________________________

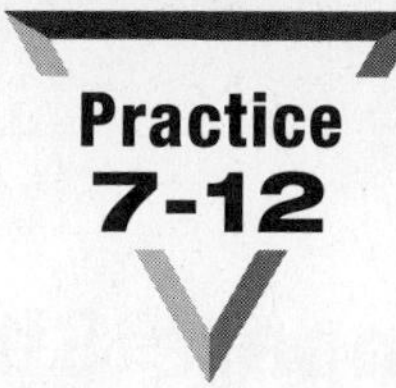

Exploring Even and Odd Numbers

1. Even numbers have 0, ______, 4, ______, or ______ in the ones place.

2. Odd numbers have 1, ______, ______, 7, or ______ in the ones place.

Write odd or even for each. You may use color cubes to help.

3. 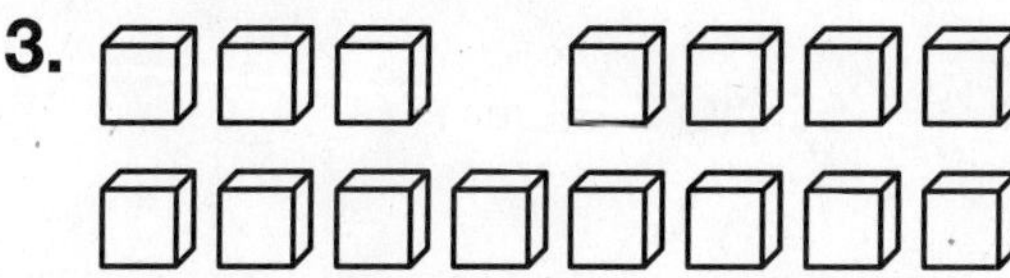

______

4. 

______

5. 6 ______ **6.** 19 ______ **7.** 9 ______ **8.** 24 ______

9. 18 ______ **10.** 17 ______ **11.** 11 ______ **12.** 23 ______

13. Start with 14 and name the next 5 even numbers. Explain how you know which numbers are even.

____

____

14. Add the pairs of odd numbers.
Do you get even or odd sums? ______

a. 7 + 5 ______ **b.** 3 + 9 ______ **c.** 11 + 7 ______

d. Can you think of any two odd numbers where the sum of the numbers will be odd? ______

15. Add the pairs of even and odd numbers.
Do you get even or odd sums? ______

a. 5 + 16 ______ **b.** 8 + 7 ______ **c.** 14 + 5 ______

d. Can you think of any two numbers, one even and the other odd, in which the sum is an even number? ______

16. Tenisha has two pages in her photo album to fill. She puts 7 photos on each page. Did she have an even or odd number of photos?

Explain. ______________________________

Name ______________________________

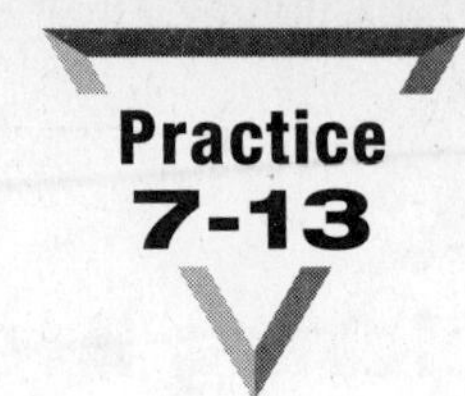

Compare Strategies: Use Objects and Make an Organized List

Use any strategy to solve.

1. Anita received 12 new stickers and a new sticker album on her birthday. She wants to put an equal number of stickers on each page that she uses.

a. How many pages could Anita use in her sticker album?

____

b. How many stickers could be on each page?

____

c. List all the ways Anita could put the stickers in her sticker album.

____

____

2. Paul has a collection of action figures. He wants to arrange the figures in equal rows. If Paul has 30 action figures, what are all the ways to arrange the figures?

____

____

3. Juan has 2 pairs of sneakers, one black pair and one white pair. He has 3 baseball caps, one red, one blue and the other orange. What are all the combinations of shoes and caps he could wear?

____

____

____

4. Rosalind must read an 18-page book. She wants to read an equal number of pages every day. List all the possible ways she could divide her reading.

____

____

Name ______________________________

Exploring Algebra: Balancing Scales

Find all the ways to balance each scale. Make a table to record each way. You may use color cubes to help.

1. a. Box A has 8 cubes inside. How many cubes can be in boxes B and C?

Fill in the missing numbers in the table.

A	8	8	8	8	8	8	8	8	8
B	8	7							0
C	0		2	3					

b. 2 cubes have been removed from box A. How many cubes are now in the boxes? Fill in the missing numbers in the table.

A							
B		5			2		0
C	0			3			

2. Box B has 7 cubes inside. Box C has 5 cubes inside. How many cubes are in each box A?

____

3. Box A has 15 cubes inside. How many cubes are in each box B?

____

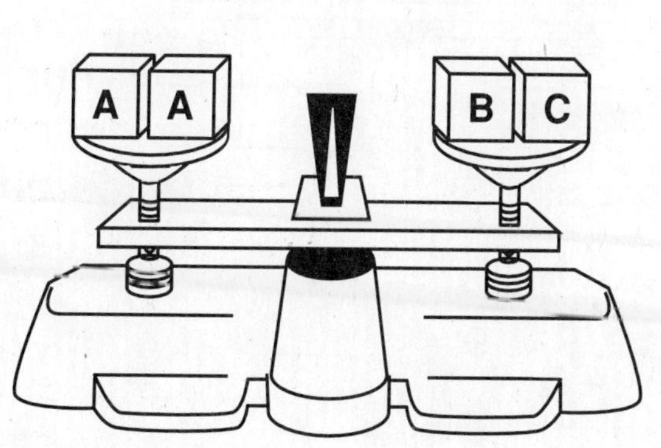

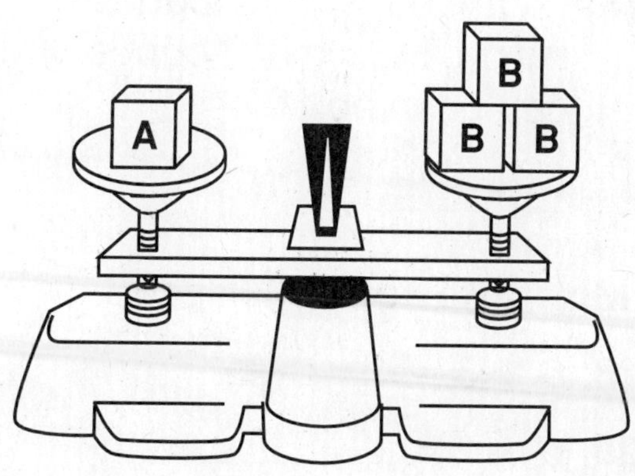

Name ________________________________

Review and Practice

Vocabulary Match the set of numbers with the word describing it.

1. even ________ **a.** 26, 32, 24, 48

2. odd ________ **b.** 31, 47, 19, 21

(Lessons 10 and 11) Find each quotient.

3. 12 ÷ 6 = ________ **4.** 16 ÷ 8 = ________

5. 21 ÷ 7 = ________ **6.** 28 ÷ 7 = ________

7. 18 ÷ 9 = ________ **8.** 45 ÷ 9 = ________

9. 24 ÷ 8 = ________ **10.** 18 ÷ 6 = ________

11. Divide 49 by 7. ________ **12.** Divide 56 by 8. ________

(Lesson 12) Write odd or even. You may use color cubes to help.

13. 17 ________ **14.** 36 ________ **15.** 15 ________

(Lesson 13) Use any strategy to solve.

16. Hunter wants to take a picture of his class. There are 24 students in his class. He wants them to stand in equal rows. What are all the ways he could arrange them?

____

____

(Lesson 14) Solve. You may use color cubes to help.

17. Each box A has 4 cubes inside. How many cubes can be in box B?

____

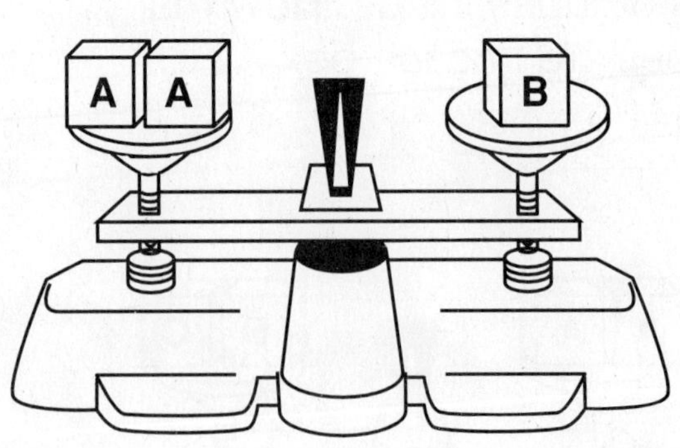

(Mixed Review) Multiply.

18. 6 × 8 = ________ **19.** 9 × 9 = ________

20. 5 × 7 = ________ **21.** 4 × 8 = ________

Name ____________________

Practice
Chapters 1–7

Cumulative Review

(Chapter 2 Lesson 5) Make a list or use any strategy to solve.

1. Chelsea sells flower bulbs to gardeners. She has 48 bulbs that can be packed in boxes of 8 or 4. How many ways can she pack the bulbs? ____________

Boxes of 8:							
Boxes of 4:							

(Chapter 6 Lessons 3, 4 and 8) Multiply.

2. $\begin{array}{r} 3 \\ \times 6 \\ \hline \end{array}$ **3.** $\begin{array}{r} 7 \\ \times 3 \\ \hline \end{array}$ **4.** $\begin{array}{r} 4 \\ \times 8 \\ \hline \end{array}$ **5.** $\begin{array}{r} 7 \\ \times 6 \\ \hline \end{array}$ **6.** $\begin{array}{r} 9 \\ \times 7 \\ \hline \end{array}$

7. $\begin{array}{r} 8 \\ \times 8 \\ \hline \end{array}$ **8.** $\begin{array}{r} 6 \\ \times 4 \\ \hline \end{array}$ **9.** $\begin{array}{r} 3 \\ \times 8 \\ \hline \end{array}$ **10.** $\begin{array}{r} 7 \\ \times 7 \\ \hline \end{array}$ **11.** $\begin{array}{r} 9 \\ \times 6 \\ \hline \end{array}$

12. $7 \times 8 =$ ________ **13.** $8 \times 6 =$ ________

14. $7 \times 4 =$ ________ **15.** $5 \times 6 \times 0 =$ ________

16. $2 \times 3 \times 8 =$ ________ **17.** $1 \times 7 \times 8 =$ ________

18. $2 \times 4 \times 3 =$ ________ **19.** $2 \times 2 \times 7 =$ ________

(Chapter 7 Lessons 6 and 7) Find each quotient.

20. $15 \div 3 =$ ________ **21.** $10 \div 5 =$ ________

22. $25 \div 5 =$ ________ **23.** $36 \div 4 =$ ________

24. $35 \div 5 =$ ________ **25.** $24 \div 4 =$ ________

26. $21 \div 3 =$ ________ **27.** $15 \div 5 =$ ________

28. $3\overline{)27}$ **29.** $4\overline{)28}$ **30.** $5\overline{)20}$ **31.** $3\overline{)9}$

Name ______________________

Practice 8-1

Exploring Solids

1. Color the figures with flat faces red.
2. Color the figures that roll blue.

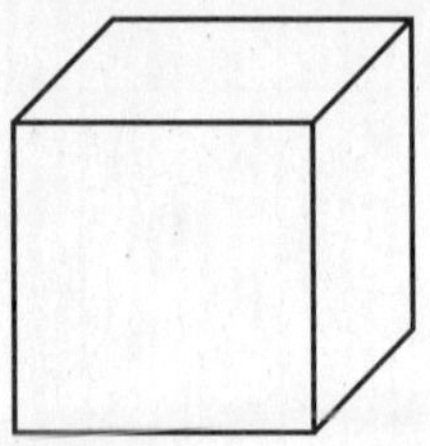
Cube

Sphere

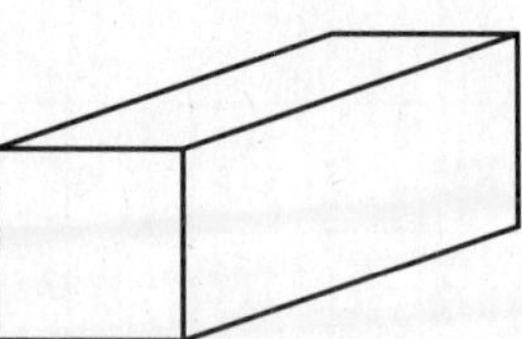
Rectangular Prism

Cone

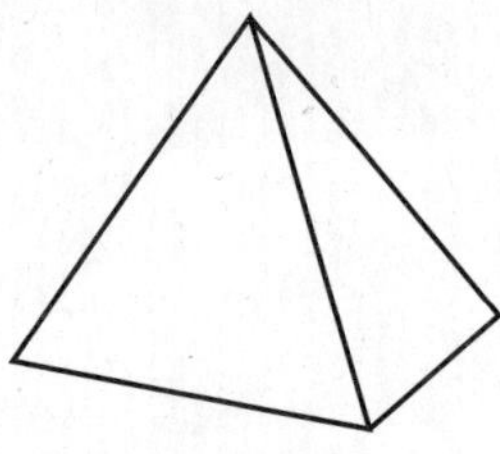
Pyramid

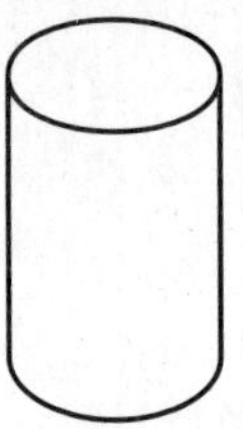
Cylinder

3. Which figures were colored twice? ______________________

Name the solid figure that each object looks like.

4. 

5. 

6. 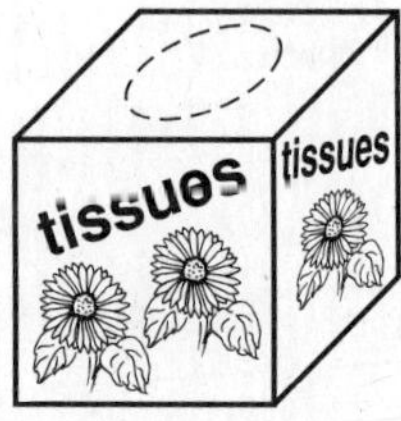

______________ ______________ ______________

7. What solid figure does a baseball look like? ______________
8. What solid figure does a drum look like? ______________
9. What solid figure does a book look like? ______________

Name ______________________________

Practice
8-2

Exploring Solids and Shapes

Name the shapes of the dotted faces on each solid figure.

1. 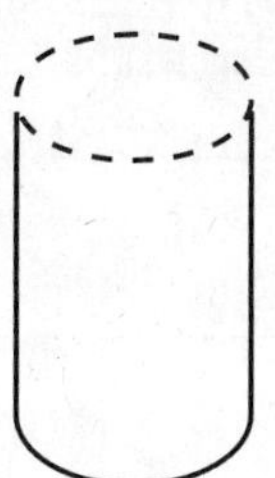

____

2. 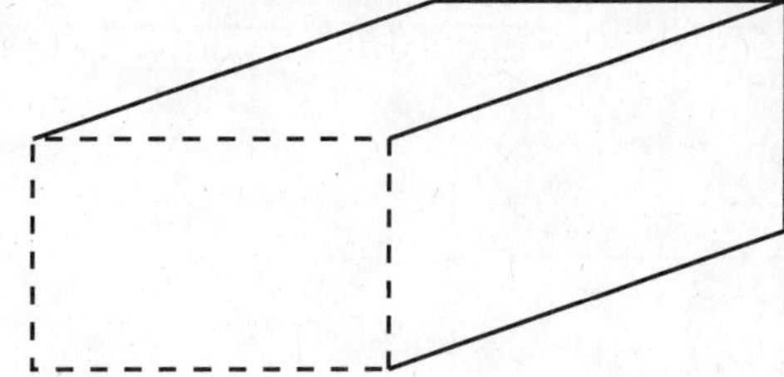

____

3. 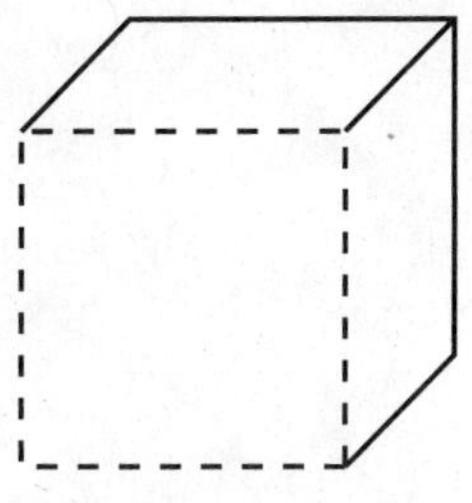

____

4. 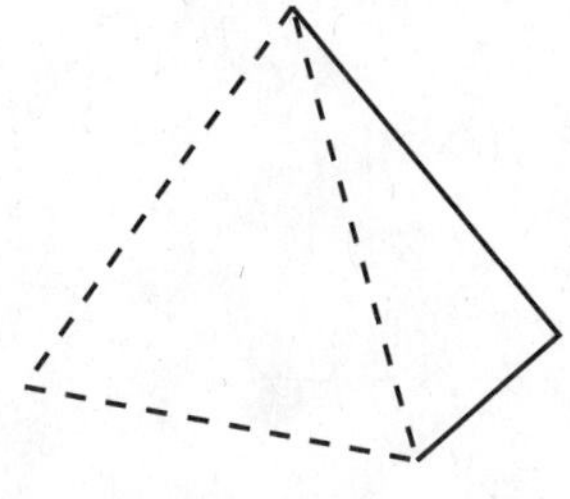

____

Name the shape that each object looks like.

5. 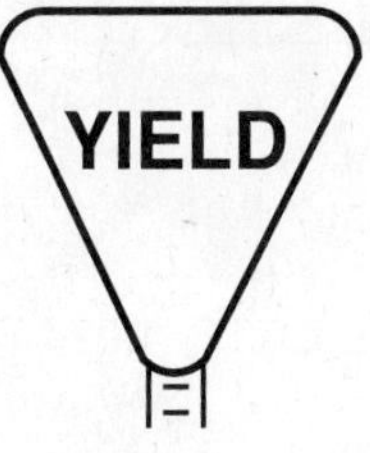

____

6. 

____

7. 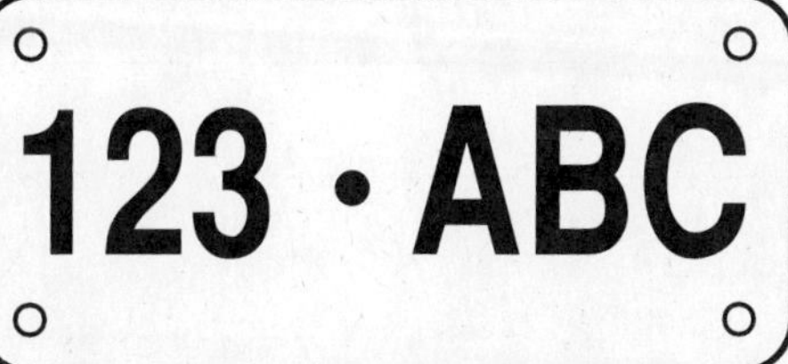

____

8. 

____

9. How many sides does a rectangle have? ______________

10. How many sides does a circle have? ______________

Name ______________________________

Practice 8-3

Lines and Line Segments

Write the name for each.

1. ______________

2. ______________

3. ______________

4. 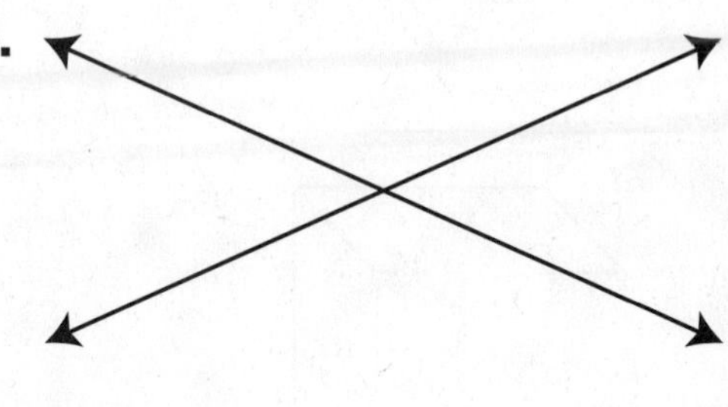

____

5. ______________

6. ______________

7. How many endpoints does a line segment have? __________

8. How is a line segment like a ray? How is it different?

____

____

9. If two lines intersect, can they also be parallel? Explain.

____

10. Draw a line segment.

11. Draw 2 parallel lines.

Name ____________________

Practice 8-4

Exploring Angles

1. Write the number 1 by the right angle.
2. Write the number 2 by the angle that is less than a right angle.
3. Write the number 3 by the angle that is greater than a right angle.

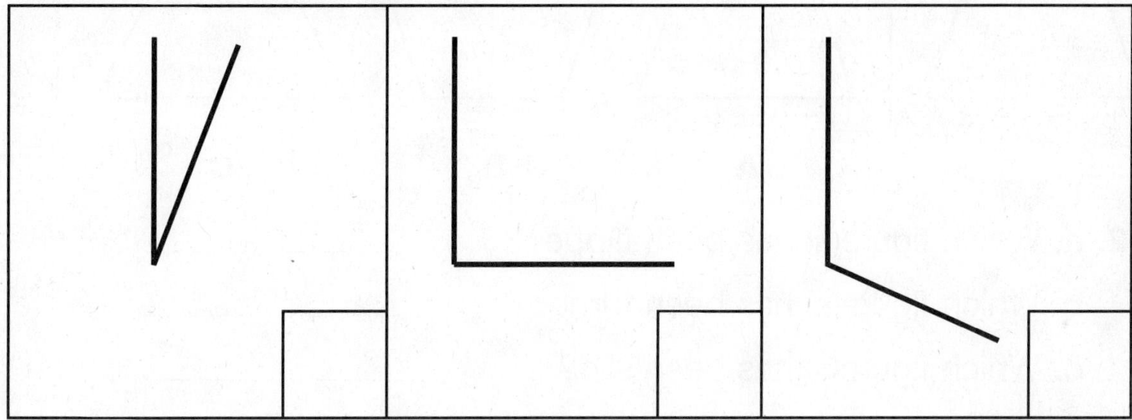

Write whether each angle is a right angle, less than a right angle, or greater than a right angle.

4.

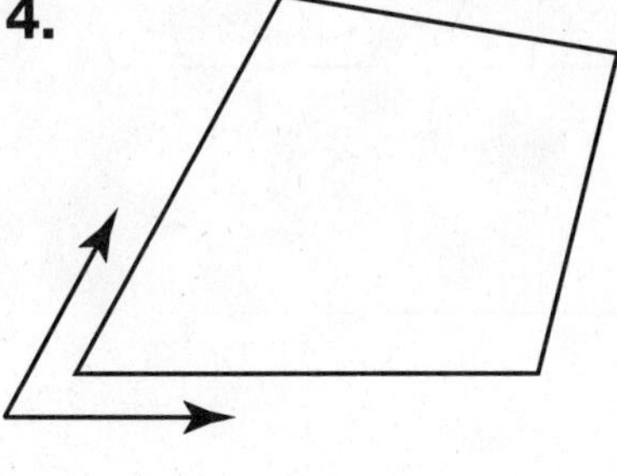

____

____

5.

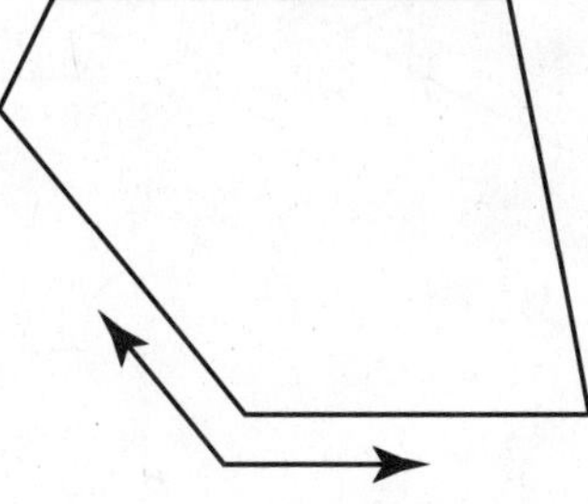

____

____

6.

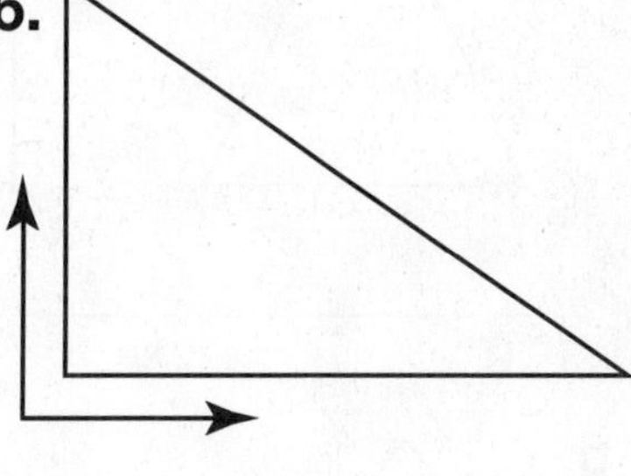

____

____

Write the number of right angles in each polygon.

7.

____

8.

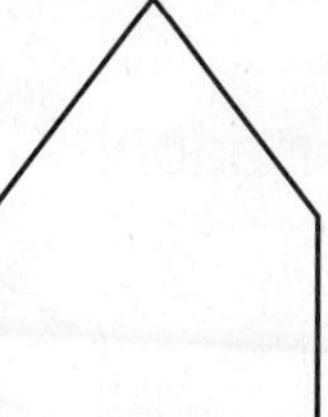

____

9.

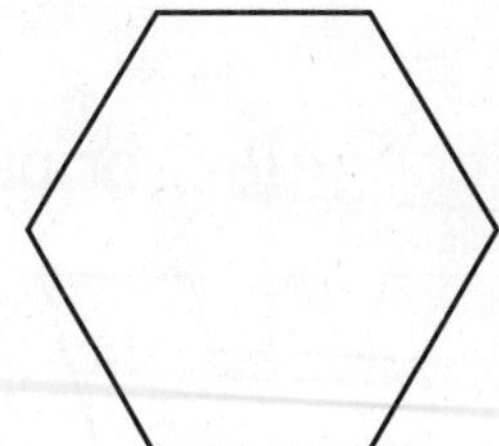

____

Name ______________________________

Practice
8-5

Exploring Slides, Flips, and Turns

Congruent figures have the same size and shape.

1. Color the figures that are congruent to the first figure blue.

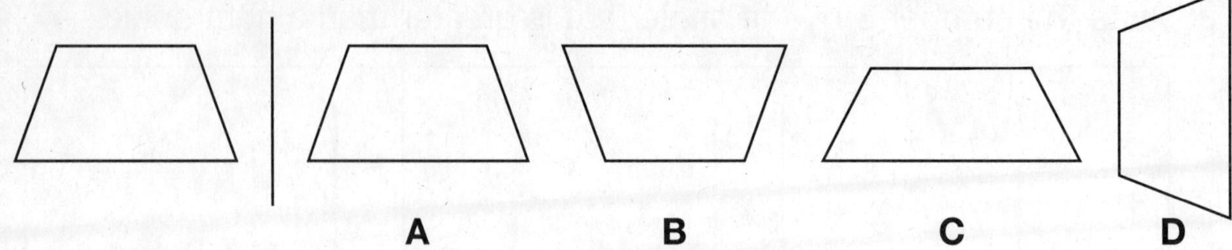

2. a. Which figure(s) has been flipped? ____________

b. Which figure(s) has been turned? ____________

c. Which figure(s) has been slid? ____________

Write slide, flip, or turn for each.

3.

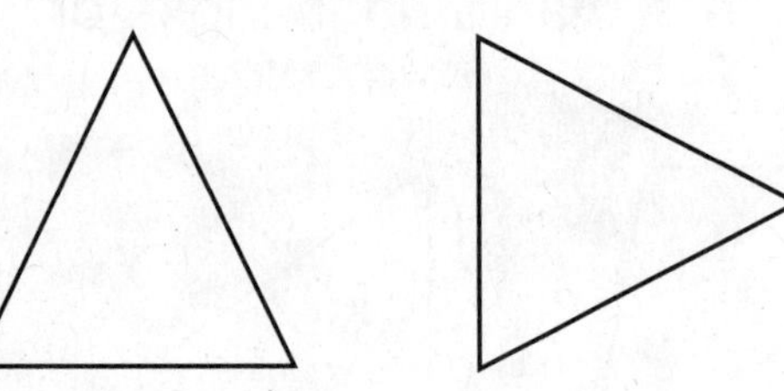

____

4.

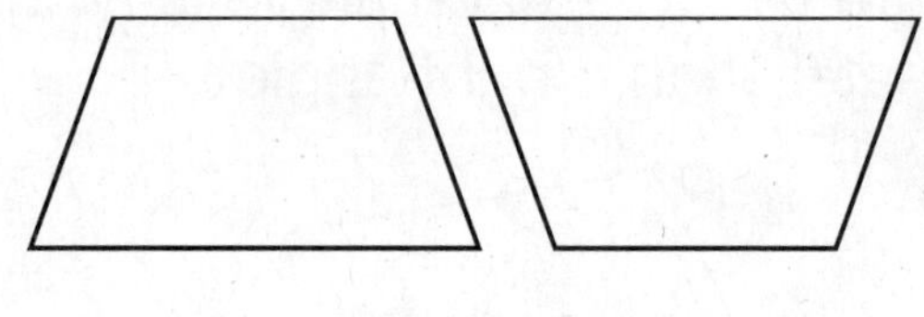

____

5.

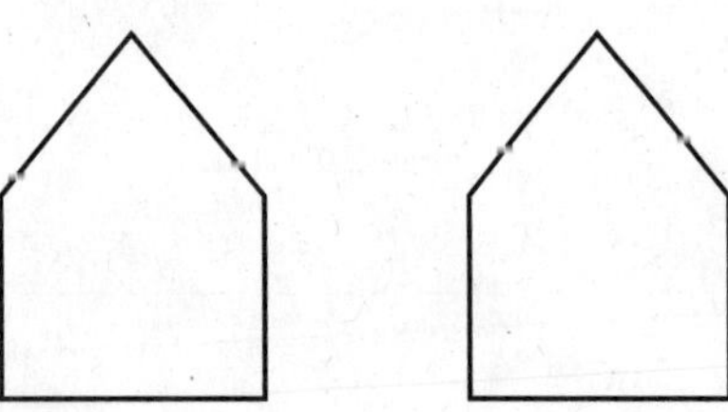

____

6.

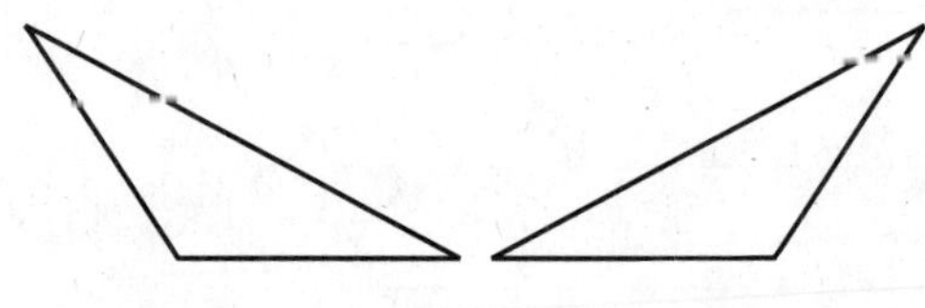

____

Write congruent or not congruent for each.

7.

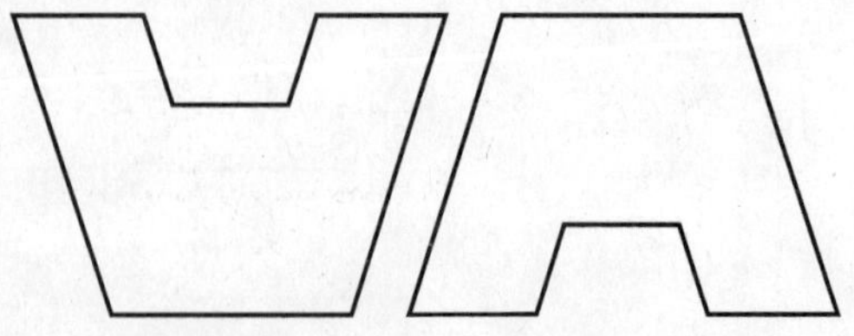

____

8.

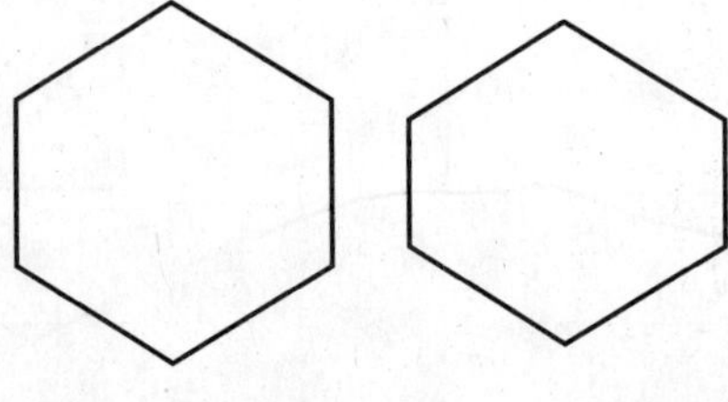

____

Name ____________________

Practice
8-6

Exploring Symmetry

A figure has a line of symmetry if you could fold the figure so both parts match exactly. Some figures have more than one line of symmetry.

1. Draw lines of symmetry on each figure. Color the figures that have only one line of symmetry.

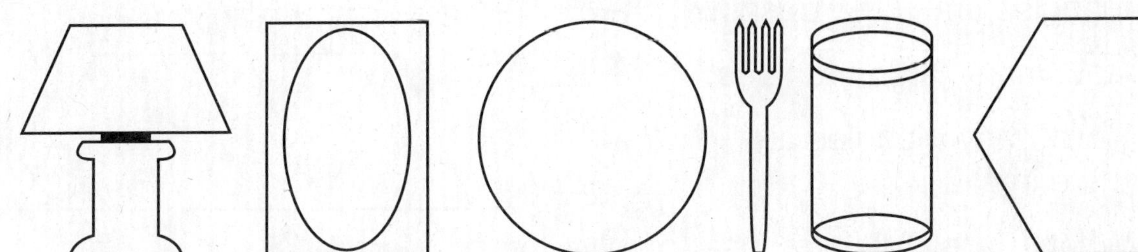

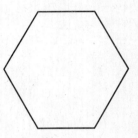

Does each figure appear to have a line of symmetry? Write yes or no.

2. 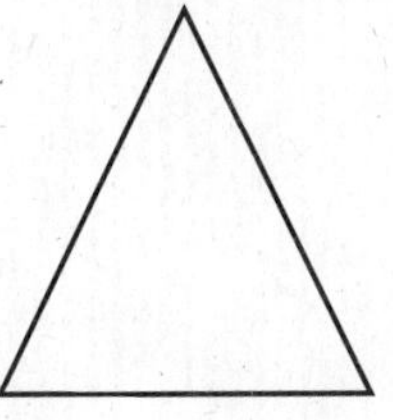

____

3. 

____

4. 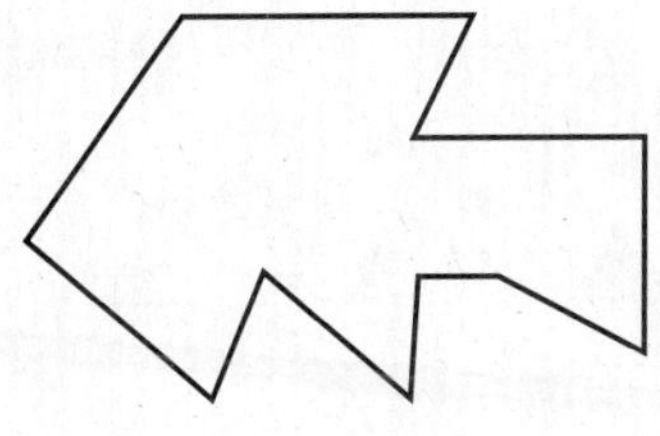

____

5. 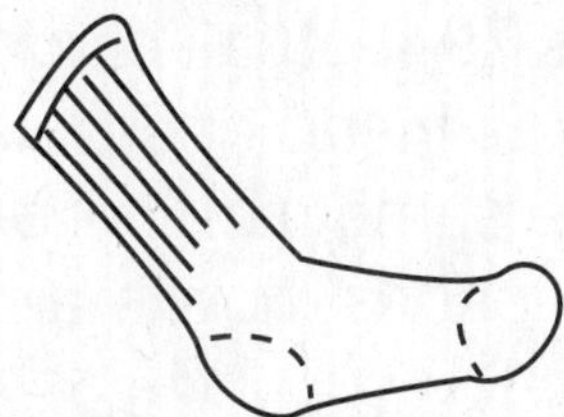

____

Does each line appear to be a line of symmetry?
Write yes or no. If not, draw a correct line of symmetry.

6. 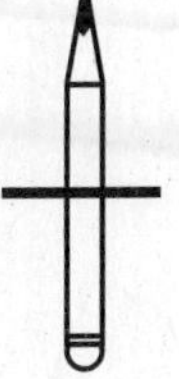

____

7. 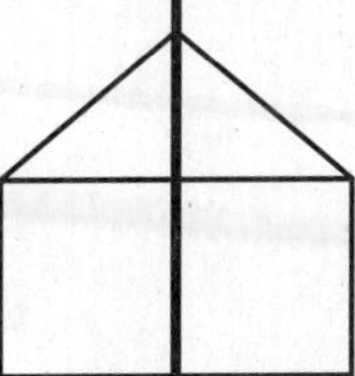

____

8. 

____

Name ______________________

Practice 8-7

Analyze Strategies: Solve a Simpler Problem

See how many triangles you can find in this design.

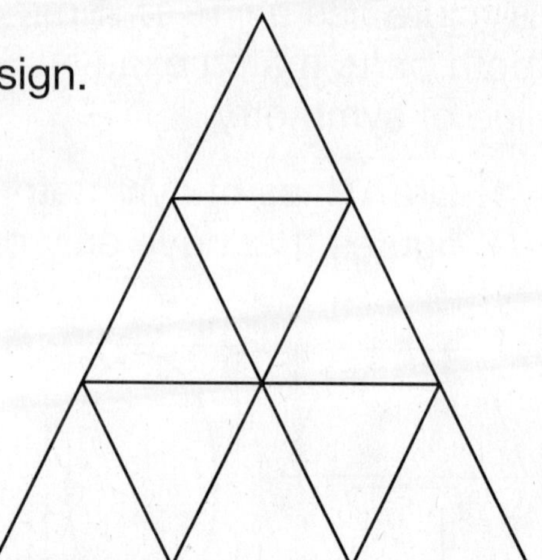

1. a. How many small triangles are in the design? ________
   b. How many medium-sized triangles are in the design? ________
   c. How many large triangles? ________
   d. How many triangles are there in all? ________
   e. What strategy did you use to solve the problem?

Use any strategy to solve each problem.

2. Sarah has three books to place together on her bookshelf. One book is red, another is blue, and the third is yellow. How many different ways can she arrange the books if she wants the blue book in the middle? ________
3. Bryan has 79 football cards in his collection. He gives seven to his friend and puts the rest in his album. He places the same number of cards on each page. If he uses nine pages, how many cards are on a page? ________
4. How many triangles can you find in this triangular design? ________

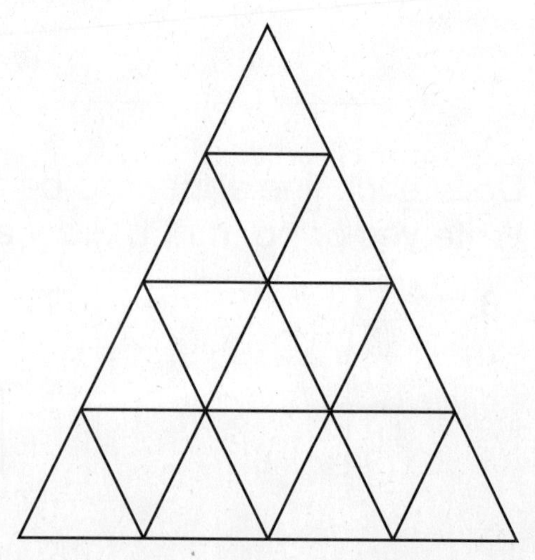

5. Four students are standing in a line. Ned is to the right of Helen. Carlos is the only one between Keith and Ned. Who is on the far left?

____

Name ______________________________

Practice
Chapter 8
Section A

Review and Practice

Vocabulary Write true or false for each.

1. A cone has no faces.

____

2. A line segment is endless in both directions.

____

3. A right angle is an angle that forms a square corner.

____

4. A corner is where two or more edges meet.

____

(Lesson 1) Name the solid figure that each object looks like.

5. 

____

6. 

____

(Lesson 2) Write the number of sides that each shape has.

7. 

____

8. 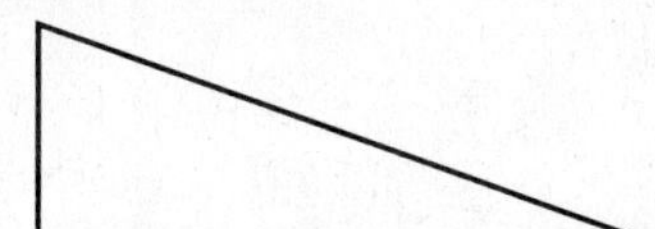

____

9. 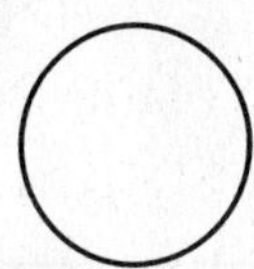

____

(Lesson 5) Write slide, flip, or turn for each.

10. 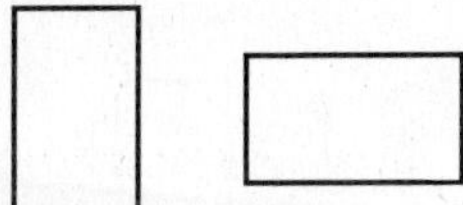

____

11. 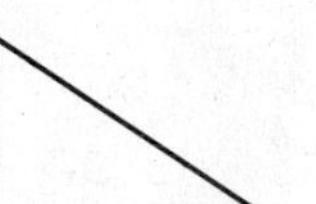

____

12. 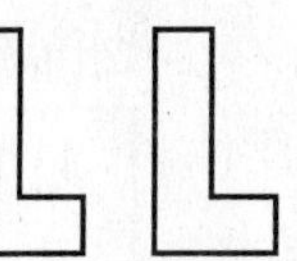

____

(Lesson 6) Is each line a line of symmetry? Write yes or no.

13. 

____

14. 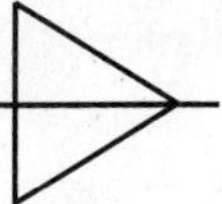

____

15. 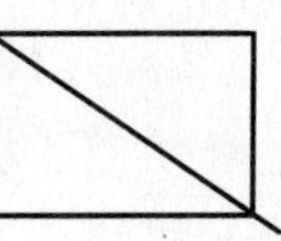

____

(Mixed Review) Find each product or quotient.

16. 8 × 8 = __________ **17.** 24 ÷ 3 = __________ **18.** 4 × 7 = __________

19. 56 ÷ 7 = __________ **20.** 49 ÷ 7 = __________ **21.** 9 × 3 = __________

Name ____________________

Practice 8-8

Exploring Perimeter

1. The perimeter is ____________________.

Find the perimeter of each.

2.

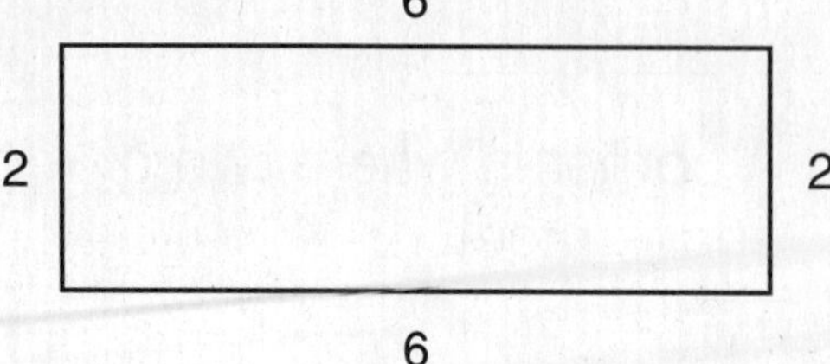

______

3.

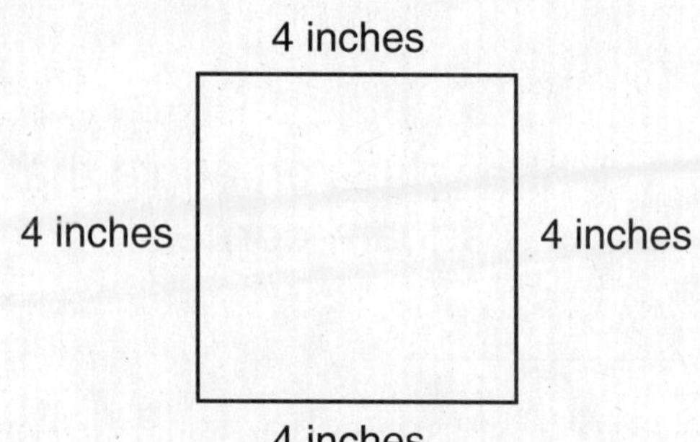

______

4.

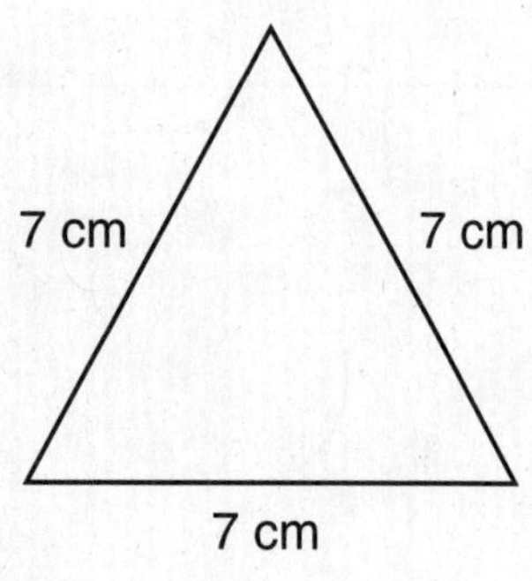

______

5.

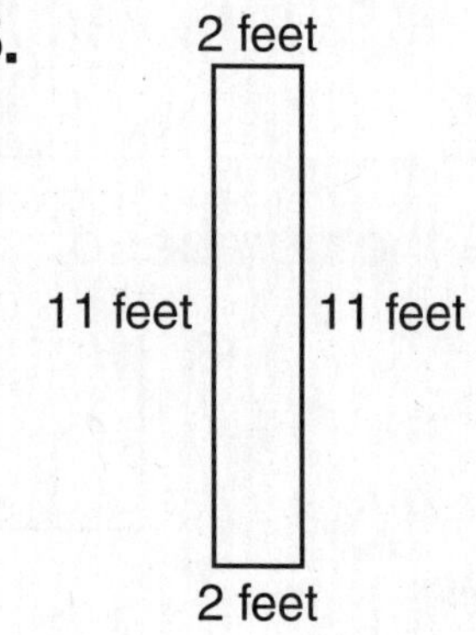

______

6.

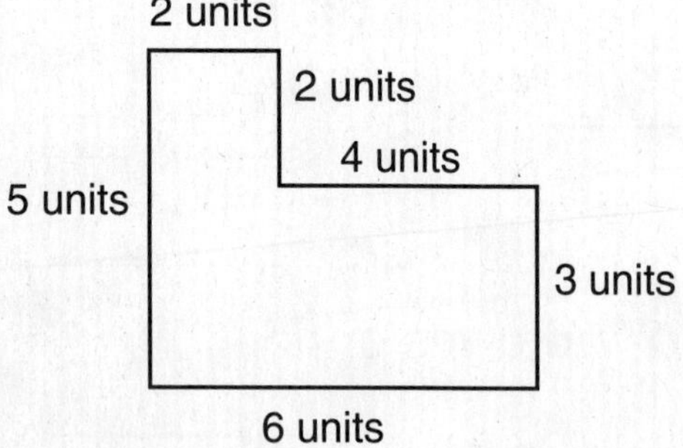

______

7.

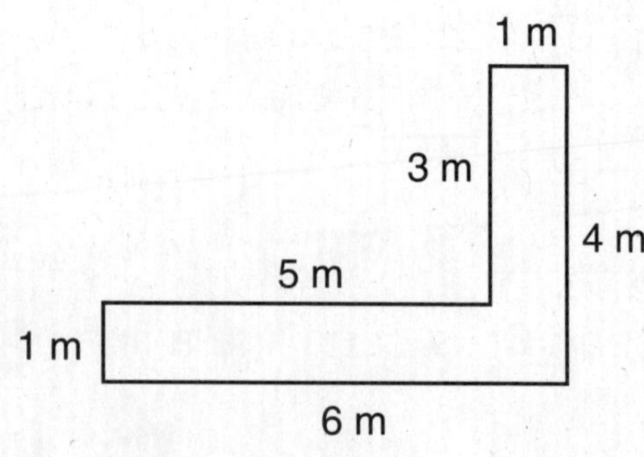

______

Use grid paper. Draw a shape with each perimeter.

8. 8 units **9.** 12 units **10.** 4 units

11. 20 units **12.** 26 units **13.** 11 units

Name ________________________________

Practice 8-9

Exploring Area

Find each area. Write your answer in square units.

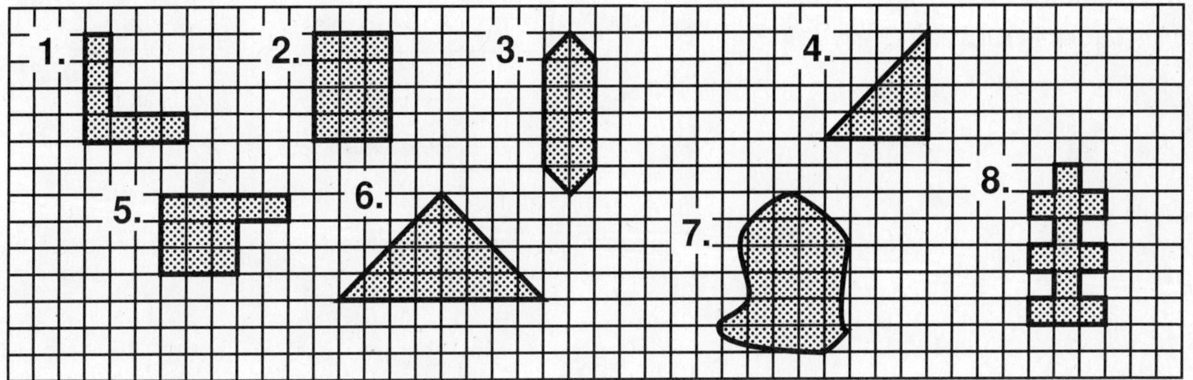

1. ____________________
2. ____________________
3. ____________________
4. ____________________
5. ____________________
6. ____________________
7. ____________________
8. ____________________

9. Use grid paper.

   a. Draw a rectangle with a perimeter that measures 10 units.

   b. What is the area of your rectangle?

   ____

   c. Draw a rectangle with the same perimeter but with a different area. What is the area of your rectangle?

   ____

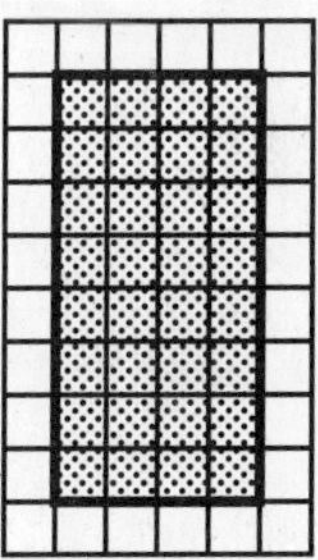

10. **a.** What is the perimeter of the rectangle?

   ____

   b. What is the area of the rectangle? ____________

   c. What happens to the perimeter if you halve each side?

   ____

   d. What happens to the area if you halve each side?

   ____

Name ______________________________

Practice
8-10

Decision Making

You want to move a desk into your bedroom. Do you have enough room?

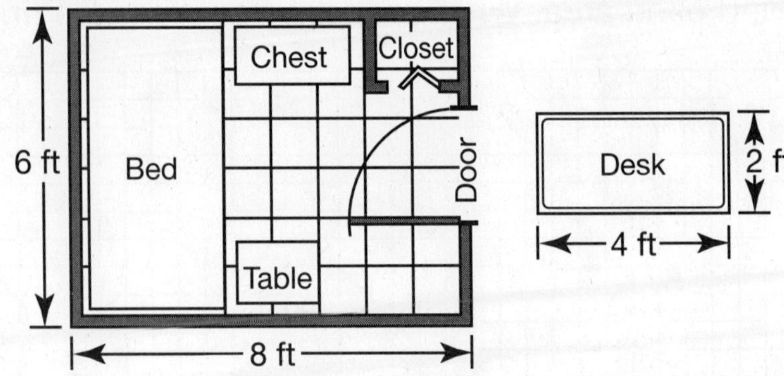

1. What do you know?

____

2. What do you need to decide?

____

3. What is the area of the desk?

____

4. What else do you have to consider other then the area of the desk?

____

5. Is there enough room for the desk?

____

Find the area of the room and the couch. Decide if the couch will fit in the room if no other furniture is moved.

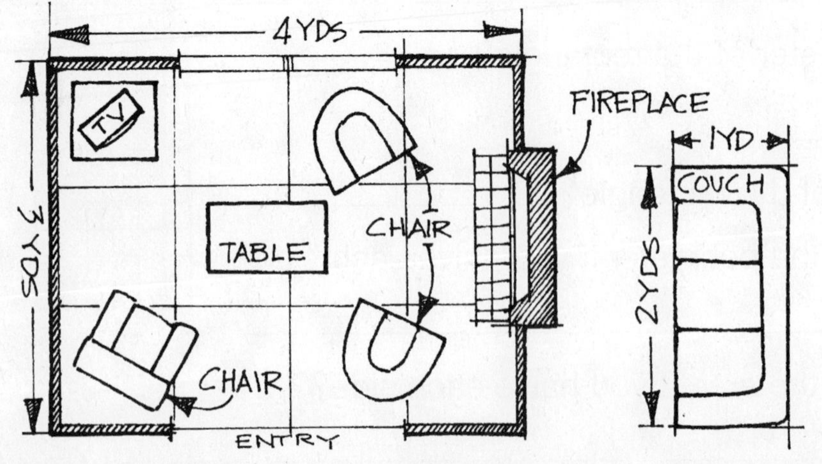

6. Area of room:

____

7. Area of couch:

____

8. Will the couch fit?

______

Name ______________________________

Practice
8-11

Exploring Volume

Write how many cubes are in each solid figure.

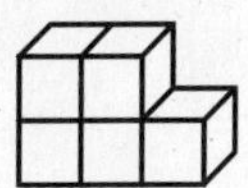

1. ____________

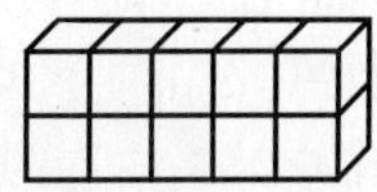

2. ____________

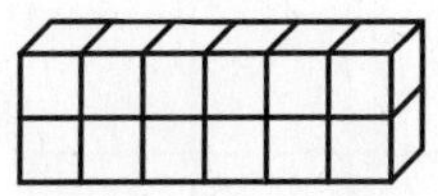

3. ____________

4. ____________

Find the volume of each. You may use cubes to help.

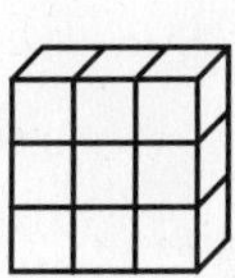

5. ____________

6. ____________

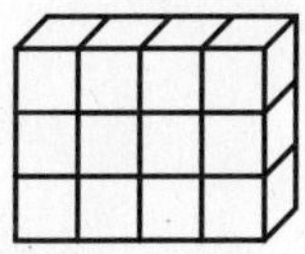

7. ____________

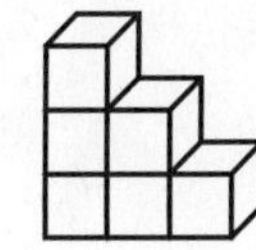

8. ____________

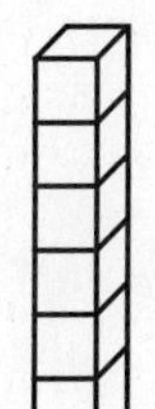
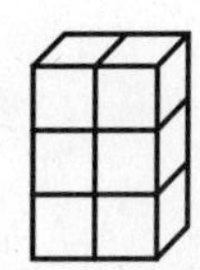
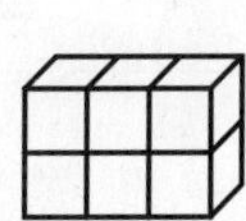
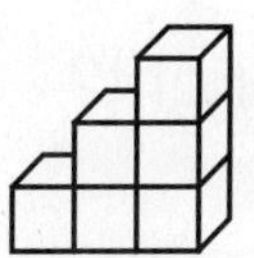

9. Is there a difference in the volumes of these solid figures?

   Explain. ______________________________

Name ______________________________

Coordinate Grids

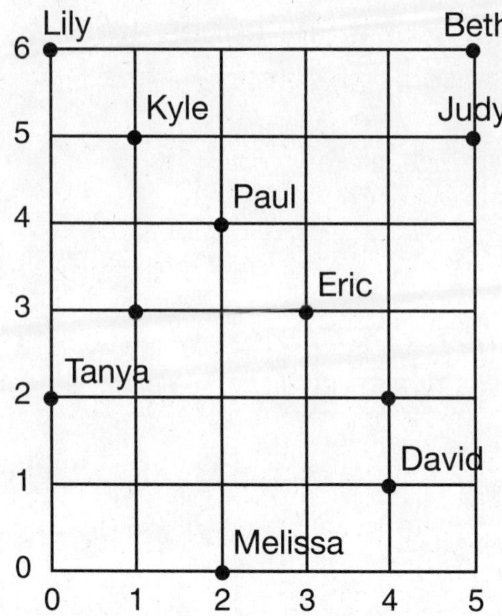

Mr. Sanders has just begun teaching at a new school. This is a grid which Mr. Sanders drew to help him remember where each of his students is sitting.

Write the ordered pair for each student's seat.

1. Kyle ________

2. David ________

3. Lily ________

4. Melissa ________

5. Beth ________

6. Tanya ________

Write the name of the student located at each ordered pair.

7. (3,3) ________

8. (5,5) ________

9. (0,2) ________

10. (2,4) ________

11. (5,6) ________

12. (2,0) ________

13. Are (0,2) and (2,0) at the same seat? Explain.

____

14. To find Beth's seat from (0,0) how many spaces do you move to the right? ________

15. To find Paul's seat from (0,0) how many spaces do you move up? ________

16. Who is seated four places to the right of (1,5)? ________

17. Who is seated four places up from (0,2)? ________

18. Two new students join the class. Miranda sits at (1,3) and June sits at (4,2). Label these points on the grid.

Name ______________________________

Review and Practice

Vocabulary Choose the correct word to complete each sentence.

Word List
cubic unit
coordinate grid
ordered pair

1. A(n) ____________________ is a graph used to locate points.

2. The unit used to measure volume is a ____________________.

3. A pair of numbers used to locate a point on a grid is a(n) ____________________.

(Lessons 8 and 9) Find the area and perimeter of each shape.

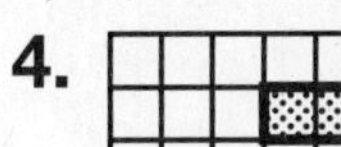
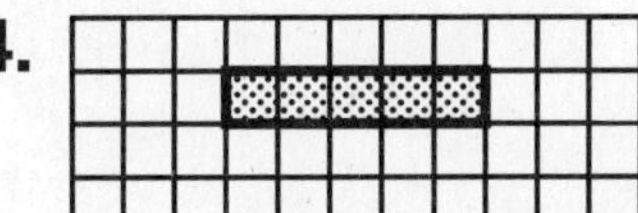

__________, ______________

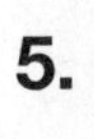
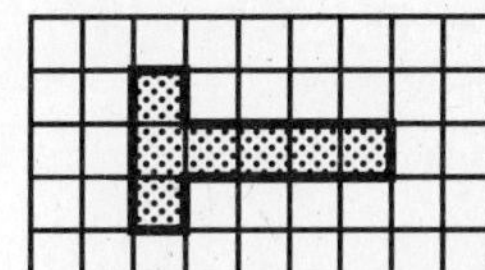

__________, ______________

(Lesson 11) Find the volume of each.

6. 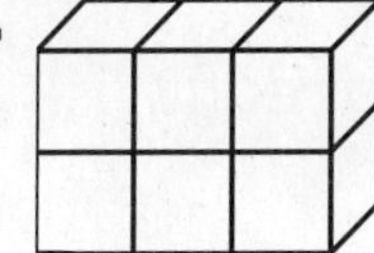

____

7. 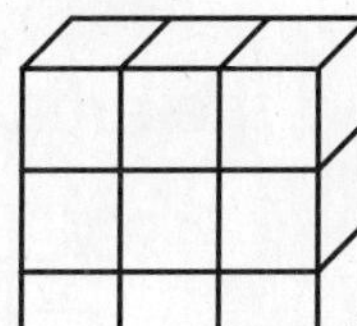

____

8. 

____

(Lesson 12) Write the ordered pair that locates each.

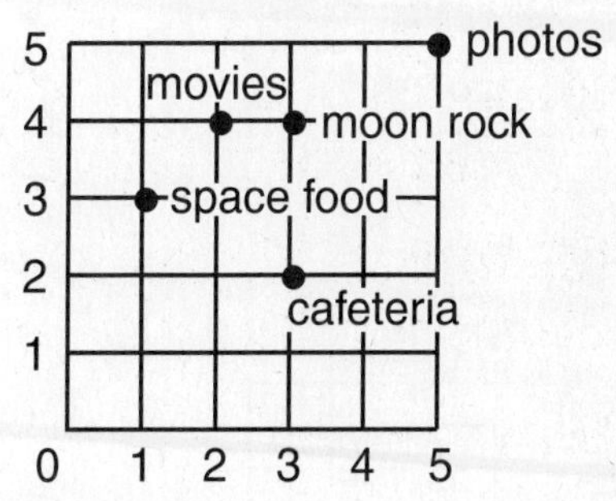

9. moon rock __________

10. movies __________

11. space food __________

12. photos __________

13. What is located at (3,2)? __________

(Mixed Review) Find each sum.

14. 24 + 25 + 24 = __________

15. 33 + 43 = __________

16. 222 + 333 + 444 = __________

17. 67 + 29 = __________

Name ______________________________

Practice
Chapters 1–8

Cumulative Review

(Chapter 4 Lesson 15) Find each difference.

1. $5.00 − 2.50

2. $3.75 − 1.58

3. $12.39 − 9.81

4. $9.52 − 6.99

(Chapter 6 Lesson 9) Solve. Use any strategy.

5. Vickie wants to fry enough sausage links so that each of her 7 guests gets to eat 4 links. The links come in packages of 6. How many packages must she buy? ______

(Chapter 7 Lessons 10 and 11) Find each quotient.

6. 18 ÷ 6 = ______ **7.** 16 ÷ 8 = ______

8. 21 ÷ 7 = ______ **9.** 63 ÷ 7 = ______

10. 56 ÷ 8 = ______ **11.** 27 ÷ 9 = ______

12. 54 ÷ 6 = ______ **13.** 63 ÷ 9 = ______

14. 8)64 **15.** 9)72 **16.** 6)36 **17.** 7)7

(Chapter 8 Lessons 8 and 9) Find the area and perimeter of each.

18.

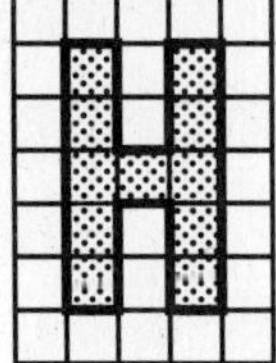

__________, ______________

19.

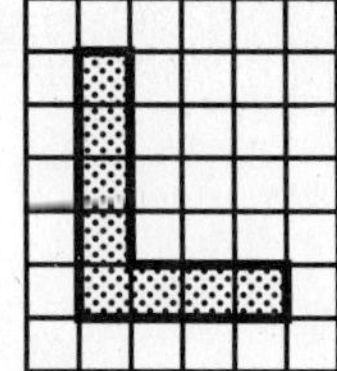

__________, ______________

20. Draw a shape with an area of 14 square units.

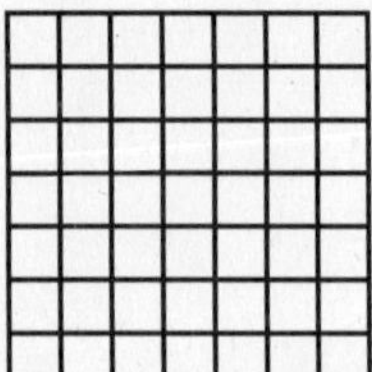

21. Draw a shape with a perimeter of 14 units.

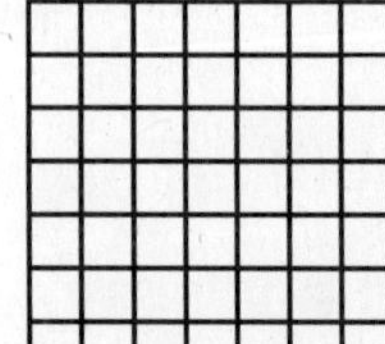

Name ______________________________

Practice
9-1

Exploring Multiplying Tens

Complete. You may use place-value blocks to help.

1. 5 groups of 7
$5 \times$ ☐ ones = ☐ ones
$5 \times 7 =$ ☐

2. 5 groups of 70
$5 \times$ ☐ tens = ☐ tens
$5 \times 70 =$ ☐

3. 5×1 ten = ☐ tens
$5 \times 10 =$ ☐

4. 2×4 tens = ☐ tens
$2 \times 40 =$ ☐

5. 3×5 tens = ☐ tens
$3 \times 50 =$ ☐

6. 2×5 tens = ☐ tens
$2 \times 50 =$ ☐

7. 3×6 tens = ☐ tens
$3 \times 60 =$ ☐

8. 4×6 tens = ☐ tens
$4 \times 60 =$ ☐

9. 7×1 ten = ☐ tens
$7 \times 10 =$ ☐

10. 3×8 tens = ☐ tens
$3 \times 80 =$ ☐

11. 4×4 tens = ☐ tens
$4 \times 40 =$ ☐

12. 2×7 tens = ☐ tens
$2 \times 70 =$ ☐

13. How can you use 7×6 to help you find 7×60?

____

____

50 PENNIES

USA USA USA USA USA
USA USA USA USA USA
USA USA USA USA USA
USA USA USA USA USA

14. How many pennies are in 3 rolls? __________

15. How many stamps are on 5 sheets? __________

Name ______________________

Practice
9-2

Exploring Multiplication Patterns

Complete.

1. 6×7 ones = ☐ ones

$6 \times 7 =$ ☐

2. 6×7 tens = ☐ tens

$6 \times 70 =$ ☐

3. 6×7 hundreds = ☐ hundreds

$6 \times 700 =$ ☐

4. $3 \times 4 =$ ☐

$3 \times$ ☐ $= 120$

☐ $\times 400 = 1{,}200$

5. $2 \times 4 =$ ☐

☐ $\times 40 = 80$

$2 \times 400 =$ ☐

6. $4 \times$ ☐ $= 20$

$4 \times 50 =$ ☐

$4 \times$ ☐ $= 2{,}000$

7. $3 \times 6 =$ ☐

$3 \times$ ☐ $= 180$

☐ $\times 600 = 1{,}800$

8. $7 \times$ ☐ $= 28$

$7 \times 40 =$ ☐

☐ $\times 400 = 2{,}800$

9. $6 \times 6 =$ ☐

☐ $\times 60 = 360$

$6 \times 600 =$ ☐

Find each product using mental math.

10. $3 \times 90 =$ ________

11. $3 \times 800 =$ ________

12. $4 \times 400 =$ ________

13. $2 \times 70 =$ ________

14. $5 \times 600 =$ ________

15. $6 \times 800 =$ ________

16. $3 \times 300 =$ ________

17. $5 \times 90 =$ ________

18. $6 \times 300 =$ ________

19. $4 \times 500 =$ ________

20. $9 \times 200 =$ ________

21. $7 \times 700 =$ ________

22. $8 \times 400 =$ ________

23. $5 \times 800 =$ ________

24. Can you use the basic fact 3×8 to find 3×800?

____

25. Can you use 5×7 to find 5×700?

____

Name ______________________

Practice
9-3

Estimating Products

Estimate each product.

1. 3×32 ______ **2.** 7×820 ______

3. 5×46 ______ **4.** 2×350 ______

5. 8×67 ______ **6.** 6×865 ______

7. 3×523 ______ **8.** 4×628 ______

9. 4×233 ______ **10.** 9×58 ______

11. 5×797 ______ **12.** 6×84 ______

13. 3×124 ______ **14.** 5×99 ______

15. 7×280 ______ **16.** 8×241 ______

17. 6×890 ______ **18.** 2×916 ______

19. 9×760 ______ **20.** 4×675 ______

21. 3×210 ______ **22.** 9×63 ______

23. 4×334 ______ **24.** 6×912 ______

25. 7×489 ______ **26.** 8×38 ______

27. Estimate the product of 6 and 34. ______

28. Estimate the product of 7 and 569. ______

29. Estimate the product of 9 and 435. ______

30. Estimate the product of 8 and 750. ______

31. Estimate to decide if 6×856 is greater than or less than 7×535. Explain.

____

32. The product of 6 and another number is about 240. Give two numbers that make this sentence true. Explain.

____

____

Name ______________________________

Practice 9-4

Exploring Multiplication with Arrays

Complete the steps to find each product.

1. 3 × 14

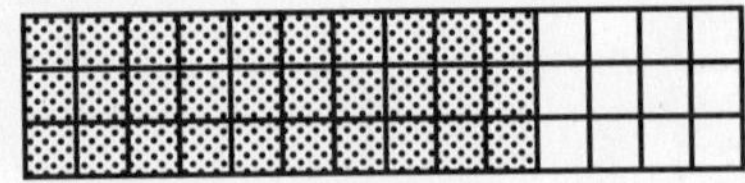

a. 3 rows of 10

3 × 10 = ☐

b. 3 rows of 4

3 × 4 = ☐

c. ☐ + ☐ = ☐

d. 3 × 14 = ☐

2. 2 × 26

a. 2 rows of 20

2 × 20 = ☐

b. 2 rows of 6

2 × 6 = ☐

c. ☐ + ☐ = ☐

d. 2 × 26 = ☐

3. 4 × 23 = ________

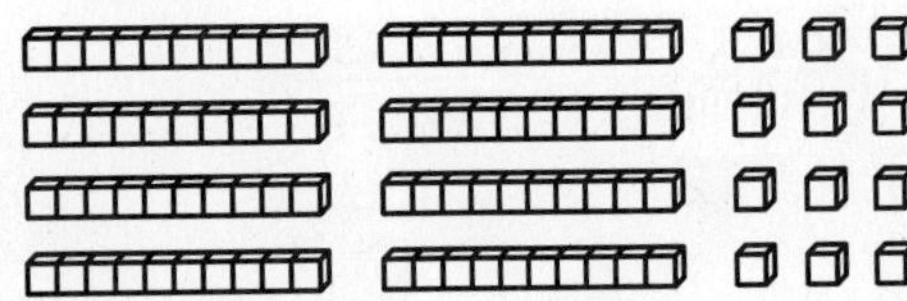

4. 5 × 13 = ________

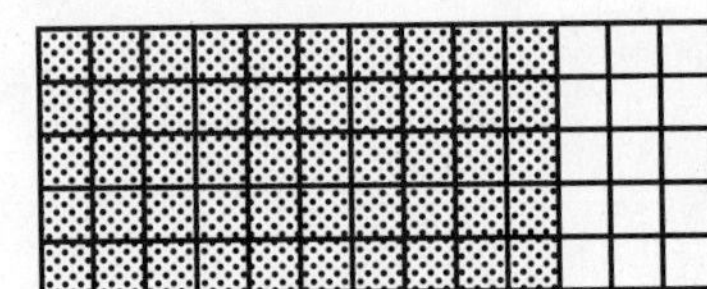

Find each product. You may use place-value blocks or grid paper to help.

5. 4 × 12 = ________

6. 6 × 13 = ________

7. 3 × 32 = ________

8. 4 × 17 = ________

9. 4 × 19 = ________

10. 2 × 47 = ________

11. 5 × 18 = ________

12. 3 × 28 = ________

13. 3 × 31 = ________

14. 2 × 39 = ________

Find the missing number. You may use grid paper or place-value blocks to solve.

15. 18 × ________ = 54

16. 12 × ________ = 84

17. 22 × ________ = 88

18. ________ × 19 = 57

19. 6 × 15 = ________

20. 5 × ________ = 70

Name ______________________________

Practice
Chapter 9
Section A

Review and Practice

(Lesson 1) Complete. You may use place-value blocks.

1. 5×1 ten = ☐ tens

$5 \times 10 =$ ☐

2. 6×4 tens = ☐ tens

$6 \times 40 =$ ☐

3. 8×3 tens = ☐ tens

$8 \times 30 =$ ☐

4. 7×2 tens = ☐ tens

$7 \times 20 =$ ☐

(Lesson 2) Complete.

5. $5 \times 3 =$ ☐

$5 \times$ ☐ $= 150$

☐ $\times 300 = 1{,}500$

6. $6 \times$ ☐ $= 36$

☐ $\times 60 = 360$

$6 \times$ ☐ $= 3{,}600$

Find each product using mental math.

7. $7 \times 50 =$ __________

8. $9 \times 600 =$ __________

9. $80 \times 9 =$ __________

10. $400 \times 8 =$ __________

(Lesson 3) Estimate each product.

11. 8×56 __________

12. 33×5 __________

13. 3×299 __________

14. 6×419 __________

15. Melissa collects stamps. She mounts them on pages that hold 63 stamps. About how many stamps will 6 pages hold? __________

(Lesson 4) Find each product. You may use place-value blocks or grid paper to help.

16. $6 \times 12 =$ __________

17. $3 \times 37 =$ __________

18. $5 \times 27 =$ __________

19. $4 \times 27 =$ __________

(Mixed Review) Add or subtract.

20. $361 + 839$

21. $308 - 149$

22. $917 - 579$

23. $608 + 55$

Name ________________________

Practice 9-5

Multiplying: Partial Products

Find each product.

1. $\begin{array}{r} 15 \\ \times\ 3 \\ \hline 15 \\ \square\square \\ \hline \square\square \end{array}$

2. $\begin{array}{r} 72 \\ \times\ 2 \\ \hline \square \\ 140 \\ \hline \square\square\square \end{array}$

3. $\begin{array}{r} 21 \\ \times\ 7 \\ \hline \square \\ \square\square\square \\ \hline \square\square\square \end{array}$

4. $\begin{array}{r} 13 \\ \times\ 6 \\ \hline \square\square \\ \square\square \\ \hline \square\square \end{array}$

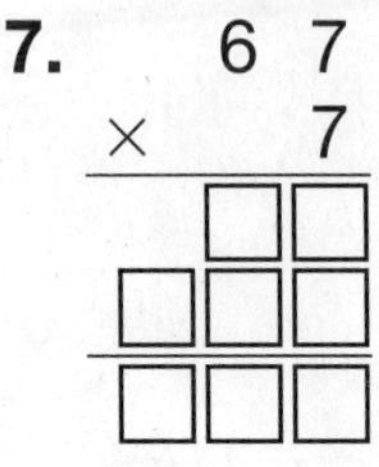

5. $\begin{array}{r} 39 \\ \times\ 7 \\ \hline \square\square \\ \square\square\square \\ \hline \square\square\square \end{array}$

6. $\begin{array}{r} 42 \\ \times\ 6 \\ \hline \square\square \\ \square\square\square \\ \hline \square\square\square \end{array}$

7. $\begin{array}{r} 67 \\ \times\ 7 \\ \hline \square\square \\ \square\square\square \\ \hline \square\square\square \end{array}$

8. $\begin{array}{r} 53 \\ \times\ 5 \\ \hline \square\square \\ \square\square\square \\ \hline \square\square\square \end{array}$

9. 43 × 5 = ________ **10.** 64 × 3 = ________

11. 88 × 7 = ________ **12.** 39 × 4 = ________

13. 67 × 8 = ________ **14.** 37 × 6 = ________

15. 45 × 4 = ________ **16.** 69 × 2 = ________

17. 36 × 2 = ________ **18.** 84 × 5 = ________

19. 18 × 6 = ________ **20.** 23 × 9 = ________

21. Explain why 9 × 34 is the same as 270 + 36.

____

22. How can you tell that 7 × 23 will be at least 3 digits?

____

____

23. Alexis says, "The product of 5 and 47 is less than 200." Is she right? Explain.

____

Name ______________________________

Practice
9-6

Multiplying 2-Digit Numbers

Find each product. Estimate to check.

1. $\begin{array}{r} 37 \\ \times\ 2 \\ \hline \end{array}$

2. $\begin{array}{r} 43 \\ \times\ 7 \\ \hline \end{array}$

3. $\begin{array}{r} 28 \\ \times\ 3 \\ \hline \end{array}$

4. $\begin{array}{r} 56 \\ \times\ 5 \\ \hline \end{array}$

5. $\begin{array}{r} 29 \\ \times\ 3 \\ \hline \end{array}$

6. $\begin{array}{r} 72 \\ \times\ 6 \\ \hline \end{array}$

7. $\begin{array}{r} 35 \\ \times\ 7 \\ \hline \end{array}$

8. $\begin{array}{r} 92 \\ \times\ 6 \\ \hline \end{array}$

9. $\begin{array}{r} 24 \\ \times\ 8 \\ \hline \end{array}$

10. $\begin{array}{r} 53 \\ \times\ 5 \\ \hline \end{array}$

11. $\begin{array}{r} 82 \\ \times\ 3 \\ \hline \end{array}$

12. $\begin{array}{r} 47 \\ \times\ 6 \\ \hline \end{array}$

13. $\begin{array}{r} 19 \\ \times\ 8 \\ \hline \end{array}$

14. $\begin{array}{r} 37 \\ \times\ 9 \\ \hline \end{array}$

15. $\begin{array}{r} 62 \\ \times\ 4 \\ \hline \end{array}$

16. $\begin{array}{r} 90 \\ \times\ 7 \\ \hline \end{array}$

17. $53 \times 5 =$ __________

18. $37 \times 3 =$ __________

19. $42 \times 8 =$ __________

20. $38 \times 7 =$ __________

21. Find the product of 17 and 9. __________

22. Find the product of 44 and 5. __________

23. Multiply 19 by 8. __________

24. Multiply 84 by 6. __________

25. Do you need to regroup ones to find the product of 42 and 3? Explain.

____

26. Do you need to regroup to find the product of 34 and 3? Explain.

____

27. How can you tell what the ones digit of the product of 38×7 will be without solving the whole problem?

____

Name ______________________

Practice
9-7

Multiplying 3-Digit Numbers

Find each product. Estimate to check.

1. 542×6
2. 374×3
3. 722×5
4. 256×7
5. 346×4
6. 117×8
7. 612×7
8. 739×2
9. 513×6
10. 757×3
11. 198×4
12. 209×8
13. 127×5
14. 508×6
15. 138×5
16. 377×9
17. $4 \times 311 =$ ______
18. $478 \times 8 =$ ______
19. $491 \times 5 =$ ______
20. $7 \times 219 =$ ______
21. $9 \times 106 =$ ______
22. $627 \times 6 =$ ______
23. Multiply 7 and 524. ______
24. Find the product of 378 and 6. ______
25. How could you use mental math to find 5×306?

____

____

26. How could you use mental math to find 3×122?

____

____

____

Name ______________________

Practice
9-8

Multiplying Money

Find each product.

1. $1.20 × 5	**2.** $0.65 × 7	**3.** $3.24 × 6	**4.** $1.75 × 5
5. $0.49 × 8	**6.** $3.19 × 4	**7.** $2.39 × 3	**8.** $4.12 × 5
9. $2.25 × 3	**10.** $1.52 × 6	**11.** $2.22 × 6	**12.** $4.33 × 7

13. 6 × $7.41 = ________ **14.** $2.29 × 4 = ________

15. $1.19 × 8 = ________ **16.** 9 × $0.79 = ________

17. $5.25 × 4 = ________ **18.** 7 × $3.50 = ________

19. What is the product of 5 and $7.44? ________

20. Multiply 6 and $0.72. ________

21. Is $0.32 the same amount as 32¢? ________

22. Mindy multiplied $1.37 and 4. She recorded $5.48.

Is she correct? ________

23. If you bought 9 cans of juice for 72¢ each, would you spend more than $5.00? Explain.

____

24. Ralph multiplied $2.69 and 5. He recorded $1345. Is he correct?

____

Name ______________________

Practice 9-9

Mental Math

Find each product using mental math.

1. 42×3 ______ **2.** 26×2 ______ **3.** 14×6 ______ **4.** 23×5 ______

5. 32×8 ______ **6.** 17×9 ______ **7.** 37×3 ______ **8.** 19×4 ______

9. 21×6 ______ **10.** 44×3 ______ **11.** 53×4 ______ **12.** 63×2 ______

13. Multiply 6 and 47. ______

14. What is the product of 92 and 7. ______

15. If you know $30 \times 4 = 120$, how could you solve 36×4 mentally?

____

16. If you know $30 \times 3 = 90$, how could you solve 29×3 mentally?

____

17. What are two ways you could use mental math to find the product of 57 and 2?

____

Name ______________________________

Practice 9-10

Analyze Strategies: Make a Table

1. This summer, a new 20-story hospital was built downtown. Electricians worked quickly to put in wiring in the building. After one week, 4 floors had wiring. After two weeks, 8 floors had wiring. After three weeks, 12 floors had wiring.

   a. Fill in the table to show what you know.

Week	1	2	3	4	5
Floors Wired	4				

   b. What multiplication pattern can help you complete the table?

   ____

   ____

   c. If the electricians continued to work at the same speed, how many weeks did it take them to put in wire in all 20 floors? ______________

2. If it takes Ginny 7 minutes to ride 1 mile on her bike, how long would it take her to ride 6 miles? ______________

3. If Todd can throw 20 curve balls in one minute, how many curve balls could he throw in 4 minutes? ______________

4. Shea is decorating a frame. She has 4 rubber stamps she could use. They are a leaf, a ladybug, a flower, and a bee. She wants to make a design with 2 rubber stamps. How many choices does she have? ______________

5. Eduardo has a red shirt, a blue shirt, and a white shirt, black trousers and blue jeans. How many different outfits can he make? ______________

Name ____________________

Practice
Chapter 9
Section B

Review and Practice

(Lessons 5–8) Find each product.

1. 43×7

2. 23×3

3. 93×6

4. 62×4

5. 308×4

6. 611×8

7. 980×4

8. 237×7

9. $\$6.18 \times 9$

10. $\$1.23 \times 6$

11. $\$0.11 \times 4$

12. $\$4.56 \times 3$

13. Sheila has 5 packets of raisins. Each packet contains 214 raisins. About how many raisins does Sheila have in all?

____

14. Jack buys 4 tickets to a concert. Each ticket costs $4.89. How much does Jack spend?

____

(Lesson 9) Use mental math to find each product.

15. $34 \times 5 =$ ________

16. $82 \times 3 =$ ________

17. $38 \times 4 =$ ________

18. $72 \times 4 =$ ________

(Lesson 10) Use any strategy to solve.

19. Kerim is saving money to buy a present. The first week he saves $1. The next week he saves $3. The third week he saves $5. If this pattern continues, how many more weeks will it be until he saves $25 in all? ________

(Mixed Review) Find each quotient.

20. $56 \div 8 =$ ________

21. $48 \div 6 =$ ________

22. $63 \div 9 =$ ________

23. $45 \div 5 =$ ________

Name ______________________

Practice 9-11

Exploring Division Patterns

Find the quotients. Use basic facts and place-value patterns to help you divide mentally.

1. 8 ones ÷ 2 = ________ ones

8 ÷ 2 = ________

8 tens ÷ 2 = ________ tens

80 ÷ 2 = ________

8 hundreds ÷ 2 =

________ hundreds

800 ÷ 2 = ________

2. 9 ones ÷ 3 = ________ ones

9 ÷ 3 = ________

9 tens ÷ 3 = ________ tens

90 ÷ 3 = ________

9 hundreds ÷ 3 =

________ hundreds

900 ÷ 3 = ________

Complete.

3. 7 ÷ 7 = ________

70 ÷ ________ = 10

________ ÷ 7 = 100

4. 8 ÷ 2 = ________

________ ÷ 2 = 40

________ ÷ 2 = 400

5. 8 ÷ 4 = ________

80 ÷ ________ = 20

________ ÷ 4 = 200

6. 10 ÷ 2 = ________

100 ÷ ________ = 50

________ ÷ 2 = 500

Find each quotient using mental math.

7. 800 ÷ 2 = ________

8. 90 ÷ 9 = ________

9. 200 ÷ 4 = ________

10. 270 ÷ 3 = ________

11. 210 ÷ 7 = ________

12. 360 ÷ 6 = ________

13. How can you use 16 ÷ 4 = 4 to help you find 160 ÷ 4?

____

Name ___

Practice 9-12

Estimating Quotients

Estimate each quotient.

1. 25 ÷ 6 ___
2. 35 ÷ 4 ___
3. 17 ÷ 4 ___
4. 29 ÷ 4 ___
5. 31 ÷ 8 ___
6. 19 ÷ 6 ___
7. 20 ÷ 3 ___
8. 14 ÷ 5 ___
9. 35 ÷ 6 ___
10. 39 ÷ 8 ___
11. 13 ÷ 6 ___
12. 65 ÷ 8 ___
13. 10 ÷ 3 ___
14. 11 ÷ 5 ___
15. 13 ÷ 4 ___
16. 73 ÷ 9 ___

17. Estimate the quotient of 25 ÷ 3. ___
18. Estimate the quotient of 41 ÷ 5. ___

19. What basic division fact can you use to help you estimate the quotient of 14 ÷ 5? Explain.

___

___

20. Is the quotient of 49 ÷ 6 greater than or less than 8? Explain.

___

___

21. Is the quotient of 53 ÷ 9 greater than or less than 6? Explain.

___

___

Name ______________________________

Practice
9-13

Exploring Division with Remainders

Find each quotient and remainder. You may use counters to help you.

1. $2\overline{)13}$ **2.** $8\overline{)29}$ **3.** $5\overline{)33}$

4. $4\overline{)25}$ **5.** $3\overline{)17}$ **6.** $6\overline{)21}$

7. $7\overline{)18}$ **8.** $5\overline{)28}$ **9.** $6\overline{)55}$

10. $5\overline{)16}$ **11.** $7\overline{)47}$ **12.** $3\overline{)26}$

13. Catherine says, "If I have 19 strawberries, I can give myself and 3 friends each 5 strawberries." Do you agree or disagree?

____

14. Kim says, "If I need 25 granny-squares for a quilt, I can knit 8 squares a week for 3 weeks." Do you agree or disagree?

____

15. Stefan was packing books into boxes. He had 8 boxes that would each hold 4 books. Stefan had 33 books. How many would not fit into the boxes?

____

16. Robin is putting photographs into an album. He can fit 7 photographs onto a page. The album has 7 pages and Robin has 53 photographs. How many will not fit in the album?

____

Name ______________________

Practice
9-14

Dividing

Find each quotient and remainder.

1. $2\overline{)15}$ **2.** $4\overline{)23}$ **3.** $8\overline{)56}$ **4.** $5\overline{)43}$

5. $6\overline{)25}$ **6.** $9\overline{)48}$ **7.** $6\overline{)56}$ **8.** $4\overline{)33}$

9. 42 ÷ 7 = ________ **10.** 70 ÷ 8 = ________

11. 51 ÷ 8 = ________ **12.** 26 ÷ 3 = ________

13. 22 ÷ 8 = ________ **14.** 61 ÷ 7 = ________

15. 35 ÷ 9 = ________ **16.** 48 ÷ 6 = ________

17. 47 ÷ 5 = ________ **18.** 34 ÷ 8 = ________

19. Divide 55 by 7. ________ **20.** Divide 66 by 8. ________

21. Divide 44 by 6. ________ **22.** Divide 33 by 4. ________

23. Divide 22 by 5. ________ **24.** Divide 88 by 9. ________

25. 12 volunteers will paint 4 walls. How many volunteers should work on each wall? ________

26. Suppose you want at least 15 rolls of film for your vacation. How many 4-roll packages should you buy? ________

27. How many traffic lights can you fill with a case of 24 light bulbs? (There are 3 lights on each traffic light.) ________

28. How many take-out boxes can you fill from a crate of 50 muffins if there are 6 muffins per take-out box? ________

29. Suppose 1 bottle of juice serves 5 people. How many bottles will you need for 27 people? ________

Name ____________________

Practice
9-15

Decision Making

You are planning a race. You need a water station every 3 miles. How many water stations will you need if the race is:

1. 12 miles long? ____________________

2. 21 miles long? ____________________

3. 15 miles long? ____________________

4. 18 miles long? ____________________

5. 24 miles long? ____________________

6. 30 miles long? ____________________

7. 26 miles long? ____________________

8. 20 miles long? ____________________

9. There are 36 runners in your race. They must be divided into equal starting groups. Find 3 different ways to divide 36 runners into equal groups.

a. _____ groups of _____ = 36

b. _____ groups of _____ = 36

c. _____ groups of _____ = 36

10. What if there are only 12 runners? Find 3 different ways to divide 12 runners into equal groups.

a. _____ groups of _____ = 12

b. _____ groups of _____ = 12

c. _____ groups of _____ = 12

Name ______________________________

Practice
Chapter 3
Section C

Review and Practice

Vocabulary Underline the term that will complete the sentence correctly.

1. The (quotient, product) is the answer to a division problem.

2. The (quotient, remainder) is the number left over after dividing.

(Lesson 11) Use mental math to find each quotient.

3. 300 ÷ 6 = ________ **4.** 320 ÷ 8 = ________

5. 630 ÷ 7 = ________ **6.** 160 ÷ 4 = ________

7. Sarah's family is going on a 120-minute walk. They stop to rest 3 times. How often to they stop to rest?

____

(Lesson 12) Estimate each quotient.

8. 31 ÷ 5 = ________ **9.** 46 ÷ 9 = ________

10. 19 ÷ 3 = ________ **11.** 52 ÷ 7 = ________

(Lessons 13 and 14) Find each quotient and remainder.

12. $2\overline{)9}$ **13.** $6\overline{)43}$ **14.** $4\overline{)29}$ **15.** $5\overline{)47}$

16. 69 ÷ 9 = ________ **17.** 58 ÷ 7 = ________

18. A bottle holds 9 ounces. How many bottles are needed to hold 57 ounces? Will all the bottles be full? Explain.

____

____

(Mixed Review) Add or subtract.

19. $\begin{array}{r} 135 \\ +222 \\ \hline \end{array}$ **20.** $\begin{array}{r} 504 \\ -243 \\ \hline \end{array}$ **21.** $\begin{array}{r} 379 \\ -\ 84 \\ \hline \end{array}$ **22.** $\begin{array}{r} 803 \\ +\ 59 \\ \hline \end{array}$

Name ______________________

Cumulative Review

(Chapter 7 Lesson 9) Write which operation you would use. Then solve.

1. Mickey bought a dog collar for $5.95. He also bought a 4-pound bag of dog food for $6.19. How much money did he spend? ______________

(Chapter 8 Lesson 4) Write whether each angle is a right angle, less than a right angle, or greater than a right angle.

2. 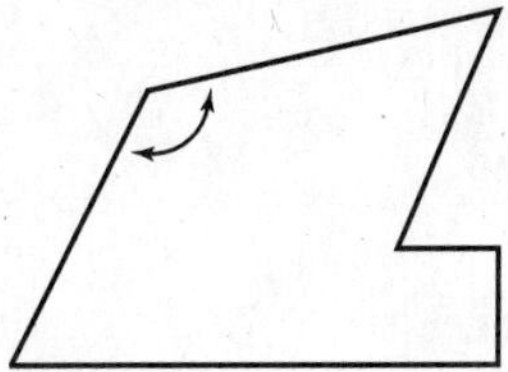

3. 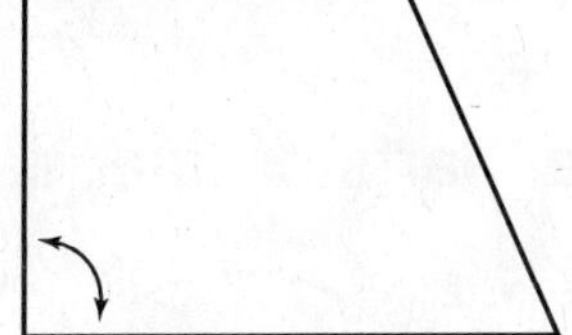

4. 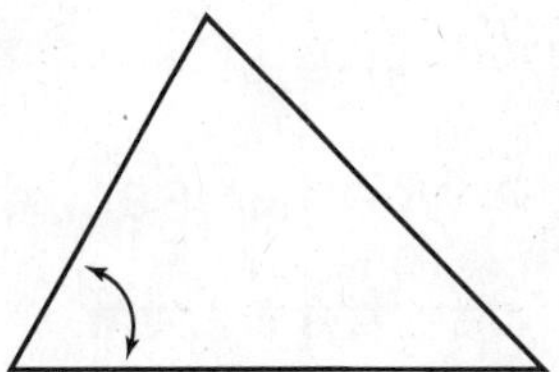

(Chapter 8 Lesson 11) Find the volume of each shape. You may use cubes to help.

5. 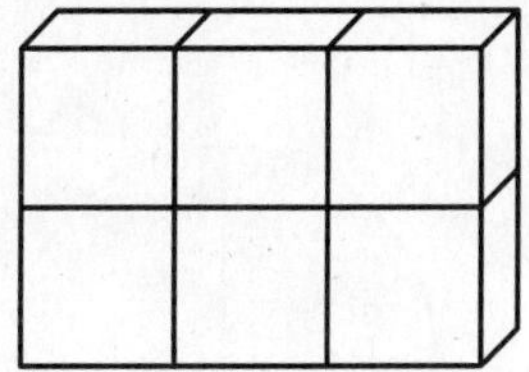

6. 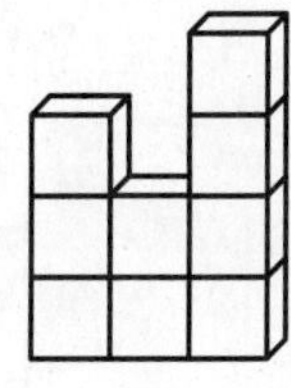

(Chapter 9 Lessons 6 and 7) Multiply.

7. 37×6

8. 21×8

9. 75×7

10. 63×4

11. 465×5

12. 307×9

13. 243×4

14. 500×3

(Chapter 9 Lesson 14)

15. $4\overline{)29}$

16. $9\overline{)71}$

17. $3\overline{)28}$

18. $6\overline{)23}$

Name ____________________

Practice 10-1

Exploring Equal Parts

Tell how many equal parts.

1. 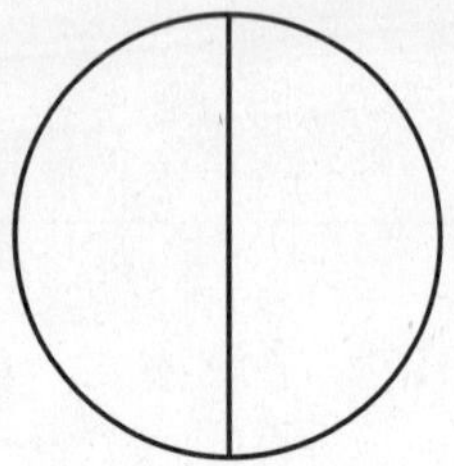

2. 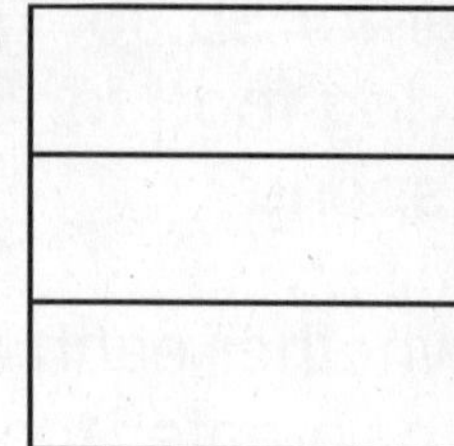

3. 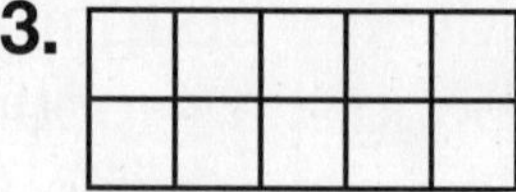

Write whether each has equal parts or unequal parts.

4. 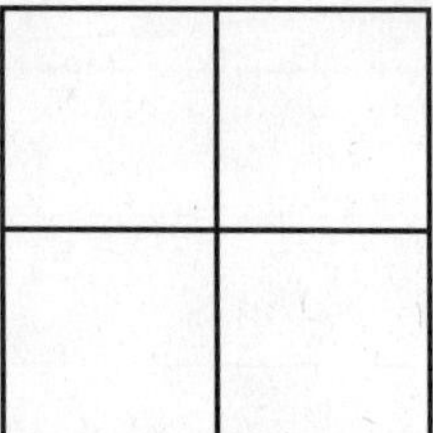

5. 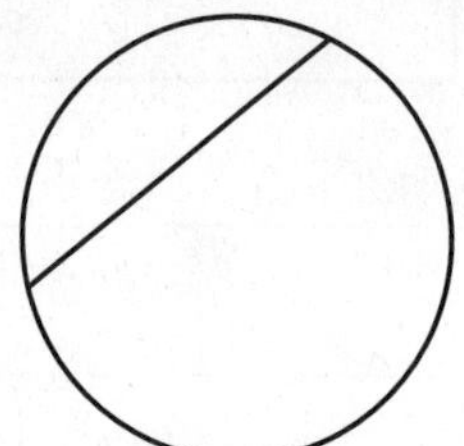

6. 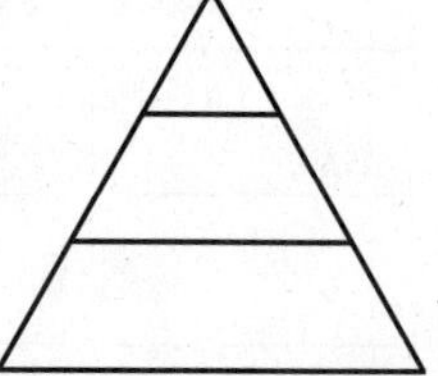

Name the equal parts of each whole.

7. 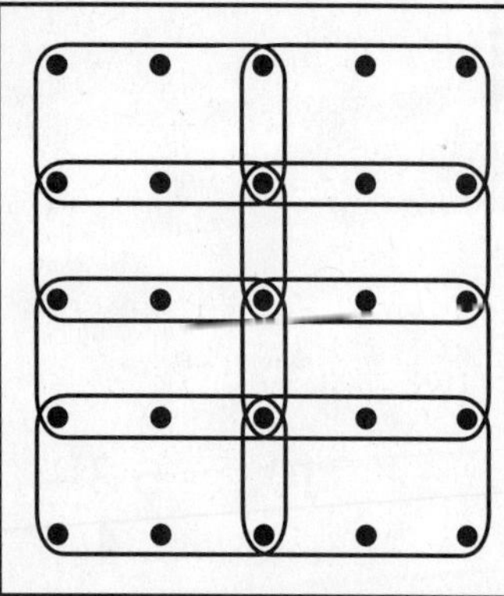

8. 

9. 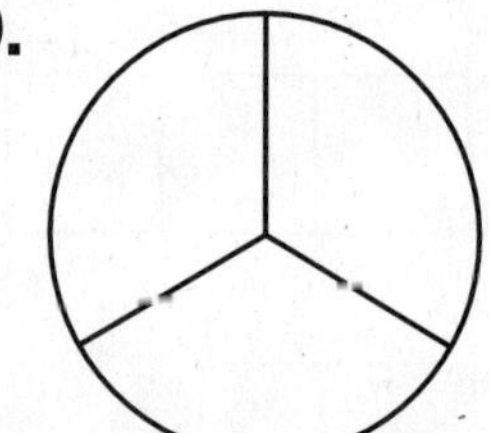

Draw a picture to show each. You may use grid paper to help.

10. thirds

11. fourths

12. tenths

Name ______________________________

Practice 10-2

Naming and Writing Fractions

Write the fraction of each figure that is shaded.

1. 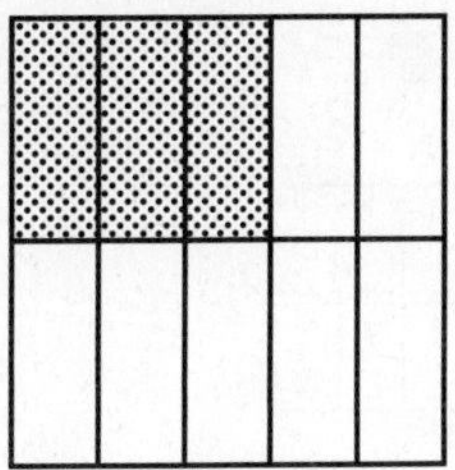

______

2. 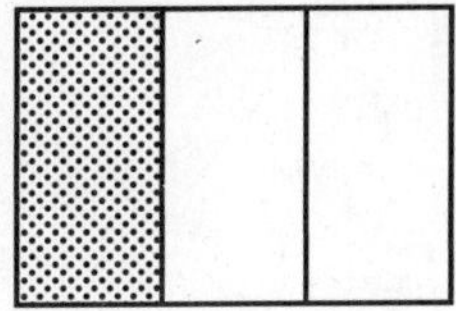

______

3. 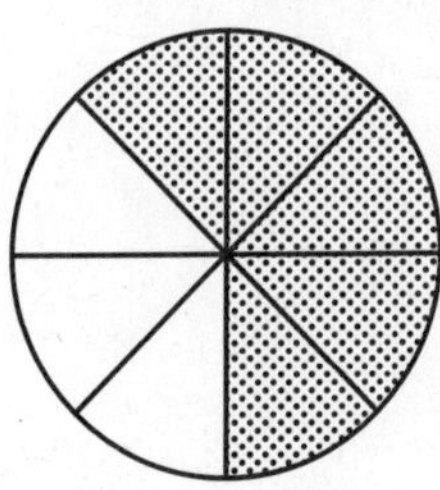

______

4. 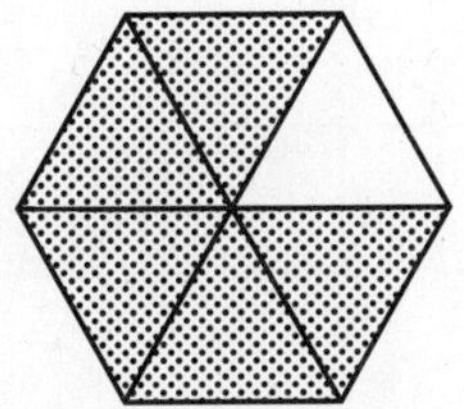

______

5. 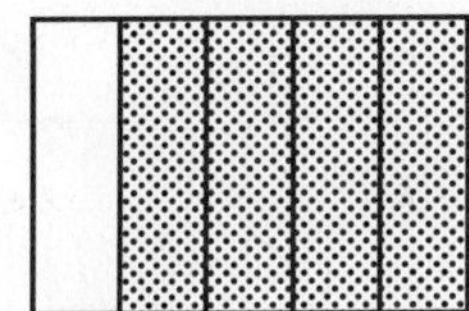

______

6. 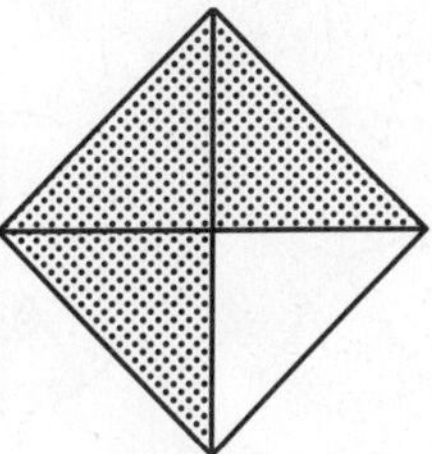

______

Draw a picture to show each fraction.

7. $\frac{3}{8}$ shaded

8. $\frac{1}{10}$ shaded

9. $\frac{7}{12}$ shaded

10. $\frac{1}{6}$ shaded

11. $\frac{3}{5}$ shaded

12. $\frac{2}{4}$ shaded

13. Khalifa says "$\frac{2}{4}$ of the Maryland flag has one design, and $\frac{2}{4}$ has another design." Do you agree or disagree? Explain.

____

____

____

Name ____________________

Practice 10-3

Exploring Equivalent Fractions

Complete. You may use fraction strips to help.

1. $\frac{1}{5} = \frac{\square}{10}$

$\frac{1}{5}$	
$\frac{1}{10}$	$\frac{1}{10}$

2. $\frac{1}{3} = \frac{\square}{6}$

$\frac{1}{3}$	
$\frac{1}{6}$	$\frac{1}{6}$

3. $\frac{2}{4} = \frac{\square}{8}$

$\frac{1}{4}$		$\frac{1}{4}$	
$\frac{1}{8}$	$\frac{1}{8}$	$\frac{1}{8}$	$\frac{1}{8}$

4. $\frac{2}{5} = \frac{\square}{10}$

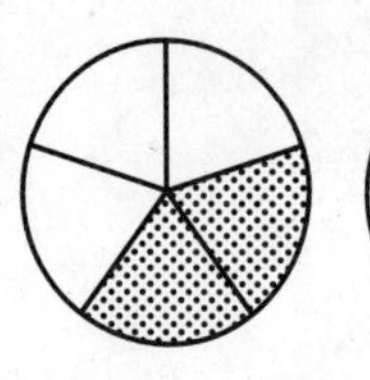
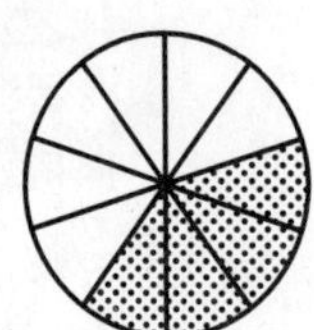

5. $\frac{1}{2} = \frac{\square}{8}$

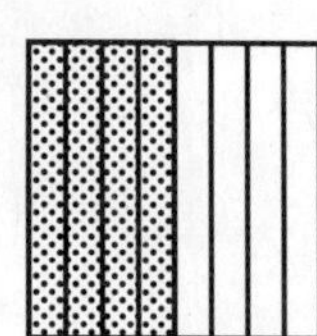

6. $\frac{2}{3} = \frac{\square}{12}$

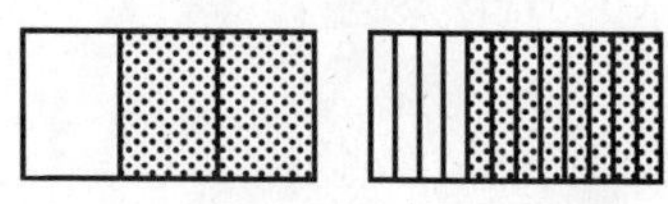

Write if the fractions are equivalent or not equivalent. You may use fraction strips to help.

7.

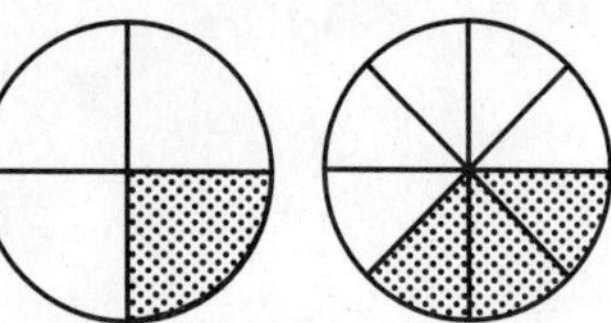

____

8.

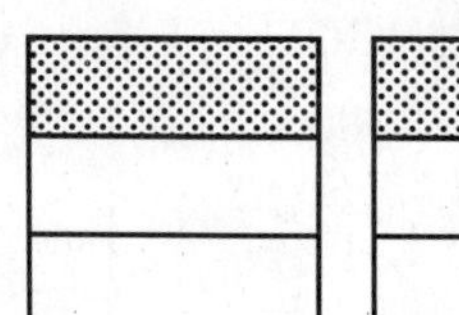

____

9.

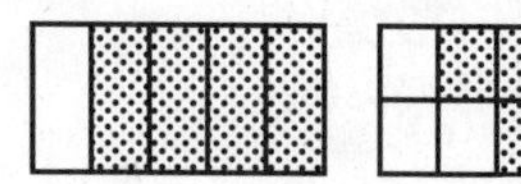

____

Look for a pattern. Complete the next three fractions.

10. a. $\frac{1}{2}, \frac{2}{4}, \frac{3}{6}, \frac{4}{\square}, \frac{5}{\square}, \frac{6}{\square}$

b. $\frac{3}{8}, \frac{6}{16}, \frac{9}{24}, \frac{\square}{32}, \frac{\square}{40}, \frac{\square}{48}$

c. $\frac{2}{5}, \frac{4}{10}, \frac{6}{15}, \frac{\square}{\square}, \frac{\square}{\square}, \frac{\square}{\square}$

Name ______________________________

Practice 10-4

Exploring Comparing and Ordering Fractions

Place the fractions in order from greatest to least. You may use fraction strips to help.

1. $\frac{1}{3}, \frac{1}{5}, \frac{1}{4}$ ______________

2. $\frac{1}{3}, \frac{2}{3}, \frac{1}{2}$ ______________

3. $\frac{3}{10}, \frac{2}{5}, \frac{1}{2}$ ______________

4. $\frac{3}{4}, \frac{1}{2}, \frac{1}{6}$ ______________

Place the fractions in order from least to greatest. You may use fraction strips to help.

5. $\frac{1}{4}, \frac{1}{2}, \frac{1}{5}$ ______________

6. $\frac{1}{2}, \frac{3}{4}, \frac{1}{3}$ ______________

7. $\frac{2}{6}, \frac{2}{3}, \frac{1}{4}$ ______________

8. $\frac{1}{10}, \frac{3}{5}, \frac{2}{8}$ ______________

Compare. Write <, >, or =. You may use fraction strips to help.

9. $\frac{1}{2}$ ◯ $\frac{5}{10}$

$\frac{1}{2}$				
$\frac{1}{10}$	$\frac{1}{10}$	$\frac{1}{10}$	$\frac{1}{10}$	$\frac{1}{10}$

10. $\frac{1}{3}$ ◯ $\frac{1}{5}$

$\frac{1}{3}$
$\frac{1}{5}$

11. $\frac{2}{8}$ ◯ $\frac{2}{5}$

$\frac{1}{8}$	$\frac{1}{8}$
$\frac{1}{5}$	$\frac{1}{5}$

12. $\frac{3}{4}$ ◯ $\frac{2}{3}$

$\frac{1}{4}$	$\frac{1}{4}$	$\frac{1}{4}$
$\frac{1}{3}$	$\frac{1}{3}$	

13. $\frac{2}{4}$ ◯ $\frac{3}{6}$

$\frac{1}{4}$	$\frac{1}{4}$	
$\frac{1}{6}$	$\frac{1}{6}$	$\frac{1}{6}$

14. $\frac{2}{3}$ ◯ $\frac{5}{6}$

$\frac{1}{3}$	$\frac{1}{3}$			
$\frac{1}{6}$	$\frac{1}{6}$	$\frac{1}{6}$	$\frac{1}{6}$	$\frac{1}{6}$

15. $\frac{6}{10}$ ◯ $\frac{2}{5}$

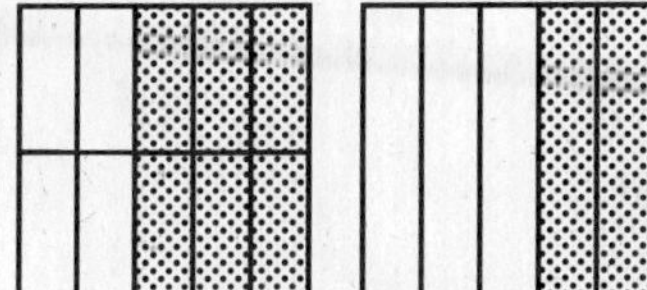

16. $\frac{1}{2}$ ◯ $\frac{2}{3}$

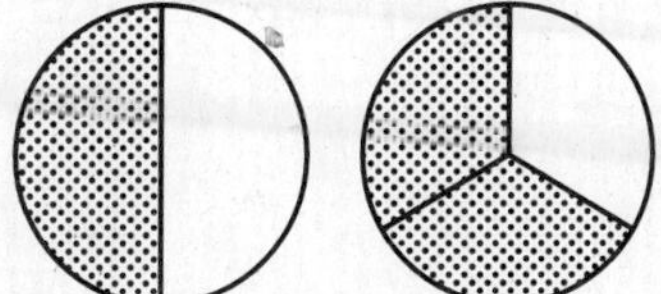

17. $\frac{2}{12}$ ◯ $\frac{1}{4}$

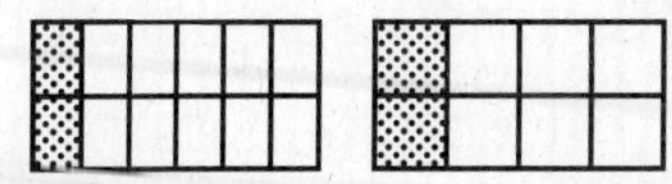

Name ________________________________

Estimating Fractional Amounts

Estimate the amount that is shaded.

1. 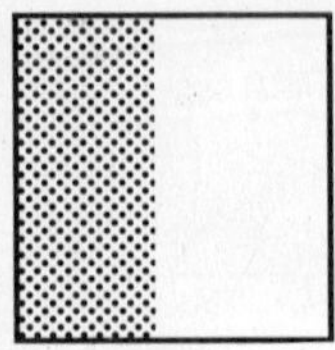

____

____

2. 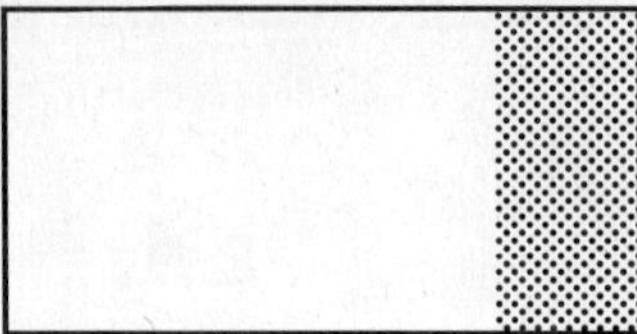

____

____

3. 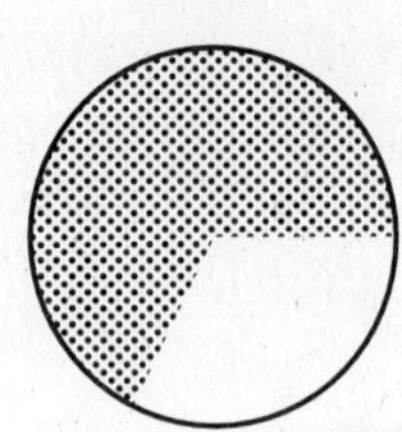

____

____

4. 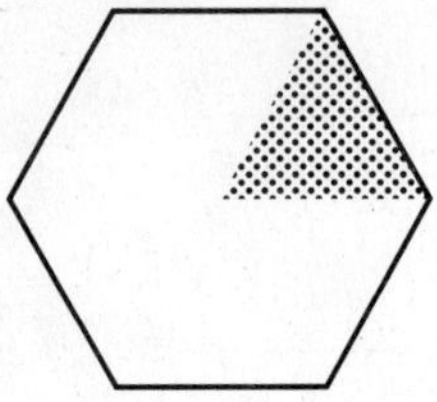

____

____

5. 

____

____

6. 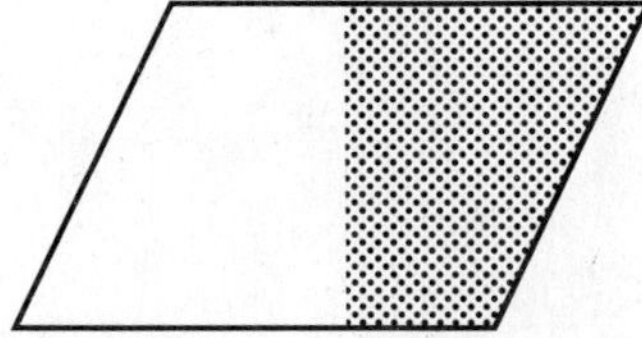

____

____

7. 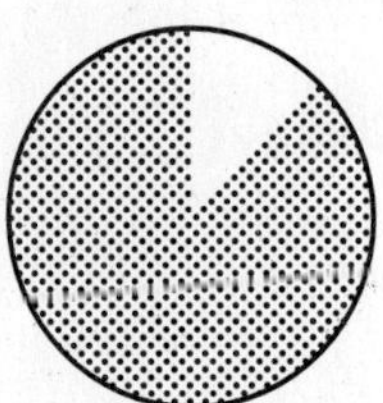

____

____

8. 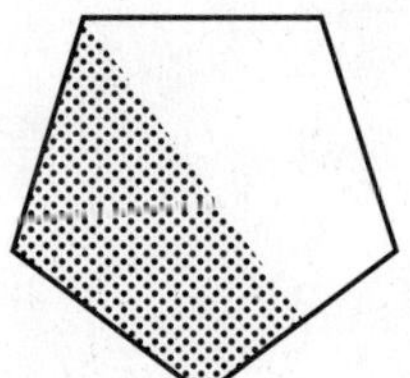

____

____

9. 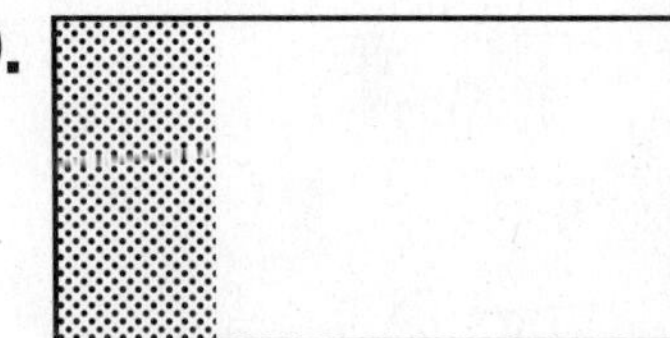

____

____

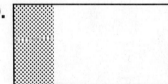

10. Tina needs about $\frac{2}{3}$ of a bar of clay to make a dinosaur. Is there enough clay left? Explain.

Name ______________________________

Review and Practice

Vocabulary Write true or false for each statement.

1. The numerator is the bottom number of a fraction and the denominator is the top number. __________

2. $\frac{3}{4}$ is a unit fraction. __________

(Lesson 1) Name the equal parts of each whole.

3. 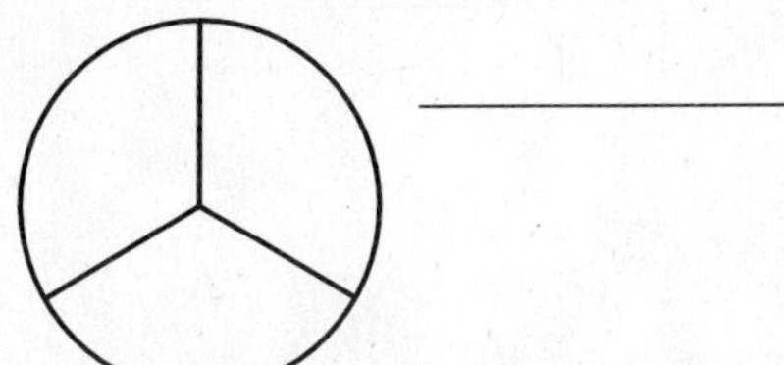 __________

4. 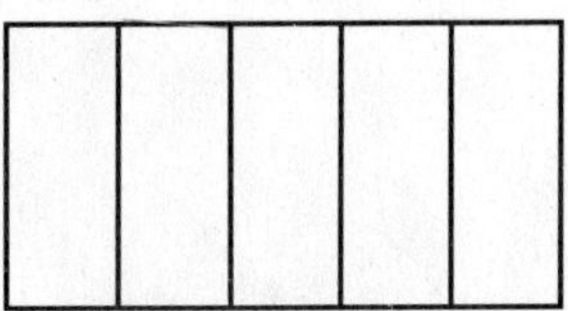 __________

(Lesson 2) Write the fraction of each figure that is shaded.

5. 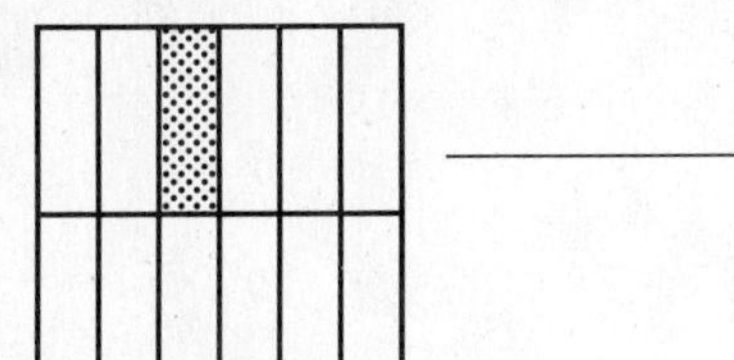 __________

6. 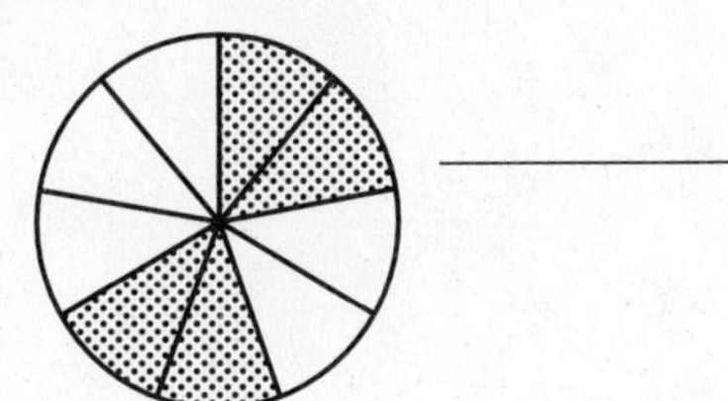 __________

(Lesson 4) Compare. Write <, >, or =. You may use fraction strips to help.

7. $\frac{2}{5}$ ◯ $\frac{3}{10}$ 8. $\frac{1}{4}$ ◯ $\frac{2}{8}$ 9. $\frac{1}{3}$ ◯ $\frac{3}{6}$

(Lesson 5) Estimate each shaded amount.

10. 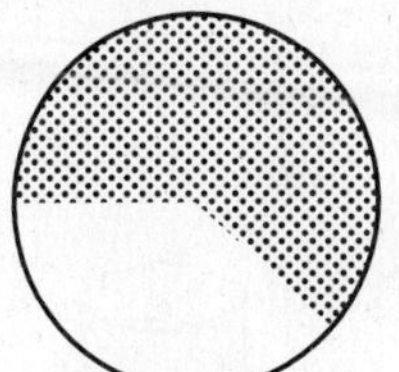

____

____

11. 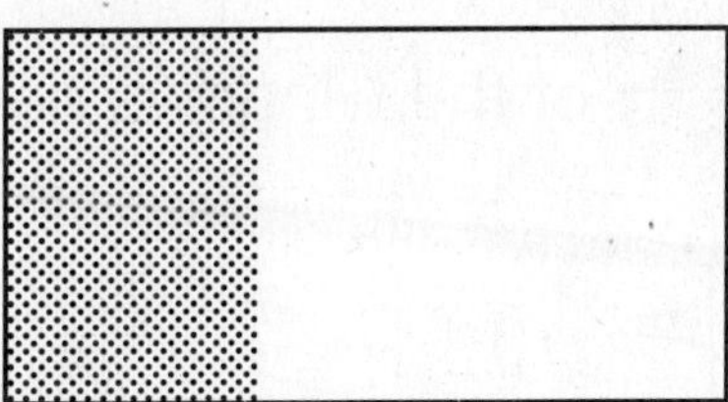

____

____

(Mixed Review) Complete.

12. 3 × ________ = 27 13. ________ × 6 = 48 14. ________ × 7 = 56

15. 47 divided by 6 is ________. 16. 23 added to 17 is ________.

Name ______________________________

Practice
10-6

Fractions and Sets

Write a fraction to tell what part of each set is circled.

1.

______

2.

______

3.

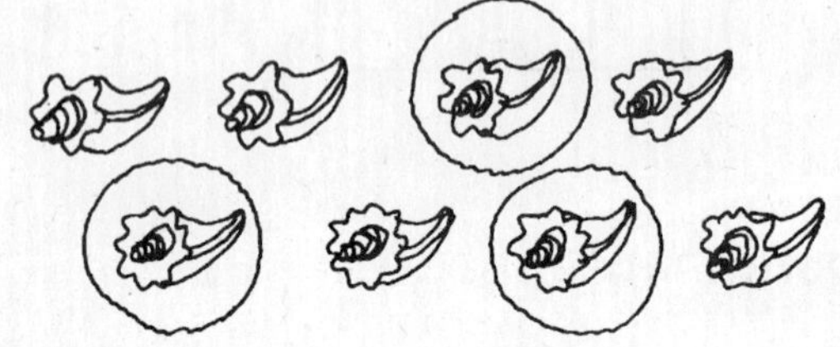

______

4.

______

Write a fraction to complete each sentence.

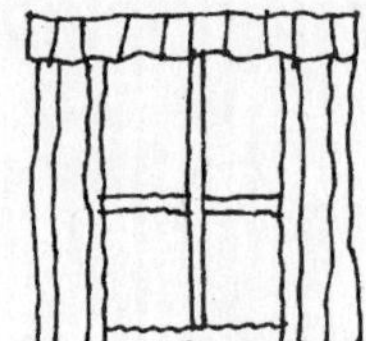  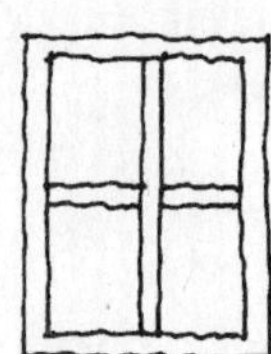  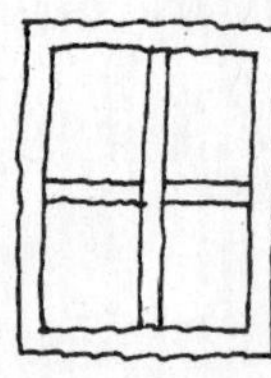

5. ______ of the windows have curtains.

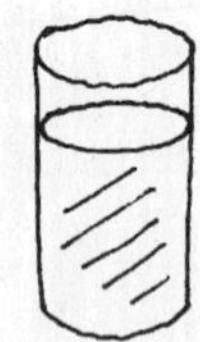 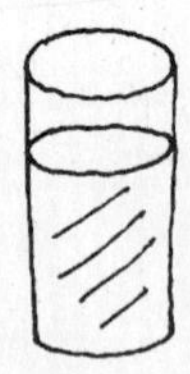 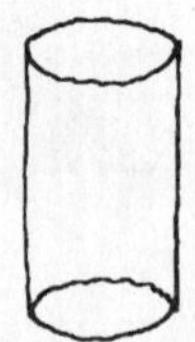   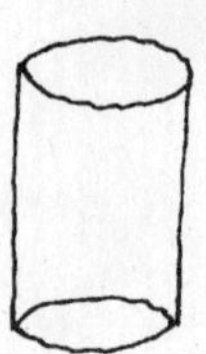 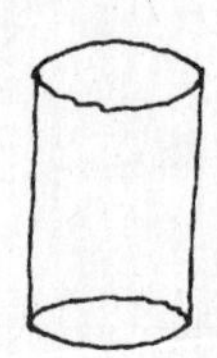

6. ______ of the glasses are empty.

7. $\frac{5}{6}$ of Sean's 6 cats are female. How many are male?

______

Name ______________________________

Practice
10-7

Exploring Finding a Fraction of a Number

Complete.

1. To find $\frac{1}{4}$ of 12 divide 12 into ______ equal groups.

2. To find $\frac{1}{3}$ of 15 divide 15 into ______ equal groups.

Solve. You may use counters or draw a picture to help.

3. $\frac{1}{2}$ of 18 = ______

4. $\frac{1}{7}$ of 21 = ______

5. $\frac{1}{10}$ of 10 = ______

6. $\frac{1}{4}$ of 8 = ______

7. Find $\frac{1}{3}$ of 9. ______

8. Find $\frac{1}{4}$ of 20. ______

9. Find $\frac{1}{5}$ of 30. ______

10. Find $\frac{1}{6}$ of 24. ______

11. What fraction of the animals are:

a. dogs? ______ **b.** cats? ______ **c.** birds? ______

12. Suppose an adult slept for $\frac{1}{4}$ of a 24-hour day. How many hours did the person sleep?

______

Name ______________________________

Practice 10-8

Mixed Numbers

Write a mixed number for each.

1. 

____

2.   

____

3.  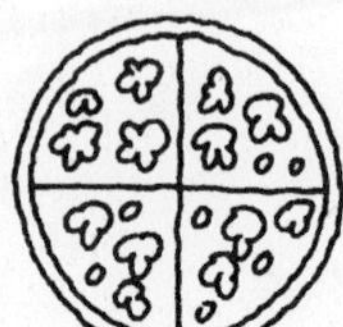

____

4.  

____

5. 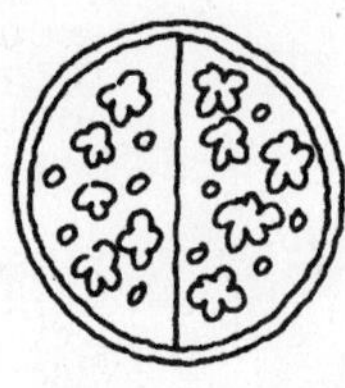 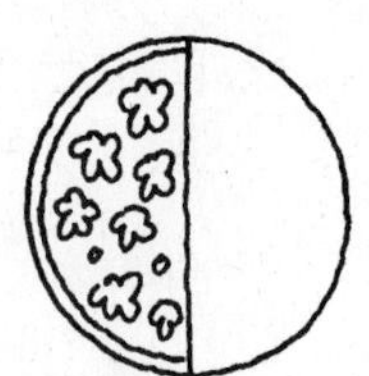

____

6.  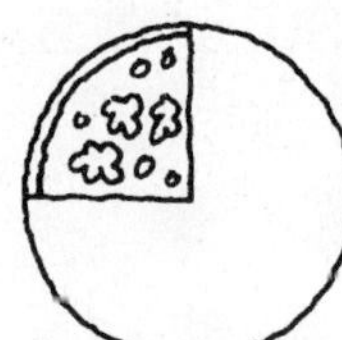

____

Answer each question.

7. Is there more or less than $1\frac{1}{4}$ pizzas? Explain.

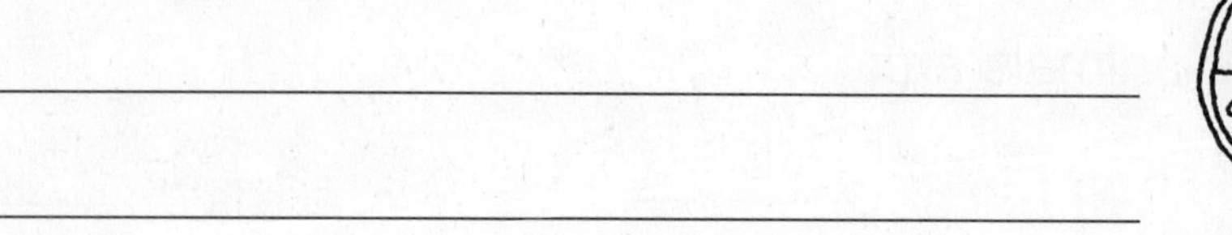

 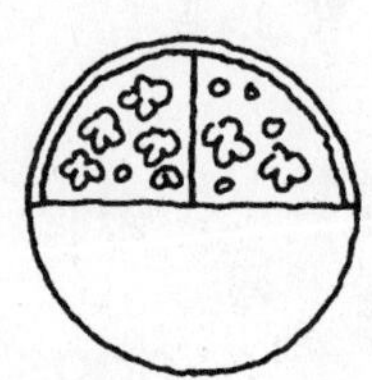

____

____

8. Leo said "$3\frac{3}{12}$ is the same as $3\frac{1}{4}$." Do you agree or disagree? Explain.

____

Name ________________________________

Practice
10-9

Exploring Adding and Subtracting Fractions

Find each sum or difference. You may use fraction strips or draw a picture to help.

1. $\frac{3}{5} + \frac{1}{5} =$ ______

2. $\frac{1}{4} + \frac{2}{4} =$ ______

3. $\frac{3}{5} - \frac{1}{5} =$ ______

4. $\frac{3}{4} - \frac{2}{4} =$ ______

5. $\frac{2}{6} + \frac{3}{6} =$ ______

6. $\frac{1}{5} + \frac{1}{5} =$ ______

7. $\frac{9}{12} - \frac{4}{12} =$ ______

8. $\frac{2}{9} - \frac{1}{9} =$ ______

9. $\frac{9}{10} - \frac{4}{10} =$ ______

10. $\frac{9}{16} + \frac{2}{16} =$ ______

11. $\frac{1}{4} + \frac{1}{4} =$ ______

12. $\frac{4}{7} - \frac{1}{7} =$ ______

13. $\frac{1}{3} + \frac{1}{3} =$ ______

14. $\frac{2}{6} - \frac{1}{6} =$ ______

15. $\frac{5}{8} - \frac{3}{8} =$ ______

16. $\frac{9}{12} - \frac{7}{12} =$ ______

17. Suppose you knocked over 9 out of 10 bowling pins. What fraction of the pins would still be standing?

______

18. Suppose 5 out of 10 bowling pins were still standing. What fraction of the pins were knocked over?

______

Name ____________________

Practice 10-10

Decision Making

Your school won the city chess championship! Your team is having a party at your house and there are 8 players to feed.

You want at least 3 pieces of pizza per player. How many pizzas will you need if . . .

1. each pizza is cut into 6 pieces? ______
2. each pizza is cut into 8 pieces? ______
3. each pizza is cut into 10 pieces? ______

You want at least 2 glasses of juice per player. How many bottles of juice will you need if . . .

4. each bottle holds 6 glasses worth of juice? ______
5. each bottle holds 10 glasses worth of juice? ______
6. each bottle holds 4 glasses worth of juice? ______
7. Don't forget the victory cake! Can you think of 2 different ways to cut it so everyone gets the same number of pieces?

   a. ________ pieces

   b. ________ pieces

8. What if the coach wants cake, too? Draw pictures to show 2 different ways to divide the cake equally among 9 people.

   a.

   b.

Name ______________________________

Review and Practice

(Lesson 6) Write a fraction that tells what part of the set is circled.

1.

______

2.

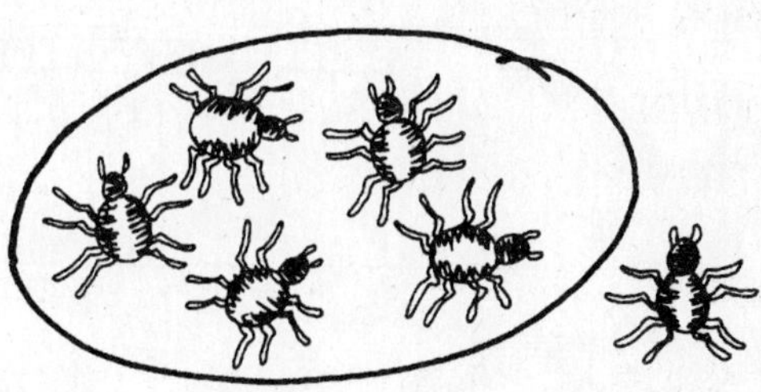

______

(Lesson 7) Solve. You may use counters or draw a picture to help.

3. Find $\frac{1}{4}$ of 24. ______

4. Find $\frac{1}{3}$ of 12. ______

5. Find $\frac{1}{5}$ of 20. ______

6. Find $\frac{1}{2}$ of 14. ______

7. Mitch has $18. He did put $\frac{1}{3}$ of the money in his savings account. How much did he put in his savings account? ______

(Lesson 8) Write a mixed number for each.

8.

______

9.

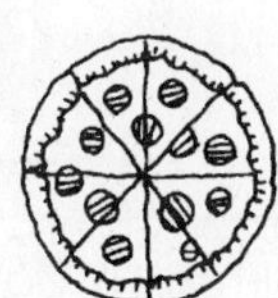
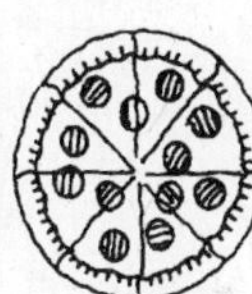

______

(Lesson 9) Find each sum or difference. You may use fraction strips or draw a picture to help.

10. $\frac{1}{6} + \frac{4}{6} =$ ______

11. $\frac{4}{5} - \frac{1}{5} =$ ______

12. $\frac{7}{9} - \frac{3}{9} =$ ______

13. $\frac{3}{8} + \frac{2}{8} =$ ______

(Mixed Review) Add or subtract.

14. $62 + 33$

15. $98 - 19$

16. $80 + 73$

17. $82 - 45$

Name ______________________________

Practice 10-11

Exploring Length

Estimate each length. Then measure to the nearest inch.

1. 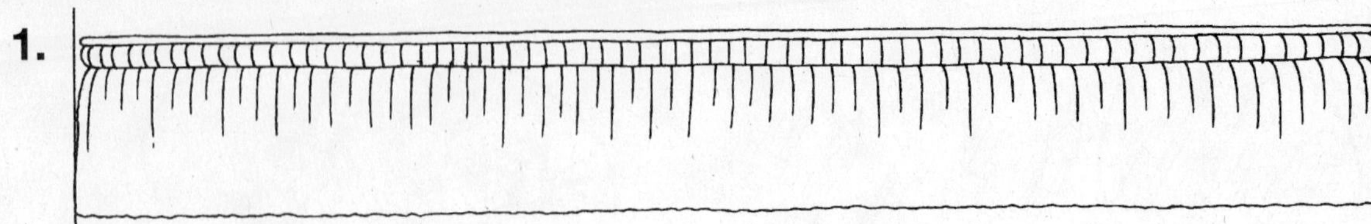

2. 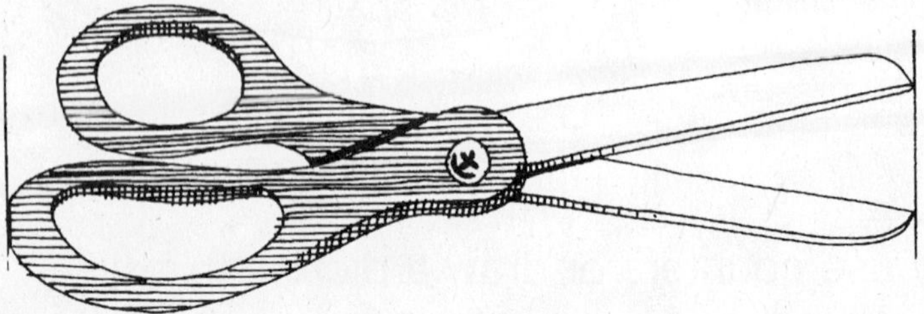 ________

3. 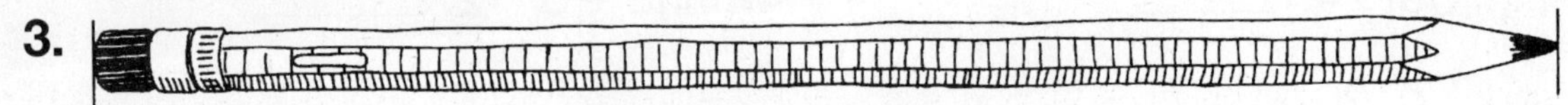 ________

4.  ________

5. 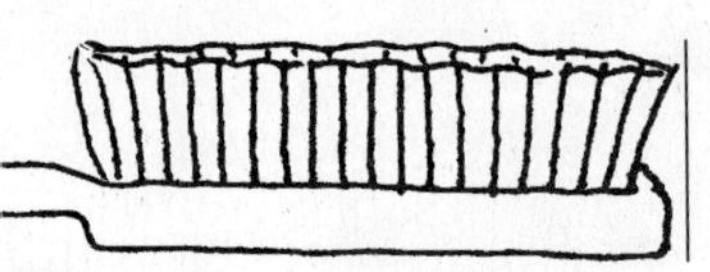 ________

6. Suppose you need at least 5 inches of wire for a project. Is this enough wire? ________

7. Measure the length of your thumb, your math book, and your arm. Write each measurement in order from greatest to least.

____

8. Use a ruler. Draw a line to show each length.

a. $2\frac{1}{2}$ inches

b. 5 inches

c. $6\frac{1}{4}$ inches

Name ______________________________

Practice 10-12

Measuring to the Nearest $\frac{1}{2}$ Inch and $\frac{1}{4}$ Inch

Measure the length of each object to the nearest $\frac{1}{2}$ inch.

1. 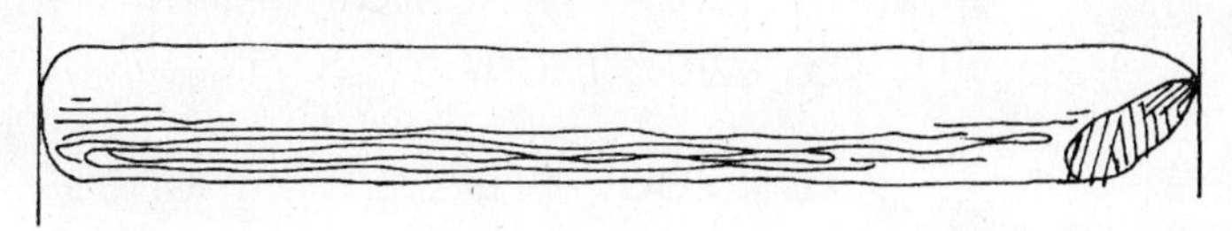

____

2. 

____

3. 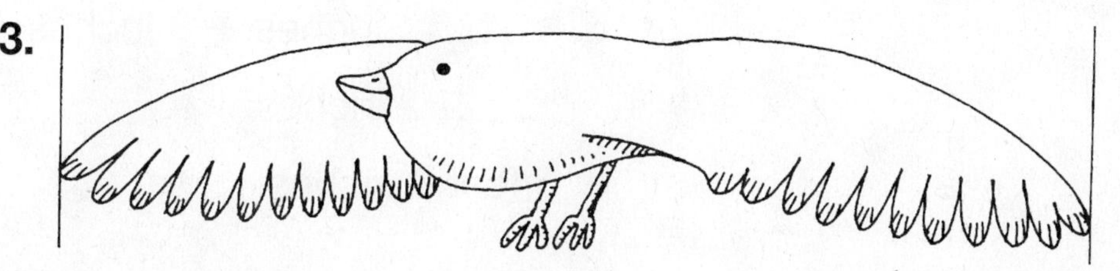

____

Measure the length of each object to the nearest $\frac{1}{4}$ inch.

4. 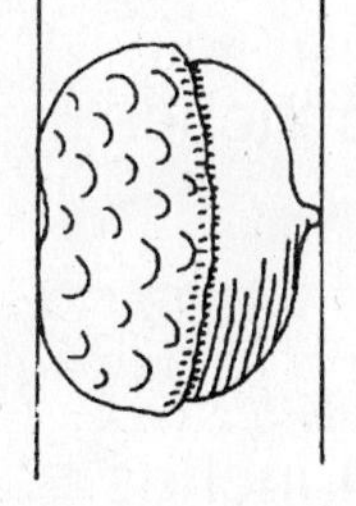

____

5. 

____

6. 

____

7. You need to measure a pebble for a science project. Does it make more sense to measure to the nearest inch or $\frac{1}{2}$ inch?

____

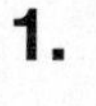

Name ______________________________

Practice
10-13

Exploring Length in Feet and Inches

You can multiply to write measurements in feet as measurements in inches.

1. How many inches are in 4 feet?

a. 1 foot = ______ inches

b. 4 feet = 4 × ______ inches

c. 4 feet = ______ inches

2. How many inches are in 5 feet 8 inches?

a. 1 foot = ______ inches

b. 5 feet = 5 × ______ inches

c. 5 feet = ______ inches

d. ______ inches + 8 inches = ______ inches

e. 5 feet 8 inches = ______________

Write each measurement in inches.

3. 4 feet 8 inches ______________

4. 2 feet 11 inches ______________

5. 5 feet 5 inches ______________

6. 1 foot 9 inches ______________

7. 6 feet 3 inches ______________

8. 4 feet 4 inches ______________

9. Does it make more sense to measure the length of your pencil in feet or inches? Explain.

____

____

10. Does it make more sense to measure the length of your classroom in feet or inches? Explain.

____

____

Name ______________________________

Practice
10-14

Feet, Yards, and Miles

Compare. Write <, >, or =.

1. 1,760 yd ◯ 1 mile
2. 3 yd ◯ 8 ft
3. 5 ft ◯ 2 yd
4. 4,000 yd ◯ 2 mi
5. 2 mi ◯ 5,280 ft
6. 6 yd ◯ 2 ft
7. 40 in. ◯ 1 yd
8. 10 ft ◯ 3 yd
9. 1 mi ◯ 3,500 yd
10. 12 ft ◯ 4 yd
11. 20 in. ◯ 2 ft
12. 3 mi ◯ 5,000 yd
13. 4,500 ft ◯ 1 mi
14. 9 yd ◯ 3 ft

Choose an estimate for each.

15. length of your bed ______ a. 1 yard
16. distance a person jogs ______ b. 1 foot
17. height of a desk ______ c. 2 yards
18. length of a football ______ d. 1 mile

19. Would it make sense to measure the distance from your home to school in feet? Explain.

____

____

20. Would it make sense to measure a bicycle in feet? Explain.

____

____

Name ____

Analyze Strategies: Use Logical Reasoning

Use logical reasoning to solve.

1. Help Peter figure out which soccer teams finished in first, second, third, and fourth place. The Wings finished in third place. The Hawks beat the Eagles and the Wings. The Tigers finished in last place.

____

2. Ramon, Max, Jenna, and Maya are all on the same soccer team. Max is the youngest. Maya is older than Ramon. Jenna is 10 years old. If each player is either 9, 10, 11, or 12 years old, how old is each person?

____

Use any strategy to solve.

3. Sean, Sharon, Ali, and Marie all have scored goals this season. Sharon has scored more goals than Ali and Sean. Sean has scored fewer goals than the three other players. Sharon has scored fewer goals than Marie. Order the players from greatest number of goals scored to fewest.

____

4. I am an even number between 20 and 30. The sum of my tens digit and my ones digit is 6. What number am I? ________

5. I am an odd number between 50 and 60. The sum of my tens digit and my ones digit is 10. What number am I? ________

6. Mickey has 5 coins. The total value of the coins is $0.60. He doesn't have any pennies and only has 1 nickel. What coins does Mickey have?

____

7. I am a number between 10 and 20. The difference between my digits is 0. What number am I? ________

Name ______________________________

Practice
Chapter 10
Section C

Review and Practice

Vocabulary Write true or false for each statement.

1. Kevin can walk 1 mile in 1 second. __________

2. This paper is about 1 foot in length. __________

(Lesson 11) Measure the length of the object to the nearest inch.

3. ________________

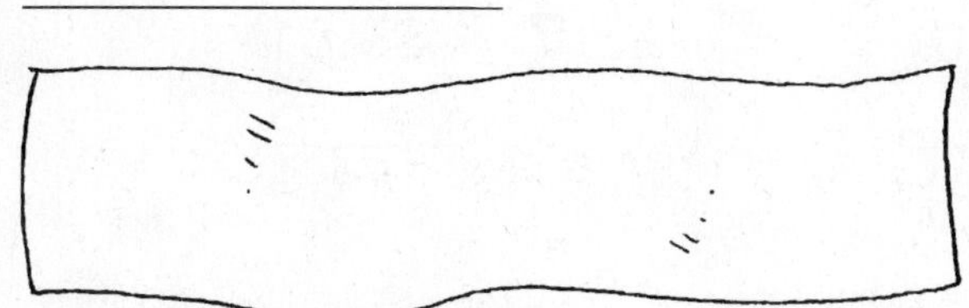

(Lesson 12) Measure the length of the object to the nearest $\frac{1}{4}$ inch.

4. ________________

(Lesson 13) Write each measurement in inches.

5. 8 feet ________ **6.** 3 feet ________ **7.** 2 feet ________

(Lesson 14) Compare. Write <, >, or =.

8. 2 feet ◯ 22 inches

9. 2 yards ◯ 6 feet

10. 5 yards ◯ 140 inches

11. 3 miles ◯ 21,120 feet

(Lesson 15) Use any strategy to solve.

12. Freda has 9 coins worth \$1. Two are quarters. None are pennies. There is 1 more nickel than there are dimes. What coins does Freda have?

____

(Mixed Review) Multiply or divide.

13. $6 \times 2 =$ ________

14. $32 \div 8 =$ ________

Name ______________________________

Practice
Chapters 1–10

Cumulative Review

(Chapter 4 Lesson 10) Subtract.

1. $\begin{array}{r} 673 \\ -\ 425 \\ \hline \end{array}$ **2.** $\begin{array}{r} 315 \\ -\ 99 \\ \hline \end{array}$ **3.** $\begin{array}{r} 830 \\ -\ 609 \\ \hline \end{array}$ **4.** $\begin{array}{r} 749 \\ -\ 73 \\ \hline \end{array}$

(Chapter 9 Lesson 8) Multiply.

5. $\begin{array}{r} \$3.29 \\ \times\ \ \ 3 \\ \hline \end{array}$ **6.** $\begin{array}{r} \$3.10 \\ \times\ \ \ 4 \\ \hline \end{array}$ **7.** $\begin{array}{r} \$9.01 \\ \times\ \ \ 5 \\ \hline \end{array}$

(Chapter 9 Lesson 13) Find each quotient and remainder. You may use counters to help.

8. $3\overline{)13}$ **9.** $5\overline{)48}$ **10.** $7\overline{)59}$ **11.** $2\overline{)19}$

(Chapter 10 Lesson 2) Write the fraction of each figure that is shaded.

12. 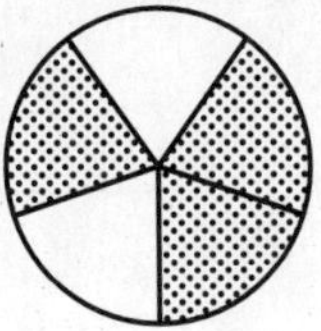
______

13. 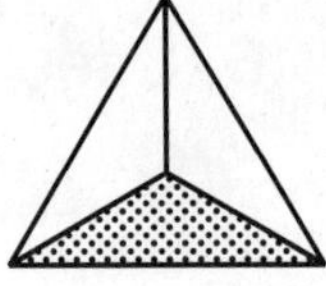
______

(Chapter 10 Lesson 4) Compare. Write <, >, or =. You may use fraction strips to help.

14. $\frac{1}{4}$ ◯ $\frac{5}{8}$ **15.** $\frac{3}{6}$ ◯ $\frac{5}{12}$ **16.** $\frac{2}{4}$ ◯ $\frac{4}{8}$

17. $\frac{4}{5}$ ◯ $\frac{5}{10}$ **18.** $\frac{1}{2}$ ◯ $\frac{2}{3}$ **19.** $\frac{3}{4}$ ◯ $\frac{8}{12}$

(Chapter 10 Lesson 9) Find each sum or difference. You may use fraction strips or draw a picture to help.

20. $\frac{6}{8} + \frac{1}{8} =$ ______ **21.** $\frac{2}{5} + \frac{3}{5} =$ ______

22. $\frac{6}{9} - \frac{3}{9} =$ ______ **23.** $\frac{7}{8} - \frac{5}{8} =$ ______

Name ____________________

Practice
11-1

Exploring Tenths

Any number in tenths can be written as a fraction or as a decimal.

Complete the table.

	Grids	Fraction or Mixed Number	Decimal	Word Name
1.			0.3	
2.				one and one tenth

Write the fraction and the decimal to name each shaded part.

3. 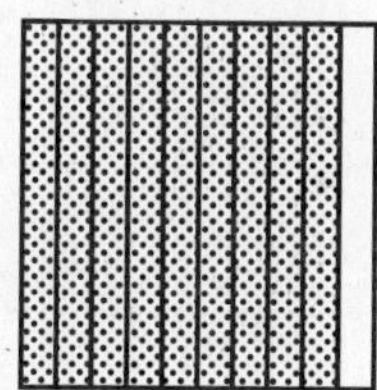

____

4. 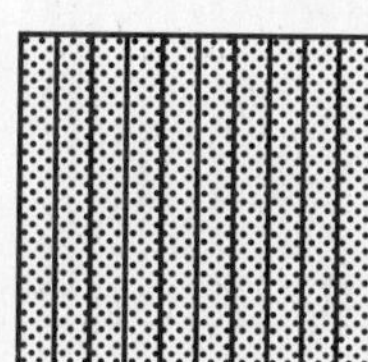 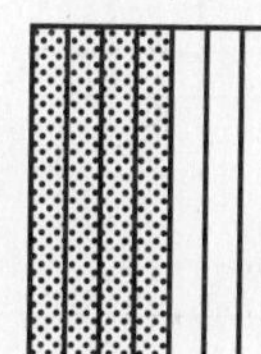

____

Write each as a decimal.

5. eight tenths ________

6. $\frac{5}{10}$ ________

7. two and two tenths ________

8. $1\frac{6}{10}$ ________

9. Write each part of the circle as a fraction and a decimal.

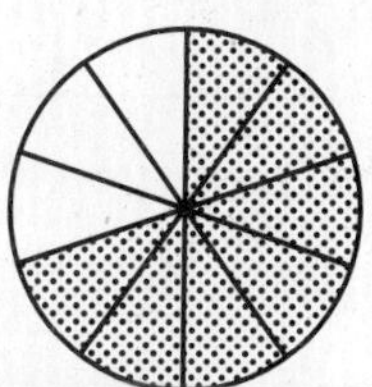

		Fraction	Decimal
a.	Shaded		
b.	Not shaded		

Name ____________________

Practice 11-2

Hundredths

Write the fraction and the decimal to name each shaded part.

1. 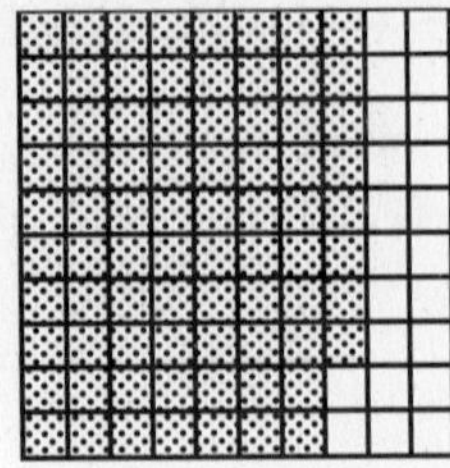

____

2. 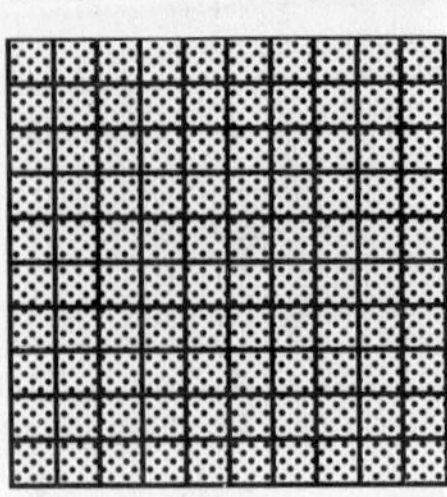

____

3. 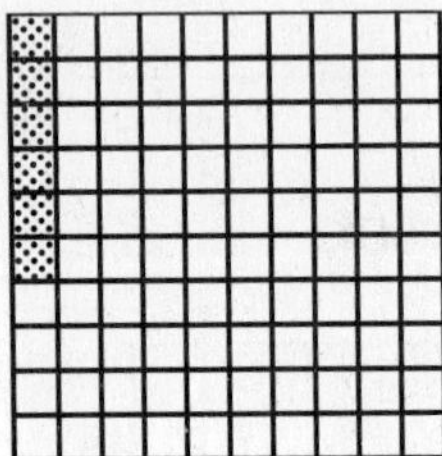

____

4. 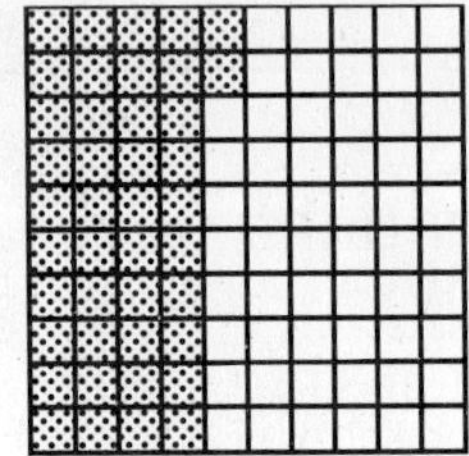

____

Write each as a decimal.

5. seventeen hundredths ________

6. nine hundredths ________

7. one and three hundredths ________

8. $\frac{22}{100}$ ________

9. fifty-one hundredths ________

10. $\frac{1}{100}$ ________

11. $2\frac{65}{100}$ ________

12. $1\frac{99}{100}$ ________

13. Is 0.70 greater than, less than, or equal to 0.7? Explain.

____

14. What is the value of each bold digit?

a. 0.8**4** ________________

b. 1.3**2** ________________

c. **3**.59 ________________

Name ______________________________

Practice
11-3

Exploring Adding and Subtracting Decimals

You can add and subtract decimals using pencil and paper. You may use tenths grids to help.

1. Add 1.4 and 0.8.

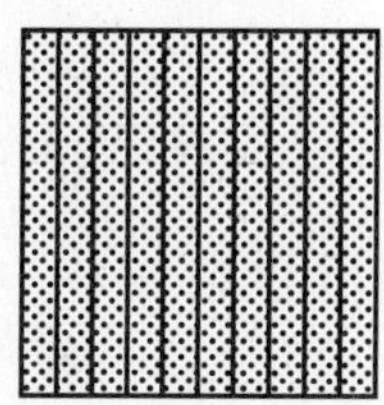
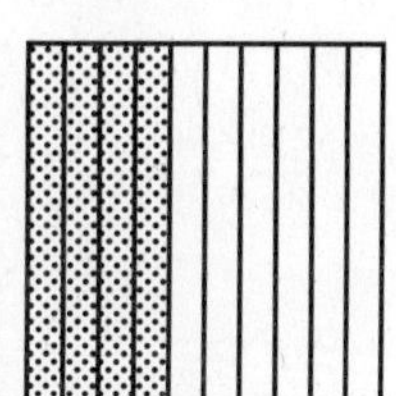
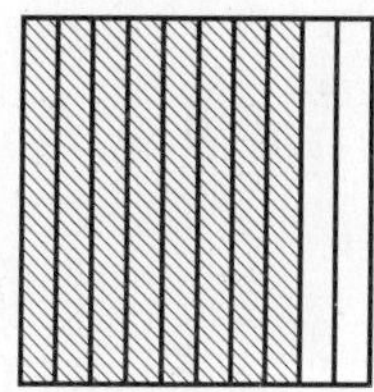

a. Write the equation vertically in the space below. Line up the decimal points.

b. Add tenths. Regroup if needed. Then add ones. What is the sum? ________

2. Subtract 1.6 from 2.5.

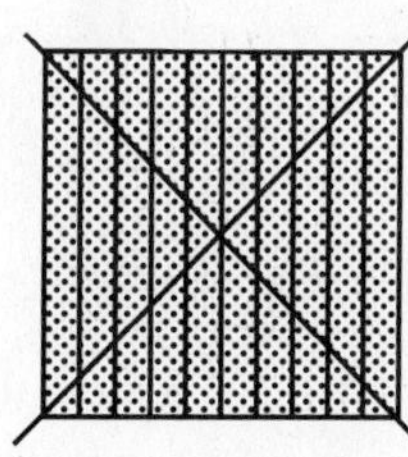
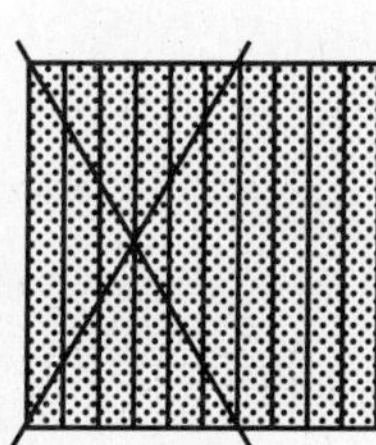
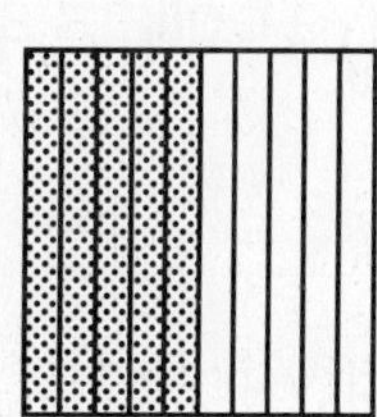

a. Write the equation vertically in the space below. Line up the decimal points.

b. Subtract tenths. Regroup if needed. Then subtract ones. What is the difference? ________

Find each sum or difference. You may use tenths grids to help.

3. $\begin{array}{r} 3.3 \\ +\ 2.2 \\ \hline \end{array}$ **4.** $\begin{array}{r} 1.9 \\ +\ 4.5 \\ \hline \end{array}$ **5.** $\begin{array}{r} 8.6 \\ -\ 3.4 \\ \hline \end{array}$ **6.** $\begin{array}{r} 6.2 \\ -\ 4.8 \\ \hline \end{array}$

7. $\begin{array}{r} 0.7 \\ +\ 0.3 \\ \hline \end{array}$ **8.** $\begin{array}{r} 2.2 \\ -\ 1.9 \\ \hline \end{array}$ **9.** $\begin{array}{r} 5.8 \\ -\ 0.7 \\ \hline \end{array}$ **10.** $\begin{array}{r} 1.5 \\ +\ 1.6 \\ \hline \end{array}$

Name ______________________

Practice 11-4

Connecting Decimals and Money

Write each as a money amount.

1. $\frac{73}{100}$ of $1.00 __________

2. $\frac{39}{100}$ of $1.00 __________

3. $1\frac{15}{100}$ of $1.00 __________

4. $\frac{51}{100}$ of $1.00 __________

5. $2\frac{27}{100}$ of $1.00 __________

6. $\frac{98}{100}$ of $1.00 __________

7. sixty-six cents __________

8. forty-two cents __________

9. one dollar and ninety-one cents

____

10. three dollars and three cents

____

11. five dollars and twelve cents

____

12. two dollars and eighty-eight cents

____

13. fifty-four hundredths of $1.00

____

14. three and thirty-seven hundredths of $1.00

____

15. Complete the table.

		Fraction of $1.00	Decimal Part of $1.00
a.	$0.74		
b.	$0.02		
c.	$0.19		

Name ______________________________

Practice 11-5

Decision Making

You've decided to purchase a get-well gift for a friend who is ill. You want to go to the local mall to shop for the gift. Your goal is to find the perfect present and to be home by 5:00 P.M. You are bringing $10.00 with you. Below is a copy of the bus schedule for the bus which will take you to the mall. The bus stops on Carey Ave. right outside your house.

Leave Carey Ave.	Arrive Milford Mall	Leave Milford Mall	Arrive Carey Ave.
2:00 P.M.	2:15 P.M.	3:15 P.M.	4:00 P.M.
4:00 P.M.	4:15 P.M.	4:30 P.M.	4:45 P.M.

1. What information does the schedule give you?

____

____

2. When is the latest time you could leave the mall in order to get home on time?

____

____

3. How long does it take the bus to get to the mall from your bus stop on Carey Ave.? __________

4. If the one-way bus fare is $0.50, how much spending money do you actually have?

____

5. You buy a shirt for your friend. It costs $8.00. How much money do you have left over to buy a snack? (Don't forget about the bus fare!)

____

6. A muffin costs $0.60. Do you have enough money to buy one for your snack? __________
Could you buy two muffins?

____

Name ____________________

Practice
Chapter 11
Section A

Review and Practice

Vocabulary Write true or false for each.

1. 85 cents is 85 tenths of a dollar. ________

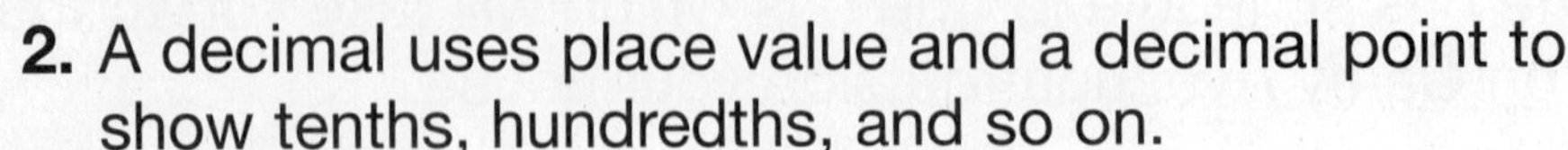

2. A decimal uses place value and a decimal point to show tenths, hundredths, and so on. ________

3. The symbol used to separate ones from tenths in decimals is a comma. ________

(Lessons 1 and 2) Write the fraction and the decimal to name each shaded part.

4. 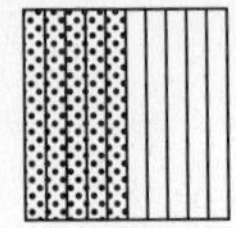

________; ________

5. 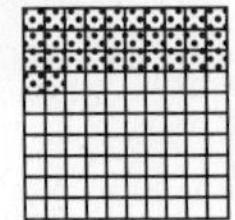

________; ________

6. 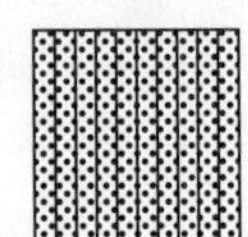 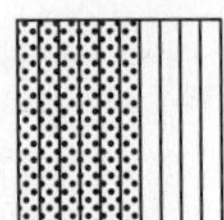

________; ________

Write each as a decimal.

7. twenty-nine hundredths ________

8. $5\frac{3}{100}$ ________

9. two and four tenths ________

10. $\frac{8}{10}$ ________

(Lesson 3) Find each sum or difference. You may use tenths grids to help.

11. $3.8 + 5.4$

12. $8.3 - 6.5$

13. $2.6 + 3.4$

14. $8.5 - 5.8$

15. $4.7 + 8.6$

(Lesson 4) Write each as a money amount.

16. $\frac{16}{100}$ of $1.00 ________

17. $3\frac{29}{100}$ of $1.00 ________

(Mixed Review) Complete each number sentence.

18. 18 + ________ = 29

19. 57 − ________ = 21

20. ________ × 6 = 54

21. 56 ÷ ________ = 7

Name ______________________________

Practice 11-6

Exploring Centimeters and Decimeters

1. Write 1 cm below the item that measures 1 cm. Write 1 dm below the item that measures 1 dm.

a. ________ **b.** ________

Estimate the length of each object. Then measure to the nearest centimeter.

2.

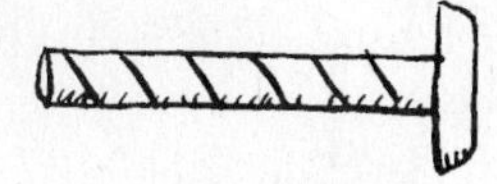

estimate ________

actual ________

3.

estimate ________

actual ________

Choose the best estimate for each.

4.

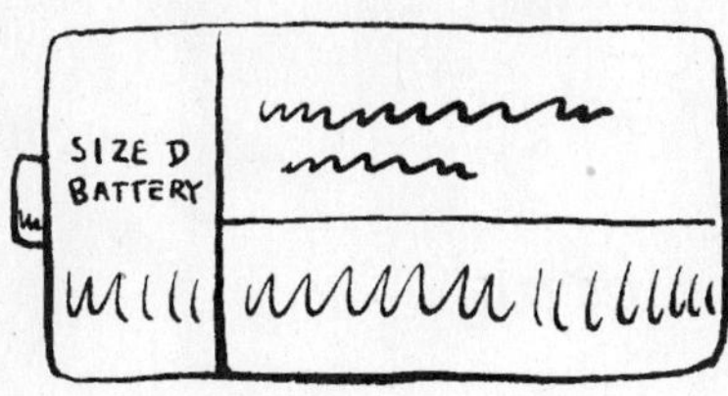

a. 5 cm ________

b. 1 dm

5.

a. 5 cm ________

b. 1 dm

Name ____________________

Practice 11-7

Meters and Kilometers

Match each with its estimate.

1. length of a hiking trail ______ a. 30 cm
2. width of a frying pan ______ b. 2 kilometers
3. height of a chimney ______ c. 3 m

Write whether you would measure each in cm, m, or km.

4. length of a nail ______
5. length of a large table ______
6. length of a hot dog ______
7. height of a mountain ______
8. length of a van ______
9. distance of a 20-minute train ride ______
10. depth of a lake ______
11. length of the Mississippi River ______
12. length of a highway bridge ______

Answer each and explain your answers.

13. Is an 87-cm rug longer or shorter than a 1-meter rug? Explain.

____

14. Is a 300-cm-long sofa longer or shorter than a meter? Explain.

____

15. Suppose your mom drove 800 meters to the shopping mall and then drove home again. Did she drive at least one kilometer? Explain.

____

Name ______________________

Practice
11-8

Compare Strategies: Use Objects and Draw a Picture

Use any strategy to solve.

1. A bus starts off on its route. At the first stop 18 passengers get on. At the second stop 10 more board, but 2 get off. At the third stop 3 passengers get on and 1 passenger gets off. How many passengers are on board when the bus arrives at the fourth stop? ______

2. The same bus departed the terminal at 10:00 A.M. It arrived at the first stop 20 minutes later. It was delayed at this stop for 2 minutes. It took another 10 minutes for the bus to arrive at the second stop. At what time did the bus arrive at the second stop? ______

3. The same bus arrived at the third stop at 10:45. How much time went by between the time it arrived at the second stop and the time it arrived at the third stop? ______

4. Kim, Lisa, Ellen, and Martin have a jump rope contest. The jumper with the fewest misses wins. Martin wins with only 5 misses. Ellen has 3 more misses than Martin. Kim misses twice as many times as Ellen. Lisa has 2 fewer misses than Ellen. Can you give the scores for Ellen, Kim, and Lisa? Who came in second?

____

5. Some students are making a chart to show how many students in the class were born in each month of the year. There are 22 students in the class. They find out that 1 student was born in January. Three times that many students were born in February. The months of March, April, September and October each had one less birth than the month of February. The rest of the students were born in the summer months. How many students had summer birthdays? ______

Name ______________________________

Practice
Chapter 11
Section B

Review and Practice

Vocabulary. Choose the best word or words to complete each sentence. Use each word once.

meter	kilometer	centimeter	decimeter

1. A ____________ is a metric unit equal to 1,000 meters.

2. A ____________ is a metric unit equal to 10 ____________s.

3. A ____________ is a metric unit equal to 100 centimeters.

(Lesson 6) Match each with its estimate.

______ **4.** 1 m　　**a.** width of an audio cassette tape

______ **5.** 1 dm　　**b.** length of a pencil

______ **6.** 1 cm　　**c.** height of your teacher's desk

(Lesson 7) Write whether you would measure each in cm, m, or km.

7. a car trip ______　　**8.** length of a marathon ______

9. length of a car ______　　**10.** width of a book ______

11. height of a dog ______　　**12.** height of a flag pole ______

(Lesson 8) Solve. Use any strategy.

13. A shelf at the grocery store had 15 loaves of bread on it. One shopper buys 3 loaves, another buys 5 loaves. The stock person restocks the shelf with 10 more loaves, then 3 more shoppers each buy 2 loaves. How many loaves of bread are on the shelf? ____________

14. Maxine rode the elevator to the third floor, where she got off. She then climbed up 2 flights of stairs and got back on the elevator. She took the elevator down 3 floors. What floor is she now on? ____________

(Mixed Review) Find each product.

15. $\begin{array}{r} 23 \\ \times\ 5 \\ \hline \end{array}$　　**16.** $\begin{array}{r} 45 \\ \times\ 6 \\ \hline \end{array}$　　**17.** $\begin{array}{r} \$3.14 \\ \times\ \quad 9 \\ \hline \end{array}$　　**18.** $\begin{array}{r} 822 \\ \times\ \ 3 \\ \hline \end{array}$

Name ______________________

Practice
Chapters 1–11

Cumulative Review

(Chapter 3 Lesson 10) Solve. Use any strategy.

1. The sum of 2 numbers is 61. The numbers are 5 apart. What are they? ________
2. The difference of 2 numbers is 10. The sum of the numbers is 14. What are they? ________

(Chapter 4 Lesson 11) Find each difference.

3. $\begin{array}{r} 807 \\ -\ 29 \\ \hline \end{array}$

4. $\begin{array}{r} \$306 \\ -\ 168 \\ \hline \end{array}$

5. $\begin{array}{r} 900 \\ -\ 824 \\ \hline \end{array}$

(Chapter 9 Lesson 14) Find each quotient and remainder.

6. $7\overline{)60}$
7. $8\overline{)56}$
8. $3\overline{)14}$
9. $5\overline{)32}$

(Chapter 10 Lesson 6) Write a fraction to tell what part of each set is circled.

10. 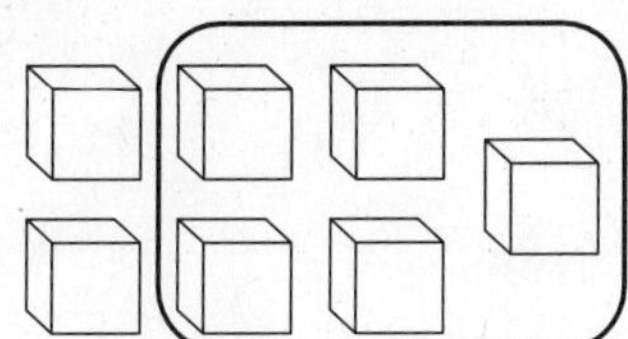
____

11. 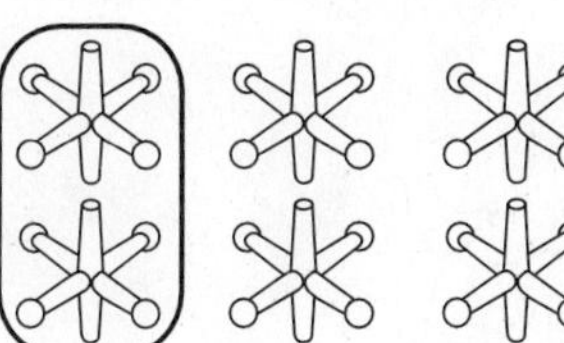
____

12. 
____

(Chapter 11 Lesson 3) Find each sum or difference.

13. $\begin{array}{r} 3.6 \\ +\ 2.3 \\ \hline \end{array}$

14. $\begin{array}{r} 9.4 \\ -\ 6.8 \\ \hline \end{array}$

15. $\begin{array}{r} 0.9 \\ +\ 7.7 \\ \hline \end{array}$

16. $\begin{array}{r} 9.9 \\ -\ 1.6 \\ \hline \end{array}$

(Chapter 11 Lesson 4) Write each as a money amount.

17. $\frac{26}{100}$ of \$1.00 ________
18. $4\frac{53}{100}$ of \$1.00 ________
19. three dollars and five cents ________
20. seventy-two hundredths of \$1.00 ________

Name ______________________________

Practice 12-1

Exploring Capacity: Customary Units

Complete.

1. ______ cups = 1 pint
2. 4 cups = ______ pints = ______ quart
3. ______ cups = 8 pints = ______ quarts = 1 gallon

Circle the best estimate for each.

4.

a. 1 cup
b. 1 quart
c. 1 pint

5.

a. 1 cup
b. 1 pint
c. 1 gallon

6.

a. 1 quart
b. 1 pint
c. 1 gallon

7.

a. 1 pint
b. 1 quart
c. 1 cup

8.

a. 1 pint
b. 1 quart
c. 1 gallon

9.

a. 1 cup
b. 1 quart
c. 1 gallon

Compare. Use $<$, $>$, or $=$.

10. 6 pints ◯ 1 gallon
11. 2 pints ◯ 3 cups
12. 2 quarts ◯ 4 pints
13. 16 cups ◯ 3 quarts

14. Suppose you want to make pudding. The recipe calls for 4 cups of milk. You have 1 quart. Do you have enough milk to make the recipe? Explain.

____

Name ______________________________

Practice 12-2

Measuring Capacity: Metric Units

Circle the better estimate for each.

1.

a. 1 mL

b. 1 L

2.

a. 300 mL

b. 300 L

3.

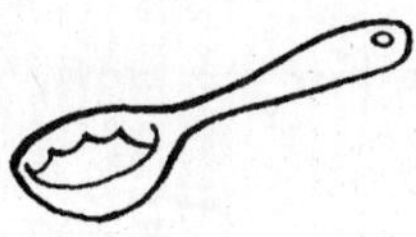

a. 10 mL

b. 10 L

4.

a. 400 mL

b. 400 L

5.

a. 2 mL

b. 2 L

6.

a. 500 mL

b. 500 L

7. Does a jar of honey hold about 600 mL or 600 L? ____________

8. Does a plastic jug of milk hold about 3 mL or 3 L? ____________

9. Suppose you estimated that you have made about 2 liters of lemonade. How could you check your estimate?

____

____

____

____

10. What kind of container might hold many liters of water?

____

Name ____

Practice 12-3

Exploring Weight: Customary Units

Compare. Use <, >, or =.

1. 16 ounces ◯ 1 pound

2. 1 ounce ◯ 1 pound

3. 18 ounces ◯ 1 pound

4. 12 ounces ◯ 1 pound

Circle the better estimate for each.

5.

a. 11 oz

b. 11 lb

6.

a. 2 oz

b. 2 lb

7.

a. 7 oz

b. 7 lb

Write whether each is less or more than a pound.

8.

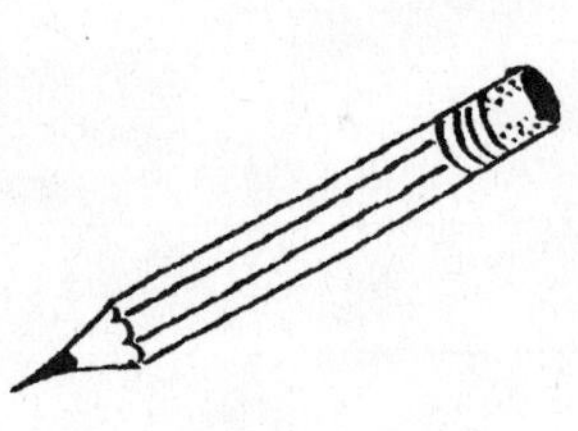

____

9.

____

10.

____

11. Suppose a dog weighs 8 pounds. How many ounces does it weigh? ______________

12. Suppose a person's brain weighs about 3 pounds. How many ounces does it weigh? ______________

13. Complete the table.

Ounces	16	32		64	80	96
Pounds	1	2				

Name ___________________________________

Practice 12-4

Grams and Kilograms

Circle the better estimate for each.

1. 

a. 2 g

b. 2 kg

2. 

a. 560 g

b. 560 kg

3. 

a. 15 g

b. 15 kg

4. 

a. 100 g

b. 100 kg

5. 

a. 4 g

b. 4 kg

6. 

a. 50 g

b. 50 kg

7. an 8-year-old boy

a. 30 g

b. 30 kg

8. a china cup

a. 350 g

b. 350 kg

9. a pen

a. 5 g

b. 5 kg

10. Remy says, "The number of grams in 2 kilograms is $2 \times 1{,}000$." Do you agree or disagree? Explain.

____

____

11. Which is heavier, a 3-kg rock or a 2,800-g rock? Explain.

____

____

Name ______________________________

Practice
12-5

Temperature

Write the temperature using °C or °F.

1.
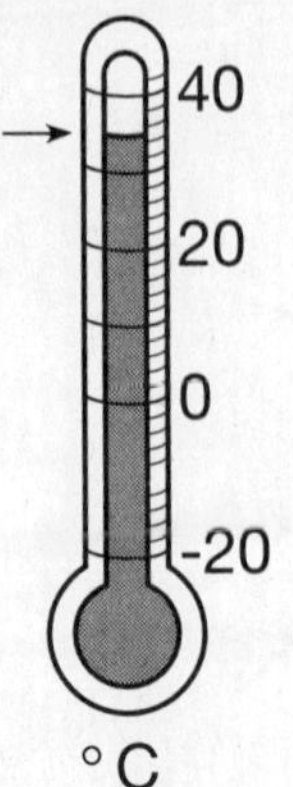

____

2.
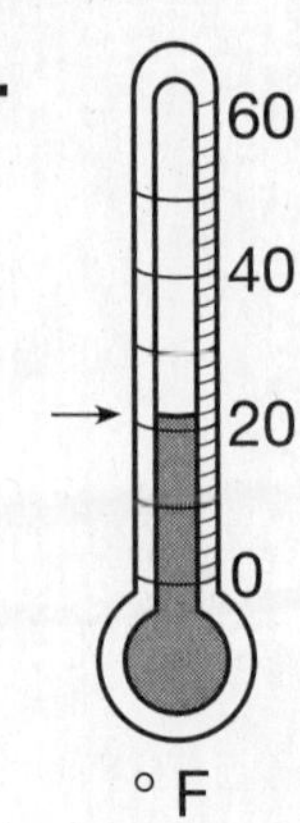

____

3.
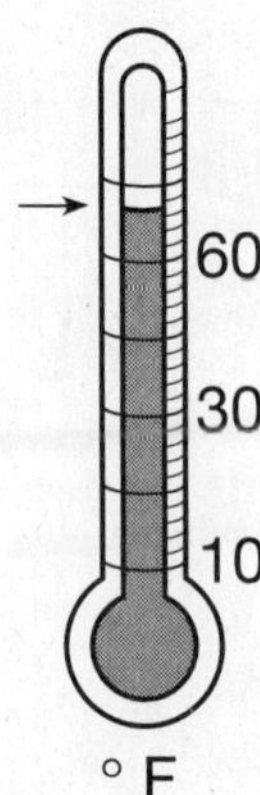

____

4.
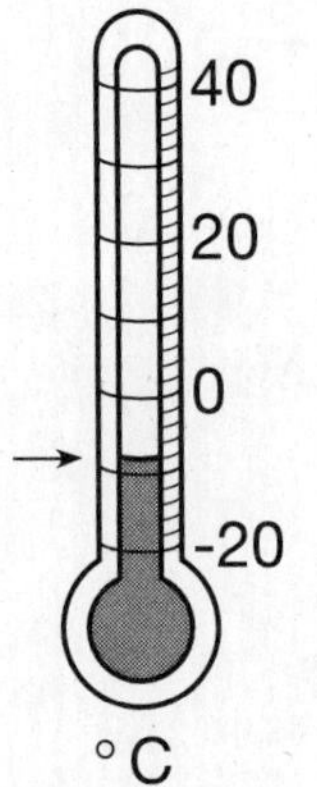

____

5.
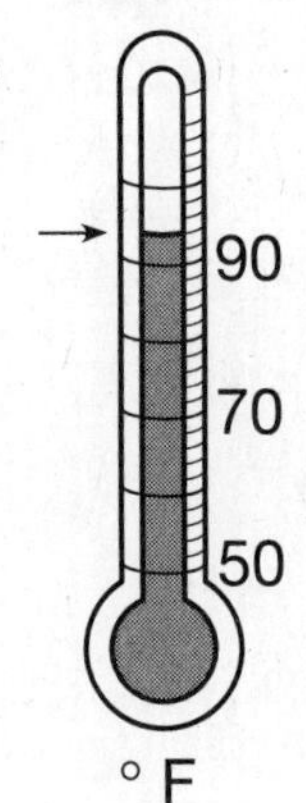

____

6.
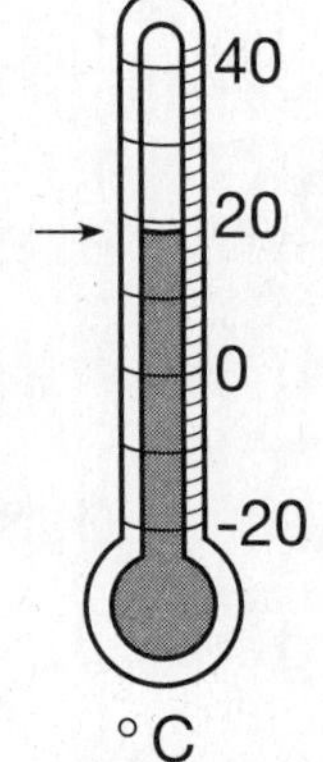

____

Circle the better estimate for each.

7.

a. 6°F

b. 68°F

8.
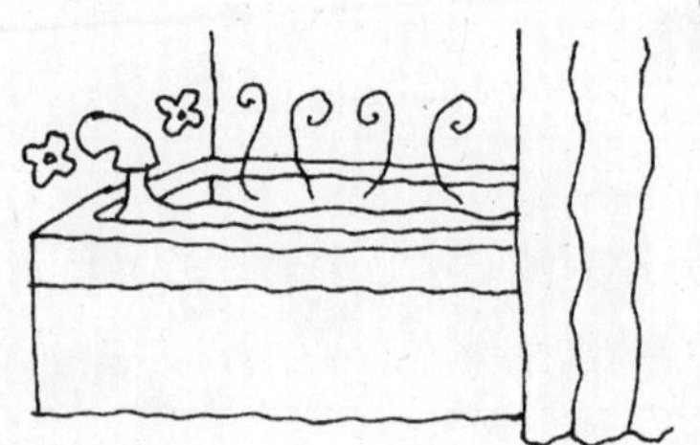

a. 7°C

b. 37°C

9.

a. 0°C

b. 20°C

10. Suppose it is 0°C outside. Should you wear a jacket?

____

Name ______________________________

Practice
12-6

Decision Making

You are going on a backpacking trip. This is what you plan to take.

Item	Weight
backpack	3 lb
3 sweaters	1 lb each
1 canteen of water	2 lb 8 oz
2 pairs of pants	8 oz each
2 mess kits	8 oz each
3 flashlights	1 lb each
1 camera	2 lb
1 tape player	1 lb
4 cassette tapes	2 oz each
socks, t-shirts, etc.	2 lb

1. What will the total weight of your backpack be when you pack all of these items?

   ____

2. If you needed to make your pack 2 lb lighter, which items would you remove? Why?

   ____

   ____

3. If you had room in your pack for 3 lb more, what would you include? (Estimate the weight of the item if it is not on the list.)

   ____

   ____

Name ______________________

Review and Practice

(Lessons 1 and 2) Circle the best estimate for each.

1.

a. 1 pint
b. 1 quart
c. 1 gallon

2.

a. 2 mL
b. 2 L

3.

a. 1 cup
b. 1 gallon
c. $\frac{1}{2}$ gallon

(Lessons 3 and 4) Circle the better estimate for each.

4.

a. 14 oz
b. 14 lb

5.

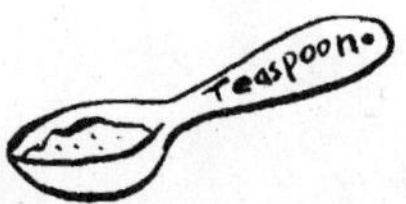

a. 2 g
b. 2 kg

6.

a. 18 kg
b. 1,800 kg

(Lesson 5) Write the temperature using °C or °F.

7.

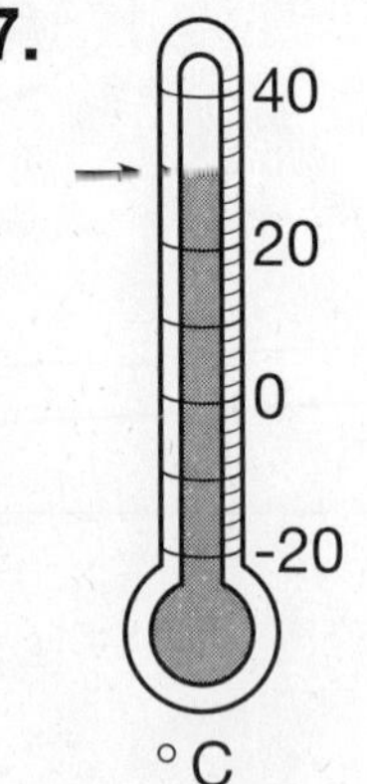

____

8.

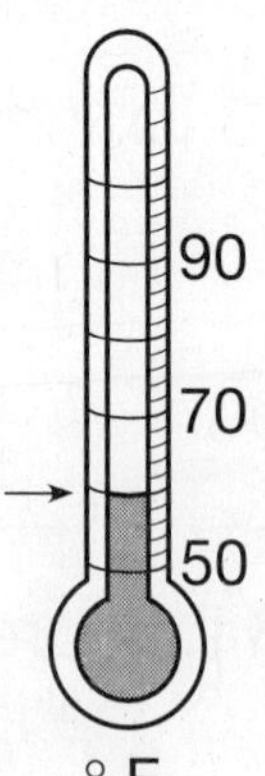

____

9.

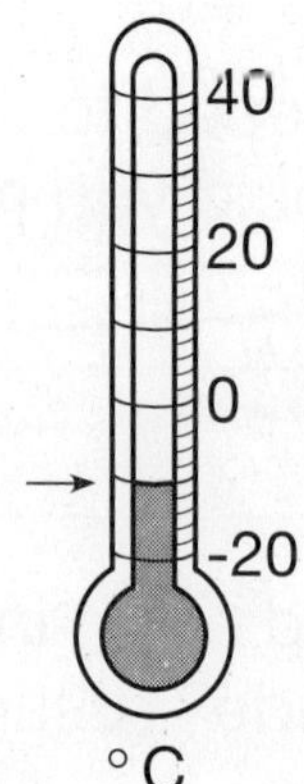

____

(Mixed Review) Add or subtract.

10. $\begin{array}{r} 318 \\ -\ 109 \\ \hline \end{array}$

11. $\begin{array}{r} 825 \\ +\ 117 \\ \hline \end{array}$

12. $\begin{array}{r} 700 \\ -\ 283 \\ \hline \end{array}$

13. $\begin{array}{r} 421 \\ -\ 89 \\ \hline \end{array}$

Name ______________________

Practice
12-7

Exploring Likely and Unlikely

1. Match each statement on the left with the best answer on the right.

a. There will be no Wednesday next week.	Certain
b. There will be clouds in the sky tomorrow.	Unlikely
c. It will snow in Florida this year.	Impossible
d. The desert will be hot this summer.	Likely

Write whether each is impossible, possible, or certain.

2. An elephant will learn how to fly. ______________

3. Many trees will lose their leaves this fall. ______________

4. A person is sleeping somewhere. ______________

Write whether each is likely or unlikely.

5. The 6 o'clock news on TV will start late today. ______________

6. Milk will be served in school cafeterias. ______________

7. Next week, all of the books in the library will be checked out.

____

8. Your hair will be the same color in five years. ______________

9. Students in your class will do some homework tonight.

____

10. It will rain daisies and roses tomorrow. ______________

11. Heather said, "It is likely that flowers will bloom this spring." Do you agree or disagree? Explain.

____

____

Name ____________________

Practice 12-8

Exploring Predictions

1. Look at the spinner. List the possible outcomes of a spin. Complete the predictions with *more, fewer, all,* or *no.*

	Possible Outcomes	Predictions
		The pointer will land on dots ______ times. It will land on stripes ______ times.

Suppose you put these cubes in a bag. Predict which cubes you are more likely to pull out.

2.

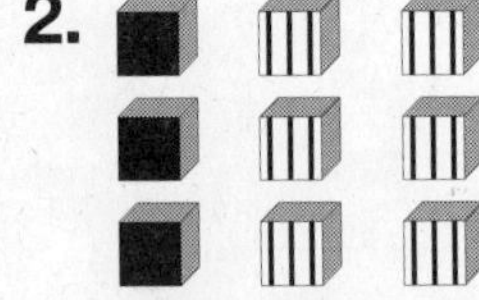

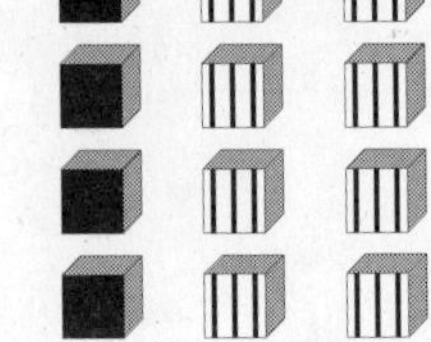

____

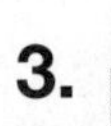

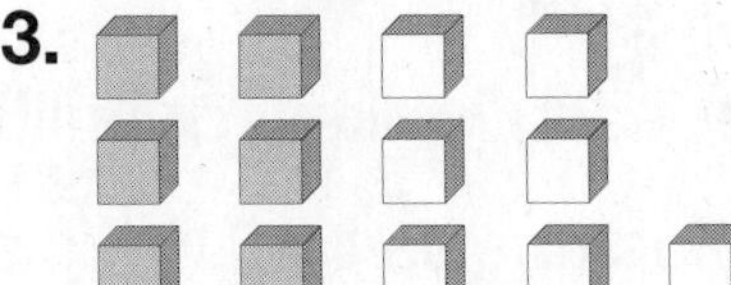

____

4.

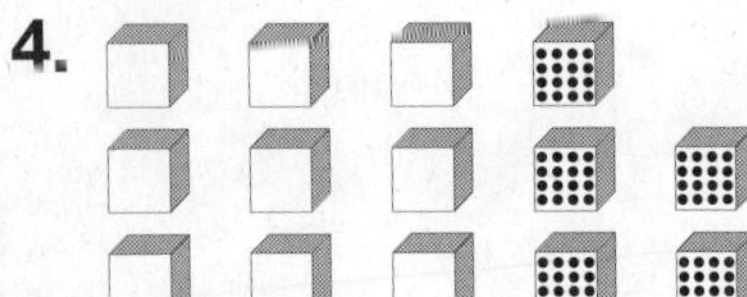

____

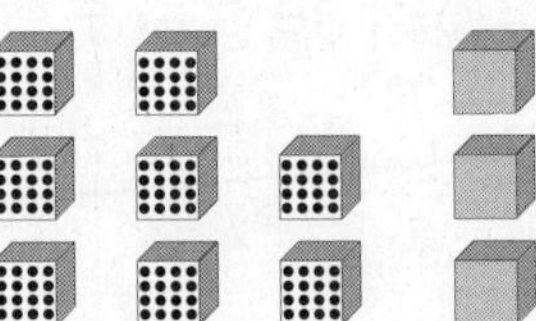

____

6. Would it be easier to guess the month or the day of the week that someone was born? Explain.

____

____

Name ______________________________________

Practice 12-9

Exploring Probability

Complete each sentence with a fraction that shows probability.

1. 3 out of 8 students are wearing blue shirts. The probability that a student is wearing a blue shirt is $\frac{\square}{8}$.
2. 2 out of 8 students are wearing red shirts. The probability that a student is wearing a red shirt is $\frac{\square}{8}$.
3. 2 out of 8 students are wearing green shirts. The probability that a student is wearing a green shirt is $\frac{\square}{8}$.
4. 1 out of 8 students is wearing a yellow shirt. The probability that a student is wearing a yellow shirt is $\frac{\square}{8}$.

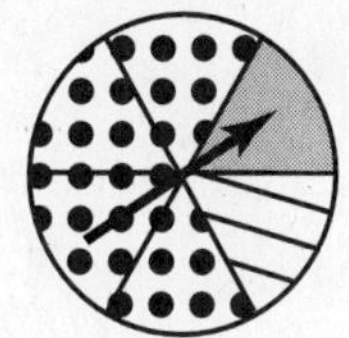

a. grey: $\square$ out of 6 or $\frac{\square}{6}$

b. striped: $\square$ out of 6 or $\frac{\square}{6}$

c. dotted: $\square$ out of 6 or $\frac{\square}{6}$

6. 1 side of a plastic cube is orange, 2 sides are pink, and 3 sides are purple.

   a. If you toss the cube, which color is most likely to land face up? ____________

   b. If you toss the cube, which color is least likely to land face up? ____________

7. A contest has the following 15 prizes: 1 trip to Hawaii, 2 CD players, 3 pairs of hiking boots, 4 radios, and 5 posters. You have been told that you won one of the prizes.

   a. Which prize are you most likely to have won? ____________

   b. Which prize are you least likely to have won? ____________

Name ______________________________

Practice 12-10

Exploring Fair and Unfair

1.

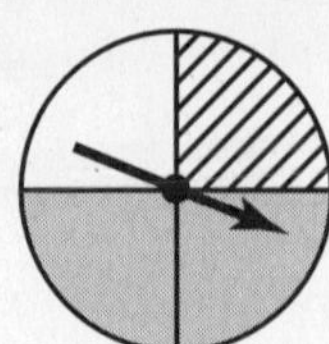

a. ☐ out of 4 equal sections are gray.

b. The probability of spinning gray is $\frac{\square}{4}$.

c. Is spinning gray likely?

____

2.

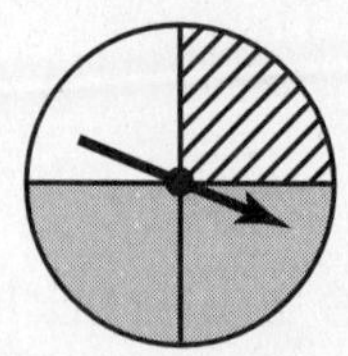

a. ☐ out of 4 equal sections are white.

b. The probability of spinning white is $\frac{\square}{4}$.

c. Is spinning white likely?

____

3. Are the spinners shown in 1 and 2 fair? __________

Write whether each spinner is fair or unfair.

4.

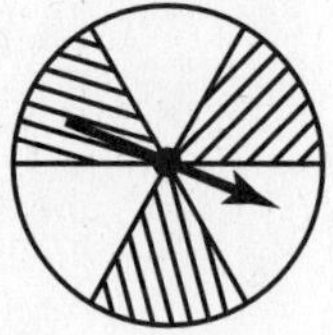

____

5.

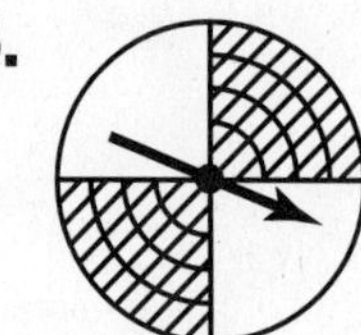

____

6.

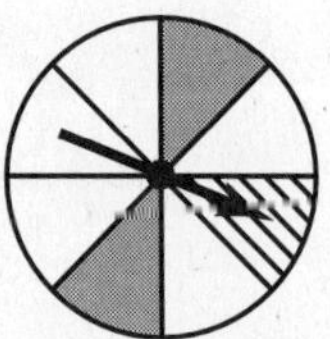

____

7.

____

8. If there are 2 red cubes and 6 white cubes in a box, are the chances of picking a red cube likely, unlikely, or equally likely? Explain.

____

9. There are 3 green and 3 blue cubes in a box. Are the chances of picking a green cube likely, unlikely, or equally likely to picking a blue cube? Explain.

____

Name ______________________________

Practice
12-11

Analyze Strategies: Work Backward

Work backward or use any strategy to solve each problem.

1. Kim must be at the airport at 8:00 A.M. She needs 45 minutes to shower, dress, and eat breakfast. She needs 1 hour to drive to the airport. She wants to allow an extra 30 minutes for traffic. She needs 8 hours and 45 minutes of sleep the night before her trip. What time should she go to sleep?

____

2. Jody said, "I am thinking of a number. If I add 24 to the number, then subtract 6, then add 12, and then multiply by 2, I end up with 84." What number did Jody start with? ______________

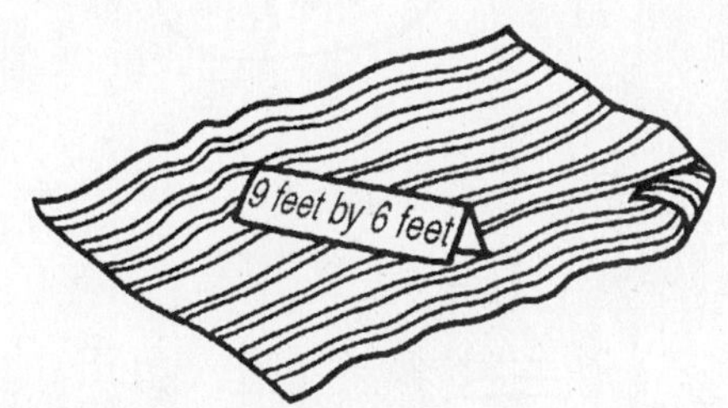

3. Skyler has a large piece of blue fabric. She wants to make table napkins out of it. If each napkin requires 1 square foot of fabric, how many napkins can she make from the fabric? Use the drawing to help.

____

4. Jason used the exercise machines at the gym. He worked on 2 machines for his arms. He skipped 5 arm exercises that he usually did because each of these machines was busy. Then he worked on his legs, using 6 machines. How many machines does Jason usually use?

____

5. Derek used small rocks to border the garden. He used $\frac{1}{2}$ of the rocks to border the roses. Then he used 31 rocks to border the tulips and 25 to border the daffodils. He had 24 rocks left over. How many rocks did Derek start with?

____

Name ______________________________

Review and Practice

Vocabulary Match each with its definition.

________	**1.** certain	**a.** able to happen
________	**2.** possible	**b.** a guess about what will happen
________	**3.** likely	**c.** sure to happen
________	**4.** prediction	**d.** probably will happen

(Lesson 8) Suppose you put these letters in a bag. Predict which letter you are more likely to pull out.

5.

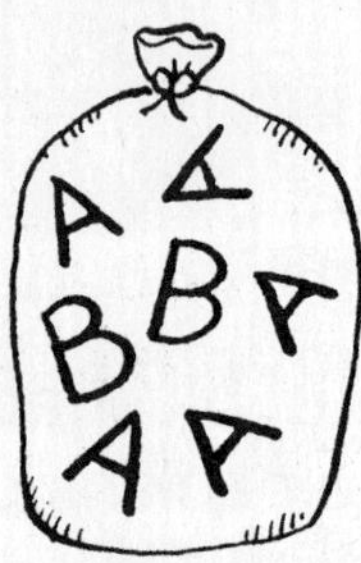

____

6.

____

7.

____

(Lesson 9) Complete.

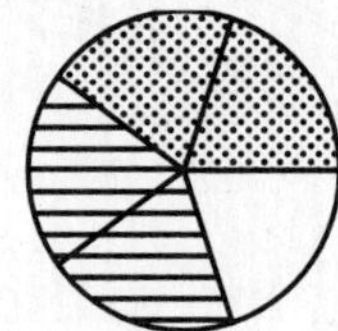

8. striped: ________ out of 5 or $\frac{\square}{5}$.

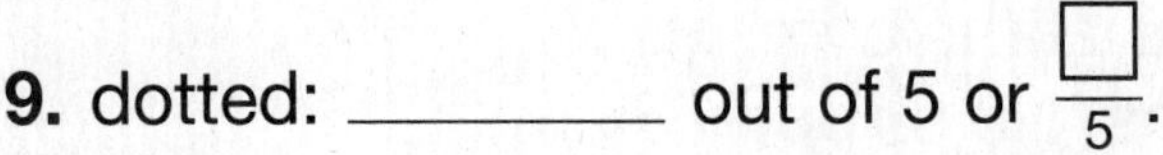

9. dotted: ________ out of 5 or $\frac{\square}{5}$.

10. white: ________ out of 5 or $\frac{\square}{5}$.

(Lesson 10) Write whether each spinner is fair or unfair.

11.

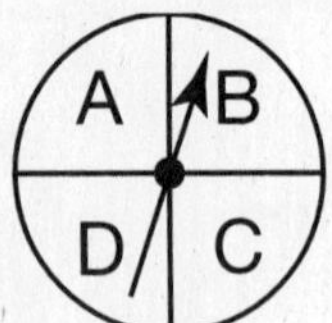

____

12.

____

13.

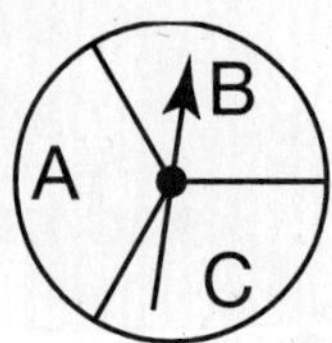

____

(Mixed Review) Divide.

14. $3\overline{)19}$ **15.** $5\overline{)49}$ **16.** $8\overline{)47}$ **17.** $4\overline{)26}$

Name ______________________________

Practice
Chapters 1–12

Cumulative Review

(Chapter 8 Lesson 2) Complete the chart.

	Shape	Number of Sides	Number of Corners
1.	triangle		
2.	circle		
3.	rectangle		

(Chapter 9 Lesson 9) Find each product using mental math.

4. $42 \times 5 =$ ______________

5. $21 \times 6 =$ ______________

(Chapter 10 Lesson 12) Measure the length to the nearest $\frac{1}{4}$ inch.

6. __________

(Chapter 11 Lesson 6) Use a ruler to measure the perimeter to the nearest centimeter.

7. __________

(Chapter 12 Lesson 5) Write the temperature. Use °C or °F.

8.

20
10
0
-10
-20
°C

____

9.

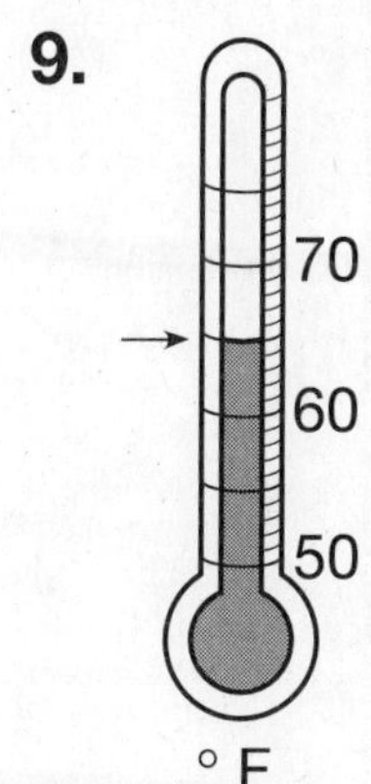

____

10.

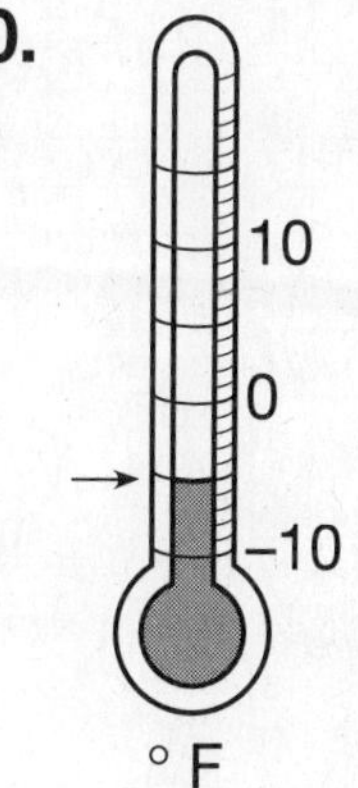

____

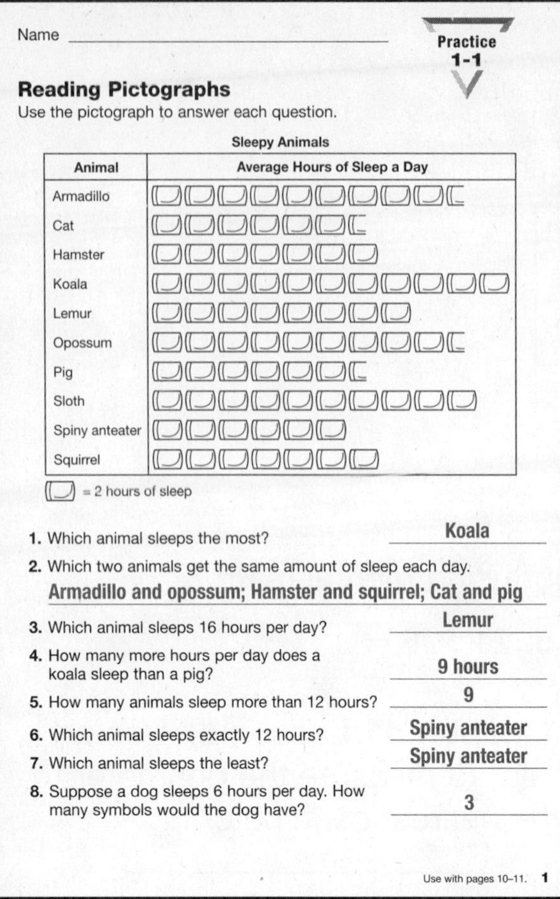

Name ______________________

Practice 1-1

Reading Pictographs

Use the pictograph to answer each question.

Sleepy Animals

Animal	Average Hours of Sleep a Day
Armadillo	
Cat	
Hamster	
Koala	
Lemur	
Opossum	
Pig	
Sloth	
Spiny anteater	
Squirrel	

= 2 hours of sleep

1. Which animal sleeps the most? **Koala**
2. Which two animals get the same amount of sleep each day. **Armadillo and opossum; Hamster and squirrel; Cat and pig**
3. Which animal sleeps 16 hours per day? **Lemur**
4. How many more hours per day does a koala sleep than a pig? **9 hours**
5. How many animals sleep more than 12 hours? **9**
6. Which animal sleeps exactly 12 hours? **Spiny anteater**
7. Which animal sleeps the least? **Spiny anteater**
8. Suppose a dog sleeps 6 hours per day. How many symbols would the dog have? **3**

Use with pages 10–11. 1

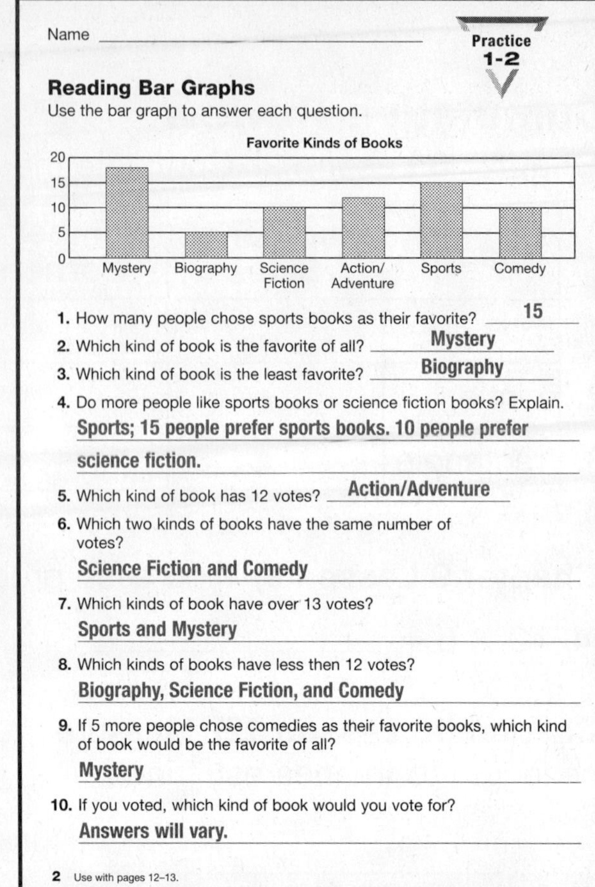

Name ______________________

Practice 1-2

Reading Bar Graphs

Use the bar graph to answer each question.

1. How many people chose sports books as their favorite? **15**
2. Which kind of book is the favorite of all? **Mystery**
3. Which kind of book is the least favorite? **Biography**
4. Do more people like sports books or science fiction books? Explain. **Sports; 15 people prefer sports books. 10 people prefer science fiction.**
5. Which kind of book has 12 votes? **Action/Adventure**
6. Which two kinds of books have the same number of votes? **Science Fiction and Comedy**
7. Which kinds of book have over 13 votes? **Sports and Mystery**
8. Which kinds of books have less then 12 votes? **Biography, Science Fiction, and Comedy**
9. If 5 more people chose comedies as their favorite books, which kind of book would be the favorite of all? **Mystery**
10. If you voted, which kind of book would you vote for? **Answers will vary.**

2 Use with pages 12–13.

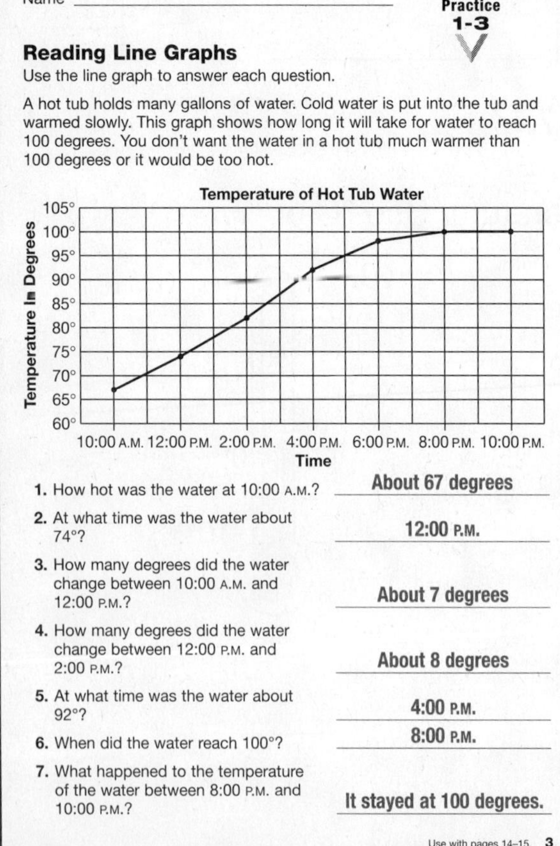

Name ______________________

Practice 1-3

Reading Line Graphs

Use the line graph to answer each question.

A hot tub holds many gallons of water. Cold water is put into the tub and warmed slowly. This graph shows how long it will take for water to reach 100 degrees. You don't want the water in a hot tub much warmer than 100 degrees or it would be too hot.

1. How hot was the water at 10:00 A.M.? **About 67 degrees**
2. At what time was the water about 74°? **12:00 P.M.**
3. How many degrees did the water change between 10:00 A.M. and 12:00 P.M.? **About 7 degrees**
4. How many degrees did the water change between 12:00 P.M. and 2:00 P.M.? **About 8 degrees**
5. At what time was the water about 92°? **4:00 P.M.**
6. When did the water reach 100°? **8:00 P.M.**
7. What happened to the temperature of the water between 8:00 P.M. and 10:00 P.M.? **It stayed at 100 degrees.**

Use with pages 14–15. 3

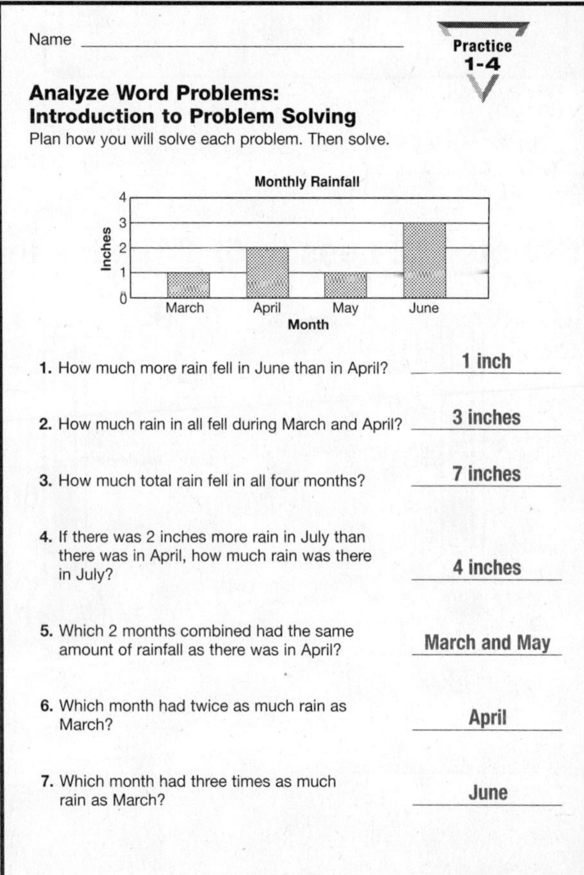

Name ______________________

Practice 1-4

Analyze Word Problems: Introduction to Problem Solving

Plan how you will solve each problem. Then solve.

1. How much more rain fell in June than in April? **1 inch**
2. How much rain in all fell during March and April? **3 inches**
3. How much total rain fell in all four months? **7 inches**
4. If there was 2 inches more rain in July than there was in April, how much rain was there in July? **4 inches**
5. Which 2 months combined had the same amount of rainfall as there was in April? **March and May**
6. Which month had twice as much rain as March? **April**
7. Which month had three times as much rain as March? **June**

4 Use with pages 16–17.

Name ______________________

Practice 1-5

Analyze Word Problems: Choose an Operation

Choose the number sentence you would use to solve. Explain.

1. Sam owns 3 lizards and 2 cats. How many pets does Sam own?

   a. 3 + 2 = 5 **b.** 3 − 2 = 1

   a; Possible answer: You need to find the total number of pets, so you add.

2. Lisa moved 9 boxes. On Monday, she unpacked 5 boxes. How many more boxes are left to unpack?

   a. 9 + 5 = 14 **b.** 9 − 5 = 4

   b; Possible answer: To compare the two amounts, subtract.

3. Tony baked 4 dozen muffins in the morning and 3 dozen more in the afternoon. How many dozen muffins did he bake in one day?

   a. 4 + 3 = 7 **b.** 4 − 3 = 1

   a; Possible answer: To find the total number of muffins, add.

Write which operation you would use. Then solve.

4. Sarah bought 10 cherries on Saturday. On Sunday, she ate 5. How many cherries does she have now?

   Subtraction; 10 − 5 = 5 cherries remaining

5. Francis bought 7 cans of beans and 6 cans of corn. How many cans did he buy?

   Addition; 7 + 6 = 13 cans

6. Judy is in a 10-kilometer road race. She has run 6 kilometers already. How many more kilometers will she run?

   Subtraction; 10 − 6 = 4 more kilometers

Name ______________________

Practice 1-6

Exploring Algebra: What's the Rule?

1. A rule describes what to do to the **In** number to get the **Out** number. What is the rule? **Subtract 3.**

In	8	9	10	11	12	13
Out	5	6	7	8	9	10

Complete each table. Write the rule for each.

2.

In	4	6	2	5	10	8
Out	8	10	6	**9**	**14**	**12**

Rule: **Add 4.**

3.

In	8	4	3	5	11	6
Out	6	2	1	**3**	**9**	**4**

Rule: **Subtract 2.**

4.

In	10	7	6	4	12	3
Out	15	12	11	**9**	**17**	**8**

Rule: **Add 5.**

5.

In	9	11	8	4	6	7
Out	5	7	4	**0**	**2**	**3**

Rule: **Subtract 4.**

Name ______________________

Practice Chapter 1 Section A

Review and Practice

(Lesson 1) Use the pictograph to answer each question.

1. How many letters were received? **6**
2. Which type of mail was received the most? **Advertisements**
3. How many symbols would there be if 20 greeting cards were received? **5**

Mail Received This Month

Letters	✉ ◧
Greeting cards	✉ ✉
Advertisements	✉ ✉ ✉ ✉
Bills	✉ ✉ ✉

✉ = 4 items of mail

(Lesson 2) Use the bar graph to answer each question.

4. Which fruit was the least favorite? **Oranges**
5. Which fruit did 10 people vote for? **Bananas**
6. How many more voted for apples than oranges? **3**

(Lesson 3) Use the line graph to answer each question.

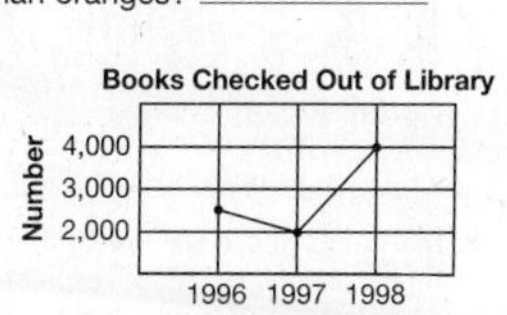

7. In what year were the most books checked out? **1998**
8. In what year were only 2,000 books checked out? **1997**

(Lesson 5) Tell which operation you would use. Then solve.

9. There are 12 boys in the class. 8 have brown eyes. How many do not have brown eyes? **Subtraction; 4**

(Mixed Review) Add or subtract.

10. 6 + 9 = **15** 11. 8 − 6 = **2** 12. 7 + 7 = **14**

Name ______________________

Practice 1-7

Exploring Organizing Data

1. This tally table shows students' votes for their favorite colors. Write the number of students who voted for each color.

Favorite Colors

Color	Tally	Number
a. Blue	𝍸	**5**
b. Purple	𝍸 ||||	**9**
c. Red	|	**1**
d. Green	𝍸	**5**
e. Yellow	𝍸 |	**6**

2. Complete the tally table.

Our Favorite After-School Activities

Activity	Tally	Number
a. Bike Riding	|||	**3**
b. Crafts	𝍸	**5**
c. Sports	𝍸 ||	**7**
d. Reading	||||	**4**

3. Explain why a tally table is a useful way to present survey results.

   Possible answer: Results are organized in easy-to-read rows and columns.

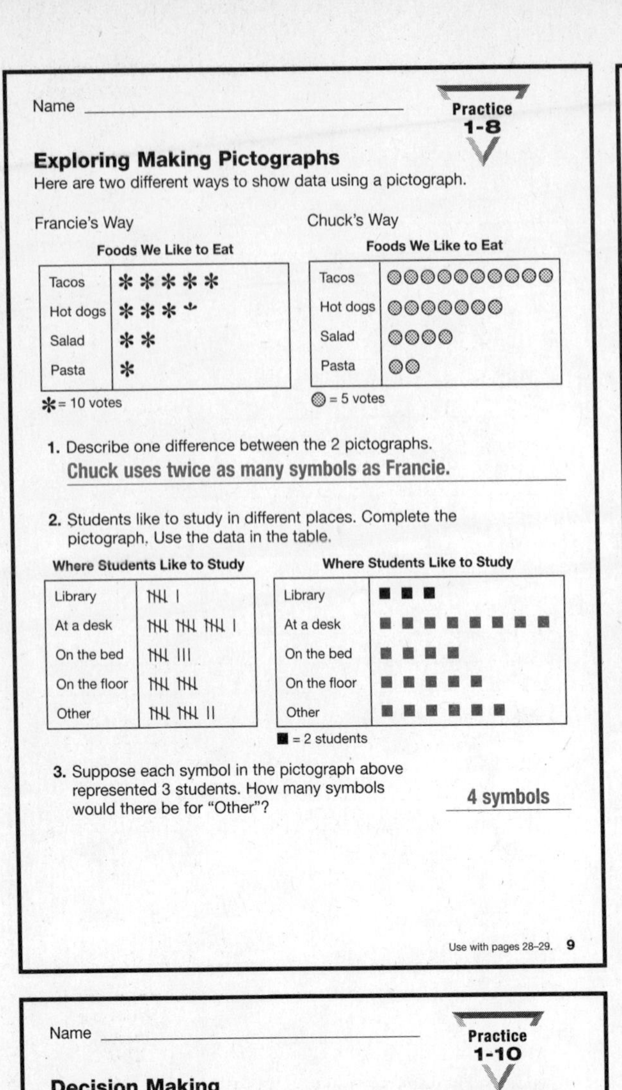
Name ______________________

Practice 1-8

Exploring Making Pictographs

Here are two different ways to show data using a pictograph.

Francie's Way

Foods We Like to Eat

Tacos	✱ ✱ ✱ ✱ ✱
Hot dogs	✱ ✱ ✱ ✱(half)
Salad	✱ ✱
Pasta	✱

✱ = 10 votes

Chuck's Way

Foods We Like to Eat

Tacos	●●●●●●●●●●
Hot dogs	●●●●●●●
Salad	●●●●
Pasta	●●

● = 5 votes

1. Describe one difference between the 2 pictographs.
   Chuck uses twice as many symbols as Francie.

2. Students like to study in different places. Complete the pictograph. Use the data in the table.

Where Students Like to Study

Library	𝍸 I
At a desk	𝍸 𝍸 𝍸 I
On the bed	𝍸 III
On the floor	𝍸 𝍸
Other	𝍸 𝍸 II

Where Students Like to Study

Library	■ ■ ■
At a desk	■ ■ ■ ■ ■ ■ ■ ■
On the bed	■ ■ ■ ■
On the floor	■ ■ ■ ■ ■
Other	■ ■ ■ ■ ■ ■

■ = 2 students

3. Suppose each symbol in the pictograph above represented 3 students. How many symbols would there be for "Other"? **4 symbols**

Use with pages 28–29. 9

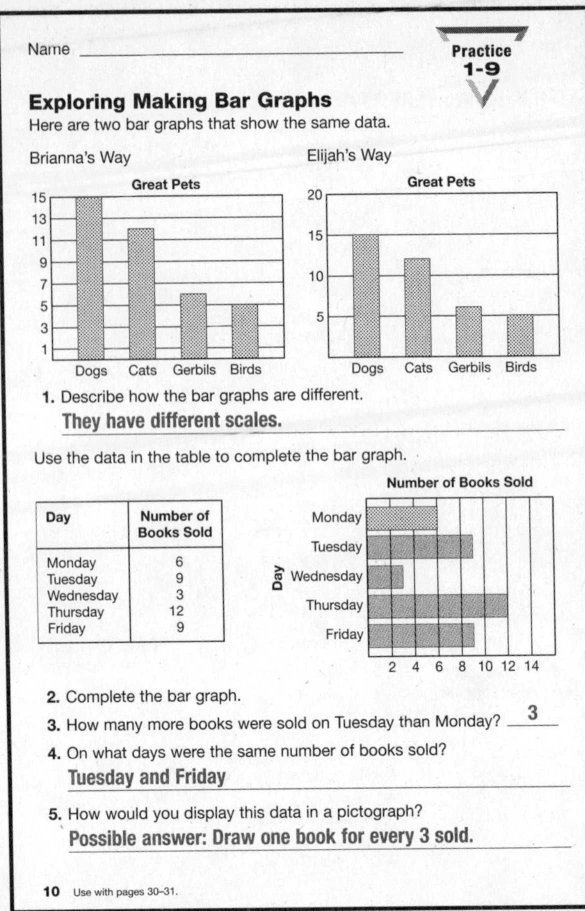
Name ______________________

Practice 1-9

Exploring Making Bar Graphs

Here are two bar graphs that show the same data.

Brianna's Way

Elijah's Way

1. Describe how the bar graphs are different.
   They have different scales.

Use the data in the table to complete the bar graph.

Day	Number of Books Sold
Monday	6
Tuesday	9
Wednesday	3
Thursday	12
Friday	9

2. Complete the bar graph.
3. How many more books were sold on Tuesday than Monday? **3**
4. On what days were the same number of books sold?
   Tuesday and Friday
5. How would you display this data in a pictograph?
   Possible answer: Draw one book for every 3 sold.

10 Use with pages 30–31.

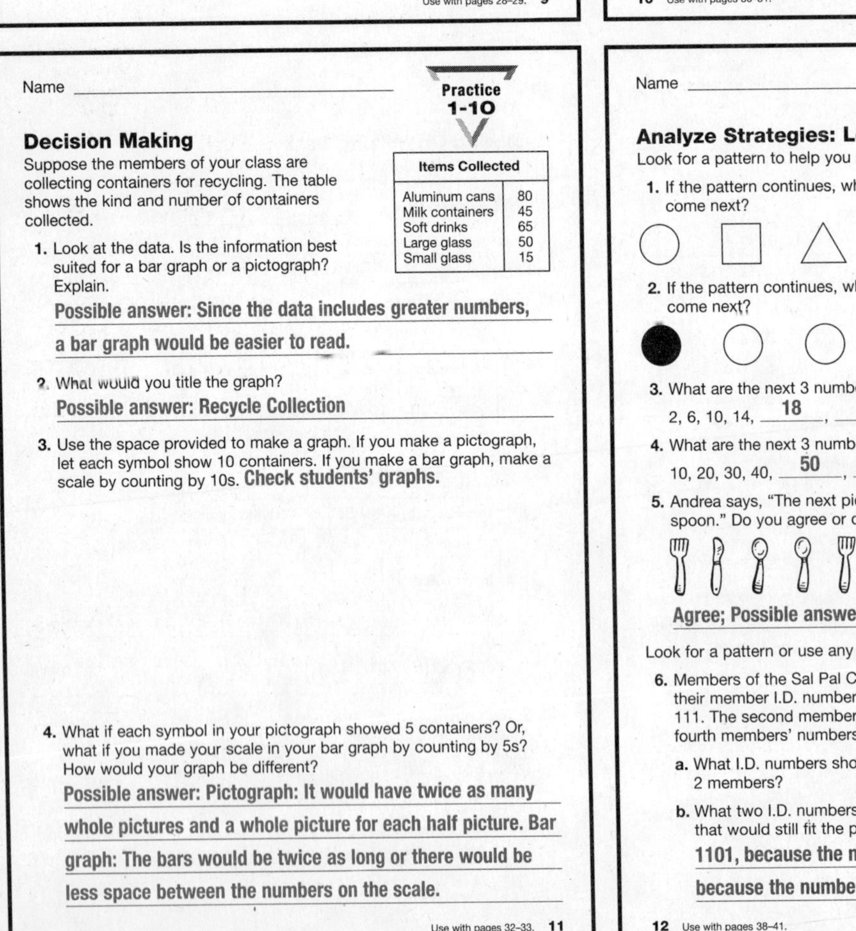
Name ______________________

Practice 1-10

Decision Making

Suppose the members of your class are collecting containers for recycling. The table shows the kind and number of containers collected.

Items Collected	
Aluminum cans	80
Milk containers	45
Soft drinks	65
Large glass	50
Small glass	15

1. Look at the data. Is the information best suited for a bar graph or a pictograph? Explain.
   Possible answer: Since the data includes greater numbers, a bar graph would be easier to read.
2. What would you title the graph?
   Possible answer: Recycle Collection
3. Use the space provided to make a graph. If you make a pictograph, let each symbol show 10 containers. If you make a bar graph, make a scale by counting by 10s. **Check students' graphs.**
4. What if each symbol in your pictograph showed 5 containers? Or, what if you made your scale in your bar graph by counting by 5s? How would your graph be different?
   Possible answer: Pictograph: It would have twice as many whole pictures and a whole picture for each half picture. Bar graph: The bars would be twice as long or there would be less space between the numbers on the scale.

Use with pages 32–33. 11

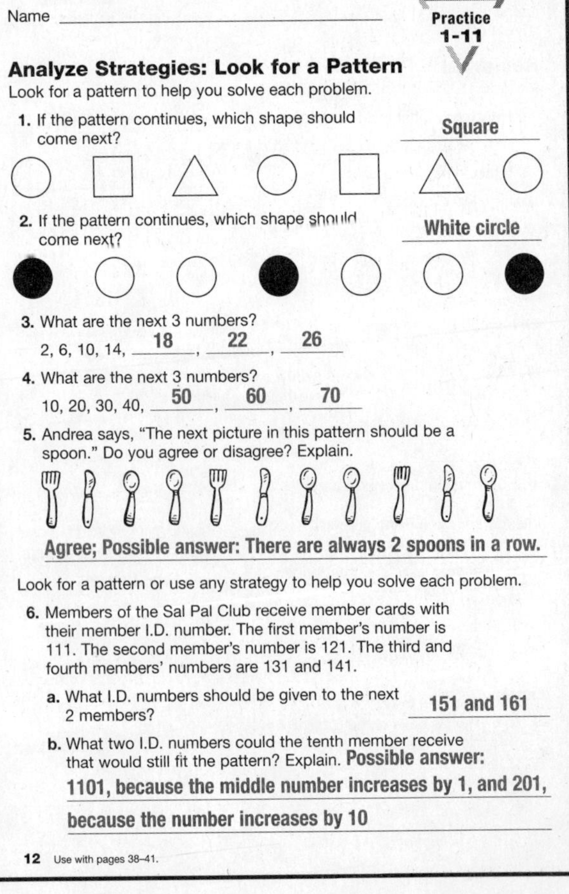
Name ______________________

Practice 1-11

Analyze Strategies: Look for a Pattern

Look for a pattern to help you solve each problem.

1. If the pattern continues, which shape should come next? **Square**
2. If the pattern continues, which shape should come next? **White circle**
3. What are the next 3 numbers?
   2, 6, 10, 14, **18**, **22**, **26**
4. What are the next 3 numbers?
   10, 20, 30, 40, **50**, **60**, **70**
5. Andrea says, "The next picture in this pattern should be a spoon." Do you agree or disagree? Explain.
   Agree; Possible answer: There are always 2 spoons in a row.

Look for a pattern or use any strategy to help you solve each problem.

6. Members of the Sal Pal Club receive member cards with their member I.D. number. The first member's number is 111. The second member's number is 121. The third and fourth members' numbers are 131 and 141.
   a. What I.D. numbers should be given to the next 2 members? **151 and 161**
   b. What two I.D. numbers could the tenth member receive that would still fit the pattern? Explain. **Possible answer: 1101, because the middle number increases by 1, and 201, because the number increases by 10**

12 Use with pages 38–41.

Name ______________________

Practice
Chapter 1
Section B

Review and Practice

(Lesson 7) Complete the tally table.

1. Number of pets in the homes of Mr. Gregory's third grade class:
   2, 1, 0, 2, 2, 0, 0, 1, 2, 1, 0, 0, 2, 1, 1, 2, 0, 0, 1, 1, 1, 1, 0

Pets	Tally	Number
0	卌 |||	8
1	卌 ||||	9
2	卌		6

(Lesson 8) Use the data in the table. Complete the pictograph.

2.

My Favorite Flavor	
Peppermint	5
Chocolate	15
Butterscotch	7

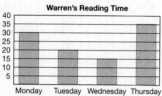

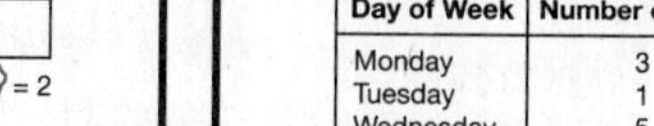

My Favorite Flavor

Peppermint	🍦🍦half
Chocolate	🍦🍦🍦🍦🍦🍦🍦half
Butterscotch	🍦🍦🍦half

Key 🍦 = 2

Check students' completed pictographs.

(Lesson 9) Use the data in the table. Complete the bar graph.

3.

Warren's Reading Time	
Day of Week	**Minutes**
Monday	30
Tuesday	20
Wednesday	15
Thursday	35

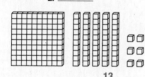

Warren's Reading Time

(Lesson 11) Solve. Use any strategy.

4. Leandra is learning to play the trombone. She increases her practice time by 3 minutes each day. Monday she practiced 8 minutes. How many minutes will she practice on Friday? **20 minutes**

(Mixed Review) Add or subtract.

5. 6 + 9 = **15**
6. 16 − 9 = **7**
7. 5 + 8 = **13**

Name ______________________

Practice
Chapter 1

Cumulative Review

(Chapter 1 Lessons 1 and 8) Use the data to complete the pictograph.

1.

Number of Rooms in Home	
Marlene	5
Patrick	4
Lois	6

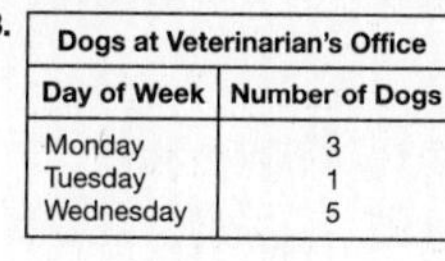

Number of Rooms in Home

Marlene	⌂⌂half
Patrick	⌂⌂
Lois	⌂⌂⌂

Key: ⌂ = 2 rooms

2. How many symbols would you use to represent 11 rooms? **5 whole and 1 half**

(Chapter 1 Lessons 2 and 9) Use the data to complete the bar graph.

3.

Dogs at Veterinarian's Office	
Day of Week	**Number of Dogs**
Monday	3
Tuesday	1
Wednesday	5

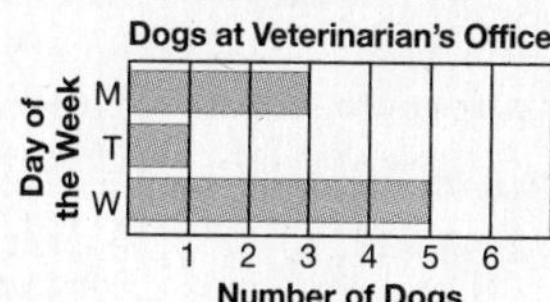

4. How many dogs were seen by the veterinarian on all three days? **9**

(Chapter 1 Lesson 3) Use the line graph to answer the questions.

5. How many children played soccer in 1996? **150**

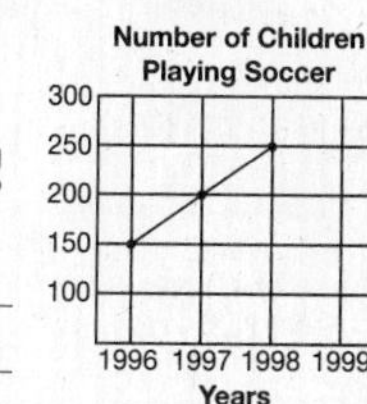

6. Do you think the number of children playing soccer in 1999 will be greater than in 1998? Explain.
   Yes; The line is going up, indicating a trend of more children playing soccer.

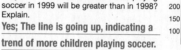

(Facts Review) Add or subtract.

7. 13 − 7 = **6**
8. 6 + 8 = **14**
9. 7 + 5 = **12**
10. 7 − 4 = **3**

Name ______________________

Practice
2-1

Place Value Through Hundreds

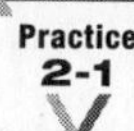

Write each number in standard form.

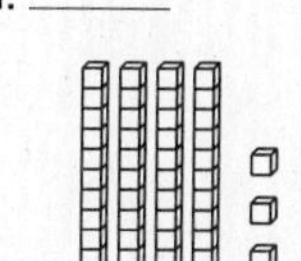

1. **43**
2. **156**

3. forty-nine **49**
4. thirteen **13**
5. 200 + 70 + 8 **278**
6. 100 + 30 + 2 **132**
7. 300 + 30 **330**
8. sixty-five **65**
9. 200 + 2 **202**
10. 500 + 40 + 5 **545**
11. two hundred sixty-two **262**
12. three hundred forty-seven **347**

Write the word name for each number.

13. 93 **Ninety-three**
14. 348 **Three hundred forty-eight**
15. 102 **One hundred two**
16. 56 **Fifty-six**
17. 210 **Two hundred ten**
18. 312 **Three hundred twelve**
19. 452 **Four hundred fifty-two**
20. 205 **Two hundred five**

21. In the number 349, which digit has the least value? Explain.
    9; 9 is less than 40 or 300.
22. To write the number three hundred ten, do you need a 0? Explain.
    Yes, the zero goes in the ones place.
23. Write the numbers five hundred ten and five hundred one.
    510; 501

Name ______________________

Practice
2-2

Exploring Place-Value Relationships

Complete.

1.	standard form **3**, 000	**400**	**160**	**17**
2.	word form **three** thousand	**four hundred**	**one hundred sixty**	**seventeen**
3.	3 thousands = **30** hundreds	4 hundreds = **40** tens	16 tens = **1** hundred, **6** tens	17 ones = **1** ten, **7** ones

Write each number in standard form.

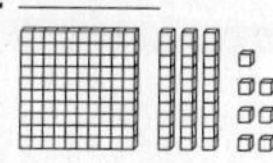

4. **137**

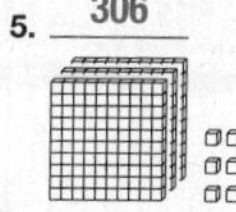

5. **306**

Complete the table.

	Number	Number of Ones	Number of Tens	Number of Hundreds
6.	100	100	**10**	**1**
7.	700	**700**	**70**	7
8.	400	**400**	40	**4**
9.	1,000	1,000	**100**	**10**

10. How many ways can you write 600? Write them.
    Possible answer: 3; 600 ones, 60 tens, 6 hundreds
11. How many ways can you write 5,000? Write them. **Possible answer: 4; 5,000 ones, 500 tens, 50 hundreds, 5 thousands**

Name ______________________

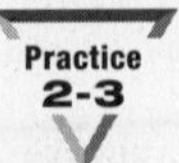
Practice 2-3

Place Value Through Thousands

Write each number in standard form.

1. 4,256

2. 2,062

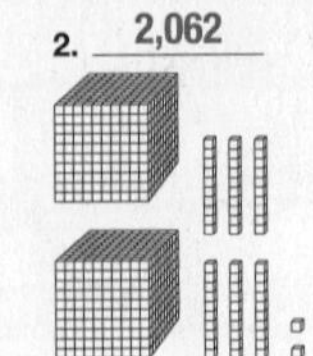

3. three thousand, four hundred seventeen 3,417
4. six thousand, seven hundred thirty-eight 6,738
5. 2,000 + 60 + 8 2,068 6. 7,000 + 100 + 40 + 5 7,145

Write the word name for each number.

7. 393 Three hundred ninety-three
8. 9,463 Nine thousand, four hundred sixty-three
9. 6,795 Six thousand, seven hundred ninety-five

Complete the table.

	Number	100 More	100 Less
10.	2,612	2,712	2,512
11.	3,911	4,011	3,811
12.	6,208	6,308	6,108

13. Is 27 hundreds the same as 27 tens? Explain.
No; 27 hundreds = 2,700 and 27 tens = 270
14. Is 100 the same as 10 ones or 10 tens? 10 tens
15. Choose a number greater than 1,000 and write it 3 ways.
Check students' answers.

Name ______________________

Practice 2-4

Place Value Through Hundred Thousands

Write each number in standard form.

1. twenty-nine thousand, five hundred sixteen 29,516
2. four hundred thirty-five thousand, seven hundred eight 435,708
3. three hundred seventy-two thousand, fifty-four 372,054
4. 20,000 + 9,000 + 700 + 80 + 1 29,781
5. 900,000 + 50,000 + 1,000 + 70 + 5 951,075
6. 700,000 + 2,000 + 400 + 80 + 2 702,482

Write the value of each underlined digit.

7. 23,045 20,000 8. 562,021 60,000
9. 803,096 800,000 10. 451,382 80
11. 12,538 500 12. 837,036 6
13. 34,789 700 14. 89,123 9,000
15. 324,598 300,000 16. 478,654 70,000

17. Which digit has the least value in 34,187? Explain.
7, it stands for 7 ones, which is less than 8 tens, 1 hundred, 4 thousands or 3 ten thousands
18. How many thousands is 100,000? How many ten thousands?
100; 10
19. Using the digits 2, 4, and 6, write a number with a 4 in the hundred thousands place and a 2 in the hundreds place.
Possible answers: 464,246; 466,226
20. Using the digits 1, 3, and 5 only once, write the greatest and least three-digit numbers you can.
Greatest: 531; Least: 135

Name ______________________

Practice 2-5

Analyze Strategies: Make an Organized List

Make a list or use any strategy to help solve each.

1. Suppose Carlos wants to order 40 light bulbs for the factory. He can buy light bulbs in boxes of 4 or 8. How many ways could he order exactly 40 bulbs?
   a. List all possible ways he could order 40 light bulbs.

boxes of 8	5	4	3	2	1	0
boxes of 4	0	2	4	6	8	10

   b. How many ways are there? 6 ways
2. Suppose Susan wants 49 boxes of light bulbs. She can order them in packs of 10 boxes or 1 box at a time. How many ways can she order 49 boxes?
5 ways: 49 boxes of 1; 4 boxes of 10 and 9 boxes of 1; 3 boxes of 10 and 19 boxes of 1; 2 boxes of 10 and 29 boxes of 1; 1 box of 10 and 39 boxes of 1
3. Pamela has a red shirt and a white shirt, black pants and a yellow skirt. How many different outfits can she make?
4 outfits: RB, RY, WB, WY
4. Three students are waiting in line to buy a venus fly trap. Barb is behind Jan. Mike is first in line. In what order are the students standing? Mike, Jan, Barb
5. Don and Carrie had 13 orders for plants in the last two days. If they had 5 orders yesterday, how many orders did they have today? 8 orders
6. When would you make a list to solve a problem?
Possible answer: In problems when there are different possible combinations of things, people, and so on

Name ______________________

Practice Chapter 2 Section A

Review and Practice

Vocabulary Choose the best number for each description.

a 1. Standard form a. 240
c 2. Expanded form b. 0, 1, 2, 3, 4, 5, 6, 7, 8, and 9
b 3. Digits c. 300 + 50 + 2

(Lesson 1) Write the word name for each number.

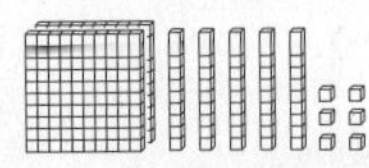

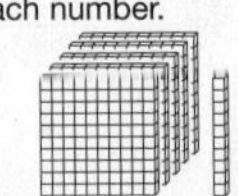

4. Two hundred fifty-six 5. Five hundred thirteen
6. 246 Two hundred forty-six 7. 80 + 2 Eighty-two

(Lesson 2) Write each missing value.

8. 60 ones = 6 tens 9. 300 ones = 3 hundreds
10. 70 tens = 7 hundreds 11. 60 tens = 600 ones

(Lesson 3) Write each number in standard form.

12. seven thousand three 7,003 13. 5,000 + 700 + 7 5,707

(Lesson 4) Write the value of each underlined digit.

14. 235,641 5,000 15. 899,002 800,000

(Lesson 5) Make a list to help solve.

16. Kara needs $35 for an aquarium for 6 fish. How can she pay with the least ten and one dollar bills?
She should use 3 tens and 5 ones.

(Mixed Review) Add or subtract.

17. 7 + 3 = 10 18. 16 − 7 = 9 19. 9 + 9 = 18

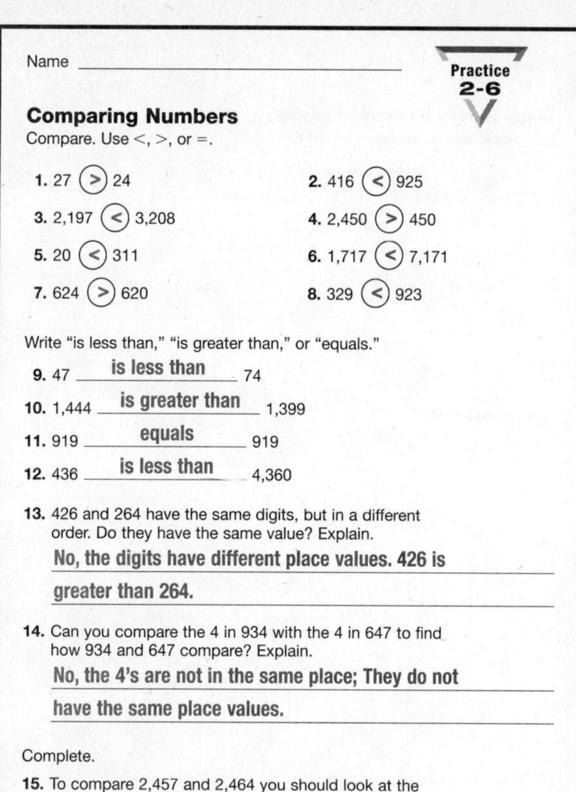

Name ______________________

Practice 2-6

Comparing Numbers

Compare. Use <, >, or =.

1. 27 (>) 24
2. 416 (<) 925
3. 2,197 (<) 3,208
4. 2,450 (>) 450
5. 20 (<) 311
6. 1,717 (<) 7,171
7. 624 (>) 620
8. 329 (<) 923

Write "is less than," "is greater than," or "equals."

9. 47 **is less than** 74
10. 1,444 **is greater than** 1,399
11. 919 **equals** 919
12. 436 **is less than** 4,360
13. 426 and 264 have the same digits, but in a different order. Do they have the same value? Explain.
No, the digits have different place values. 426 is greater than 264.
14. Can you compare the 4 in 934 with the 4 in 647 to find how 934 and 647 compare? Explain.
No, the 4's are not in the same place; They do not have the same place values.

Complete.

15. To compare 2,457 and 2,464 you should look at the digits in the **tens** place.
16. To compare 1,830 and 1,799 you should look at the digits in the **hundreds** place.

Name ______________________

Practice 2-7

Ordering Numbers

Order from least to greatest.

1. 649, 469, 964 **469, 649, 964**
2. 215, 512, 255 **215, 255, 512**
3. 375, 752, 527 **375, 527, 752**
4. 823, 838, 282 **282, 823, 838**
5. 439, 394, 934 **394, 439, 934**

Order from greatest to least.

6. 315, 153, 453 **453, 315, 153**
7. 8,042; 4,028; 2,408 **8,042; 4,028; 2,408**
8. 3,962; 2,396; 9,632 **9,632; 3,962; 2,396**
9. 484, 884, 448 **884, 484, 448**
10. 1,256; 1,652; 2,165 **2,165; 1,652; 1,256**
11. Circle the number that comes between 3,010 and 3,325.
3,001 3,332 (3,125) 3,521
12. Circle the greatest number.
2,909 (2,999) 2,990 2,900
13. Write a number between 2,458 and 3,002.
Possible answers: 2,500; 3,000
14. Write a number between 2,999 and 3,008.
Possible answers: 3,000 to 3,007

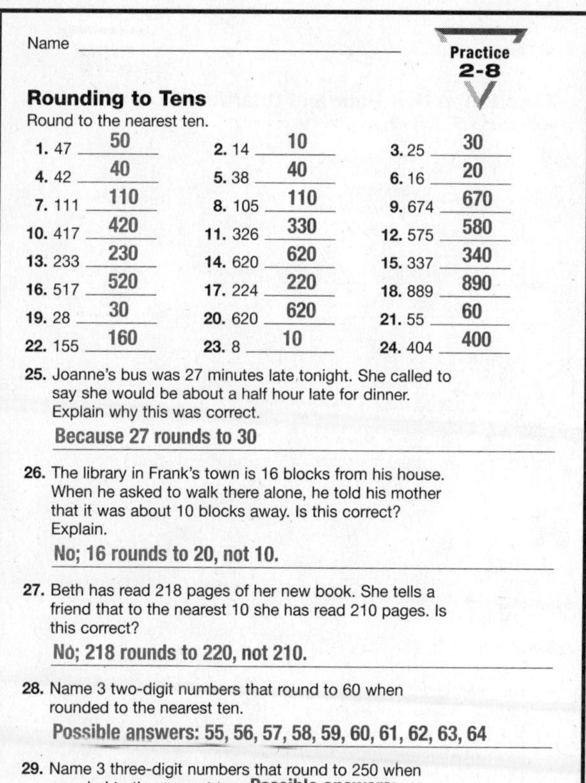

Name ______________________

Practice 2-8

Rounding to Tens

Round to the nearest ten.

1. 47 **50**
2. 14 **10**
3. 25 **30**
4. 42 **40**
5. 38 **40**
6. 16 **20**
7. 111 **110**
8. 105 **110**
9. 674 **670**
10. 417 **420**
11. 326 **330**
12. 575 **580**
13. 233 **230**
14. 620 **620**
15. 337 **340**
16. 517 **520**
17. 224 **220**
18. 889 **890**
19. 28 **30**
20. 620 **620**
21. 55 **60**
22. 155 **160**
23. 8 **10**
24. 404 **400**
25. Joanne's bus was 27 minutes late tonight. She called to say she would be about a half hour late for dinner. Explain why this was correct.
Because 27 rounds to 30
26. The library in Frank's town is 16 blocks from his house. When he asked to walk there alone, he told his mother that it was about 10 blocks away. Is this correct? Explain.
No; 16 rounds to 20, not 10.
27. Beth has read 218 pages of her new book. She tells a friend that to the nearest 10 she has read 210 pages. Is this correct?
No; 218 rounds to 220, not 210.
28. Name 3 two-digit numbers that round to 60 when rounded to the nearest ten.
Possible answers: 55, 56, 57, 58, 59, 60, 61, 62, 63, 64
29. Name 3 three-digit numbers that round to 250 when rounded to the nearest ten. **Possible answers: 245, 246, 247, 248, 249, 250, 251, 252, 253, 254**

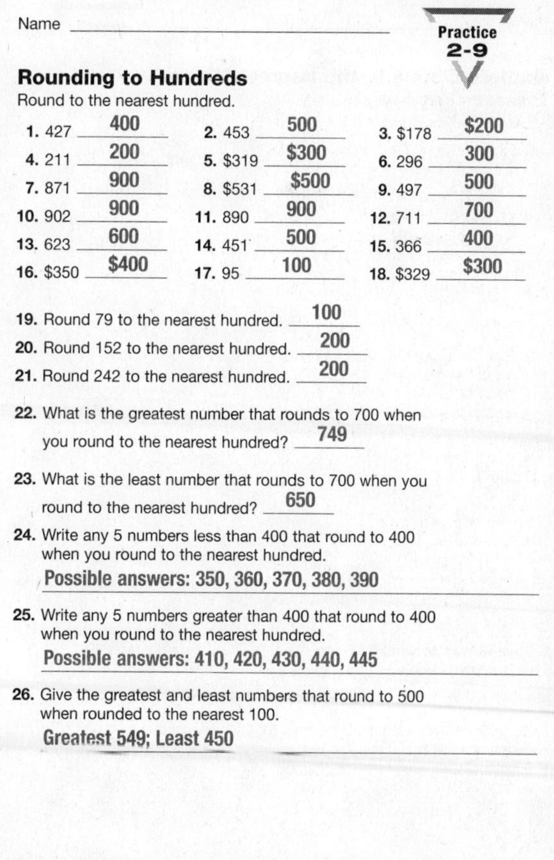

Name ______________________

Practice 2-9

Rounding to Hundreds

Round to the nearest hundred.

1. 427 **400**
2. 453 **500**
3. $178 **$200**
4. 211 **200**
5. $319 **$300**
6. 296 **300**
7. 871 **900**
8. $531 **$500**
9. 497 **500**
10. 902 **900**
11. 890 **900**
12. 711 **700**
13. 623 **600**
14. 451 **500**
15. 366 **400**
16. $350 **$400**
17. 95 **100**
18. $329 **$300**
19. Round 79 to the nearest hundred. **100**
20. Round 152 to the nearest hundred. **200**
21. Round 242 to the nearest hundred. **200**
22. What is the greatest number that rounds to 700 when you round to the nearest hundred? **749**
23. What is the least number that rounds to 700 when you round to the nearest hundred? **650**
24. Write any 5 numbers less than 400 that round to 400 when you round to the nearest hundred.
Possible answers: 350, 360, 370, 380, 390
25. Write any 5 numbers greater than 400 that round to 400 when you round to the nearest hundred.
Possible answers: 410, 420, 430, 440, 445
26. Give the greatest and least numbers that round to 500 when rounded to the nearest 100.
Greatest 549; Least 450

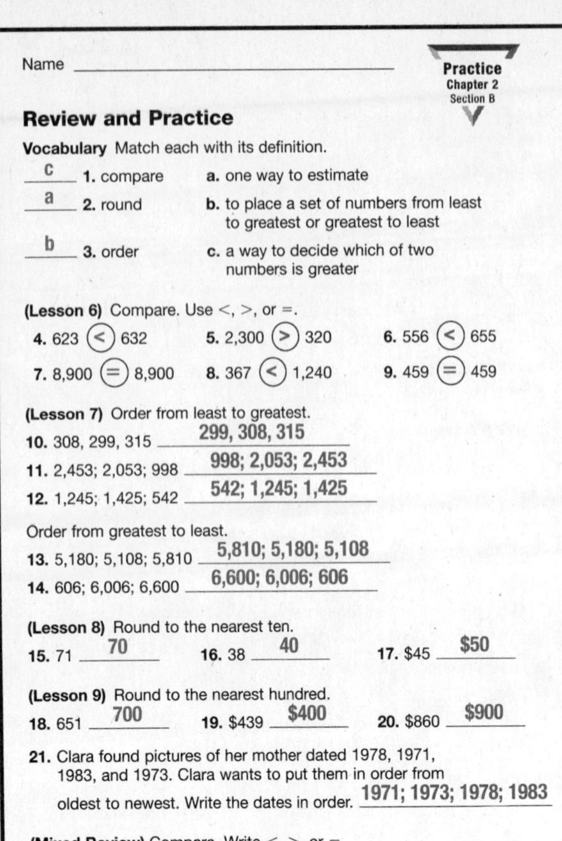

Name ____________

Practice Chapter 2 Section B

Review and Practice

Vocabulary Match each with its definition.

c 1. compare — a. one way to estimate
a 2. round — b. to place a set of numbers from least to greatest or greatest to least
b 3. order — c. a way to decide which of two numbers is greater

(Lesson 6) Compare. Use <, >, or =.

4. 623 (<) 632 5. 2,300 (>) 320 6. 556 (<) 655
7. 8,900 (=) 8,900 8. 367 (<) 1,240 9. 459 (=) 459

(Lesson 7) Order from least to greatest.

10. 308, 299, 315 **299, 308, 315**
11. 2,453; 2,053; 998 **998; 2,053; 2,453**
12. 1,245; 1,425; 542 **542; 1,245; 1,425**

Order from greatest to least.

13. 5,180; 5,108; 5,810 **5,810; 5,180; 5,108**
14. 606; 6,006; 6,600 **6,600; 6,006; 606**

(Lesson 8) Round to the nearest ten.

15. 71 **70** 16. 38 **40** 17. $45 **$50**

(Lesson 9) Round to the nearest hundred.

18. 651 **700** 19. $439 **$400** 20. $860 **$900**

21. Clara found pictures of her mother dated 1978, 1971, 1983, and 1973. Clara wants to put them in order from oldest to newest. Write the dates in order. **1971; 1973; 1978; 1983**

(Mixed Review) Compare. Write <, >, or =.

22. 6 + 9 (=) 9 + 6 23. 8 − 5 (<) 7 − 2 24. 9 + 3 (>) 15 − 4

Use with page 72. 25

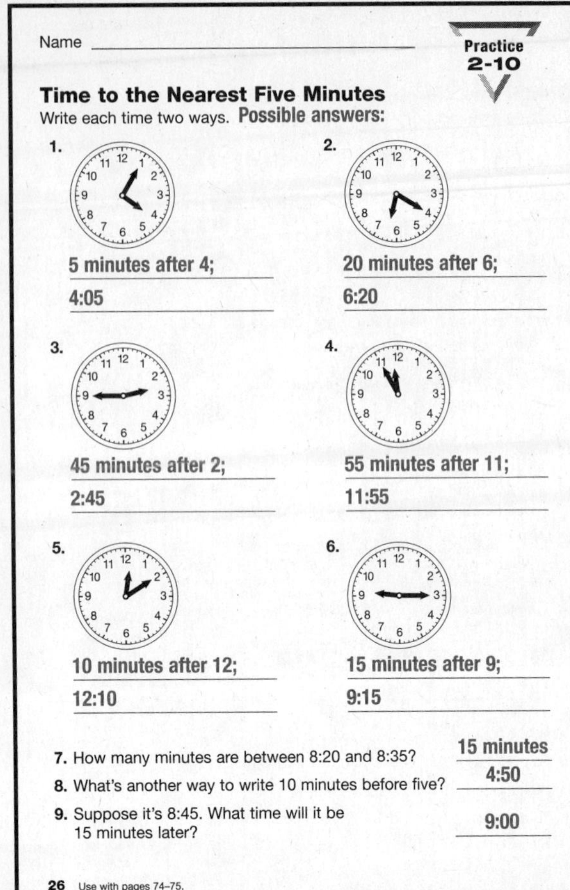

Name ____________

Practice 2-10

Time to the Nearest Five Minutes

Write each time two ways. **Possible answers:**

1. **5 minutes after 4; 4:05**
2. **20 minutes after 6; 6:20**
3. **45 minutes after 2; 2:45**
4. **55 minutes after 11; 11:55**
5. **10 minutes after 12; 12:10**
6. **15 minutes after 9; 9:15**

7. How many minutes are between 8:20 and 8:35? **15 minutes**
8. What's another way to write 10 minutes before five? **4:50**
9. Suppose it's 8:45. What time will it be 15 minutes later? **9:00**

26 Use with pages 74–75.

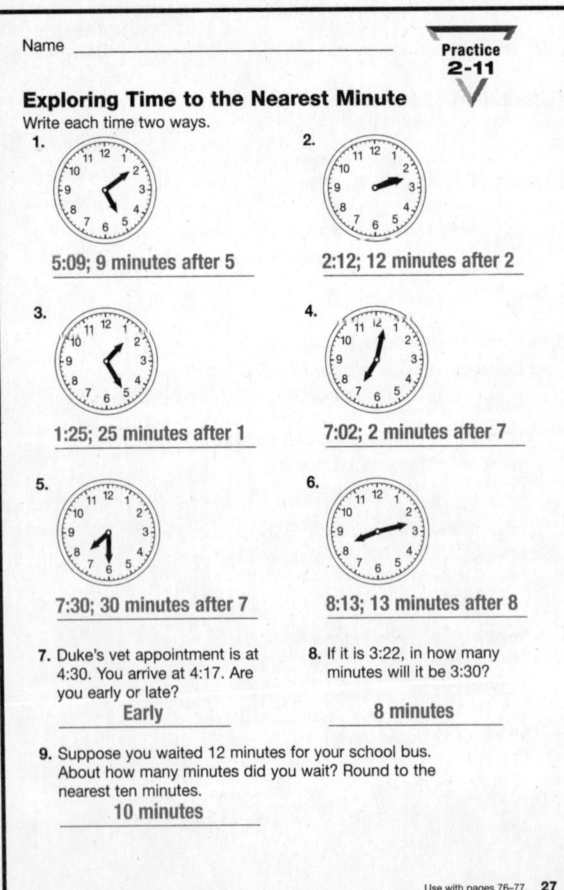

Name ____________

Practice 2-11

Exploring Time to the Nearest Minute

Write each time two ways.

1. **5:09; 9 minutes after 5**
2. **2:12; 12 minutes after 2**
3. **1:25; 25 minutes after 1**
4. **7:02; 2 minutes after 7**
5. **7:30; 30 minutes after 7**
6. **8:13; 13 minutes after 8**

7. Duke's vet appointment is at 4:30. You arrive at 4:17. Are you early or late? **Early**
8. If it is 3:22, in how many minutes will it be 3:30? **8 minutes**
9. Suppose you waited 12 minutes for your school bus. About how many minutes did you wait? Round to the nearest ten minutes. **10 minutes**

Use with pages 76–77. 27

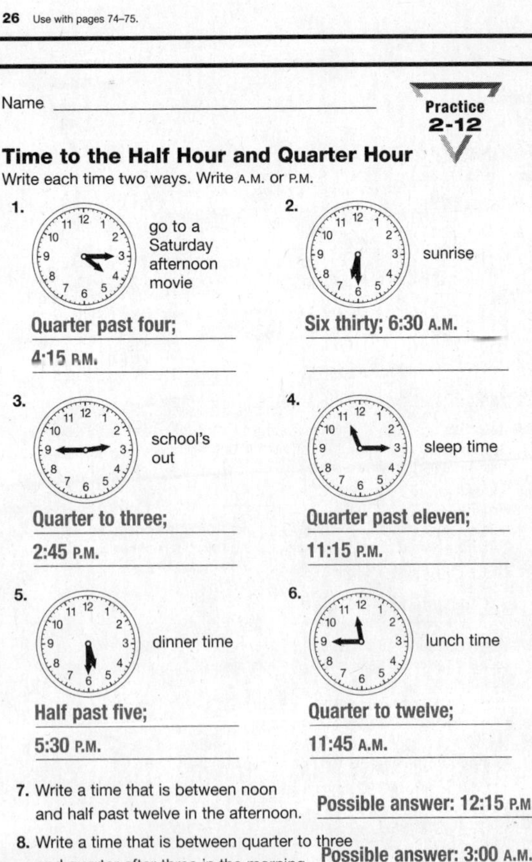

Name ____________

Practice 2-12

Time to the Half Hour and Quarter Hour

Write each time two ways. Write A.M. or P.M.

1. go to a Saturday afternoon movie — **Quarter past four; 4:15 P.M.**
2. sunrise — **Six thirty; 6:30 A.M.**
3. school's out — **Quarter to three; 2:45 P.M.**
4. sleep time — **Quarter past eleven; 11:15 P.M.**
5. dinner time — **Half past five; 5:30 P.M.**
6. lunch time — **Quarter to twelve; 11:45 A.M.**

7. Write a time that is between noon and half past twelve in the afternoon. **Possible answer: 12:15 P.M.**
8. Write a time that is between quarter to three and quarter after three in the morning. **Possible answer: 3:00 A.M.**
9. How many times in one day will the clock show 6:30? Explain. **2 times; At 6:30 A.M. and 6:30 P.M.**

28 Use with pages 78–79.

Name ______________________

Practice 2-13

Elapsed Time

1. Sam wants to let his dog run for twenty minutes. If he starts at 12:15 P.M., what time should he call the dog in? **12:35 P.M.**
2. "I tried to call you an hour ago!" says Sheila. If it is 8:45 P.M. now, what time did she call before? **7:45 P.M.**
3. "This movie lasts for 2 hours and 45 minutes," says Marc. If it begins at 7:00 P.M., what time will the movie end? **9:45 P.M.**
4. Kai started his homework at 4:35 P.M. and finished at 7:00 P.M. How much time did he spend doing homework? **2 hours and 25 minutes**
5. Carla's karate class lasts for 45 minutes. If it begins at 4:15 P.M., what time will it end? **5:00 P.M.**
6. Suppose it is 6:20 A.M. What time will it be in half an hour? **6:50 A.M.**
7. The school bus arrives at 7:15 A.M. It is now 6:35 A.M. How much time does Amir have to get ready? **40 minutes**

Three cars left school at 2:30 P.M. Each traveled for the amount of time shown. When did each car arrive at its destination?

Car	Driving Time	Arrival Time
8. Juan's car	35 minutes	**3:05 P.M.**
9. Hannah's car	60 minutes	**3:30 P.M.**
10. Beryl's car	1 hour and 5 minutes	**3:35 P.M.**

Name ______________________

Practice 2-14

Ordinal Numbers and the Calendar

Use the calendar to answer **1–6**.

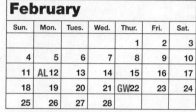

February

Sun.	Mon.	Tues.	Wed.	Thur.	Fri.	Sat.
				1	2	3
4	5	6	7	8	9	10
11	AL 12	13	14	15	16	17
18	19	20	21	GW 22	23	24
25	26	27	28			

1. How many Tuesdays are in this month? **4**
2. Abraham Lincoln was born on February 12th. What day of the week is that? **Monday** Mark it on the calendar above.
3. George Washington was born on the twenty-second of February. What day of the week is that? **Thursday** Mark it on the calendar above.
4. What day of the week is February 3rd? **Saturday**
5. What is the date of the third Saturday in February? **February 17**
6. What are the dates of the last weekend in February? **February 24–25**
7. February is the second month of the year. What is the first month? **January**
8. Name the fourth month. **April**

Name ______________________

Practice 2-15

Decision Making

1. Part of making a schedule is knowing how much time you have to get everything done. Figure out how much time you have available for each activity on this list and write it down.

Activity	Total time
a. The meeting begins at 3:15 P.M. and lasts until 4:00 P.M.	**45 minutes**
b. You have from 6:00 P.M. until 8:20 P.M. to do your homework.	**2 hours, 20 minutes**
c. Practice begins at 3:45 P.M. and ends at 5:15 P.M.	**1 hour, 30 minutes**
d. You begin your chores at 8:30 A.M. and must be done by noon.	**3 hours, 30 minutes**

2. Another step in making a schedule is estimating—or guessing—how long something will take. Give it a try. Estimate how long it would take you to:

Possible answers:

a. brush your teeth **2 minutes**
b. clean your room **15 minutes**
c. read 10 pages **15 minutes**
d. play a game of checkers **10 minutes**
e. walk to the nearest store **5 minutes**
f. make a sandwich **3 minutes**
g. change your clothes **2 minutes**
h. take a bath **15 minutes**

Name ______________________

Practice Chapter 2 Section C

Review and Practice

Vocabulary Match each word with its definition.

c 1. A.M. — a. times from noon to midnight
a 2. P.M. — b. numbers used for ordering
b 3. ordinal numbers — c. times from midnight to noon

(Lessons 10, 11, and 12) Write each time two ways. Write A.M. or P.M.

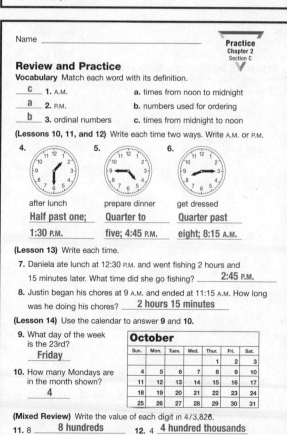

4. after lunch — **Half past one; 1:30 P.M.**
5. prepare dinner — **Quarter to five; 4:45 P.M.**
6. get dressed — **Quarter past eight; 8:15 A.M.**

(Lesson 13) Write each time.

7. Daniela ate lunch at 12:30 P.M. and went fishing 2 hours and 15 minutes later. What time did she go fishing? **2:45 P.M.**
8. Justin began his chores at 9 A.M. and ended at 11:15 A.M. How long was he doing his chores? **2 hours 15 minutes**

(Lesson 14) Use the calendar to answer **9** and **10**.

9. What day of the week is the 23rd? **Friday**
10. How many Mondays are in the month shown? **4**

October

Sun.	Mon.	Tues.	Wed.	Thur.	Fri.	Sat.
				1	2	3
4	5	6	7	8	9	10
11	12	13	14	15	16	17
18	19	20	21	22	23	24
25	26	27	28	29	30	31

(Mixed Review) Write the value of each digit in 473,826.

11. 8 **8 hundreds**
12. 4 **4 hundred thousands**
13. 7 **7 ten thousands**

Name ______________________

Practice Chapters 1–2

Cumulative Review

(Chapter 1 Lesson 2) Use the data from the graph to answer each question.

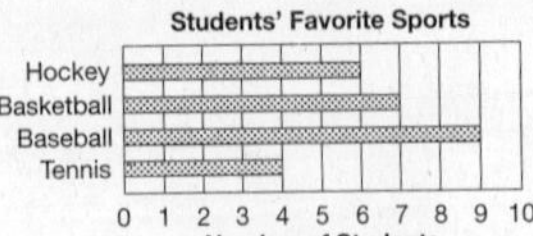

1. How many sports are the favorite of more than 5 students? **3**
2. What sport is the favorite of 9 students? **baseball**

(Chapter 1 Lesson 5) Write a number sentence and use it to solve the problem.

3. Liz read 10 books. 6 were mysteries. The rest were biographies. How many were biographies? **10 − 6 = 4; 4 biographies.**

(Chapter 1 Lesson 11) Write the next four numbers.

4. 10, 20, 30, 40, **50**, **60**, **70**, **80**
5. 29, 26, 23, 20, **17**, **14**, **11**, **8**

(Chapter 2 Lesson 4) Write the value of each underlined digit.

6. 64<u>5</u>,861 **5,000** 7. 293,<u>8</u>62 **800**

(Chapter 2 Lesson 7) Order from least to greatest.

8. 455, 450, 530, 545 **450, 455, 530, 545**
9. 4,670, 5,839, 4,668, 5,355 **4,668; 4,670; 5,355; 5,839**

(Chapter 2 Lesson 10) Write each time in two ways.

10. 

2:05; 5 minutes after 2

11. **8:35; 35 minutes after 8**

Name ______________________

Practice 3-1

Exploring Addition Patterns

Use basic facts and place value to complete each problem.

1. 3 + 4 = **7**
2. 30 + 40 = **3** tens + **4** tens = **7** tens = **70**
3. 300 + 400 = **3** hundreds + **4** hundreds = **7** hundreds = **700**
4. 3 + 5 = **8**; 30 + **50** = 80; **300** + 500 = 800
5. 4 + 9 = **13**; **40** + 90 = 130; 400 + **900** = 1,300
6. 8 + 1 = **9**; 80 + **10** = 90; **800** + 100 = 900
7. 8 + 7 = **15**; **80** + 70 = 150; 800 + **700** = 1,500

Find each sum using mental math.

8. \$20 + \$50 = **\$70**
9. 100 + 700 = **800**
10. 600 + 400 = **1,000**
11. \$30 + \$80 = **\$110**
12. 20 + 90 = **110**
13. \$60 + \$70 = **\$130**
14. There are 30 students on one school bus and 70 on another school bus. How many students are there altogether? **100**
15. Can you use the basic fact 3 + 2 to add 30 + 200? Explain. **No; Possible answer: The 3 and the 2 do not have the same place value.**

Name ______________________

Practice 3-2

Exploring Adding on a Hundred Chart

You can think about adding numbers in different ways.

1. 50 + 36 = 50 + 30 + **6** = **86**

Show how you can use the hundred chart to add 48 and 37.

2. 48 + 37 = **85**

1	2	3	4	5	6	7	8	9	10
11	12	13	14	15	16	17	18	19	20
21	22	23	24	25	26	27	28	29	30
31	32	33	34	35	36	37	38	39	40
41	42	43	44	45	46	47	48	49	50
51	52	53	54	55	56	57	58	59	60
61	62	63	64	65	66	67	68	69	70
71	72	73	74	75	76	77	78	79	80
81	82	83	84	85	86	87	88	89	90
91	92	93	94	95	96	97	98	99	100

Find each sum. You may use the hundred chart to help.

3. 43 + 20 = **63**
4. 52 + 18 = **70**
5. 27 + 6 = **33**
6. 6 + 27 = **33**
7. \$78 + \$21 = **\$99**
8. 40 + 45 = **85**
9. 37 + 14 = **51**
10. \$13 + \$29 = **\$42**
11. Find the sum of 14 and 67. **81**
12. Add 54 and 39. **93**
13. If you know the sum of 24 + 37, how can you find the sum of 37 + 24? Explain. **Possible answer: Both have the same sum because you can add the same numbers in any order.**
14. Explain how you would add 39 + 22 using mental math. **Possible answer: Think 39 and 20 more is 59. 59 and 2 more is 61.**

Name ______________________

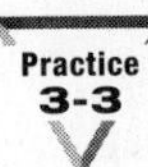

Practice 3-3

Exploring Algebra: Missing Numbers

There are two ways to find the missing number in ☐ + 4 = 21.

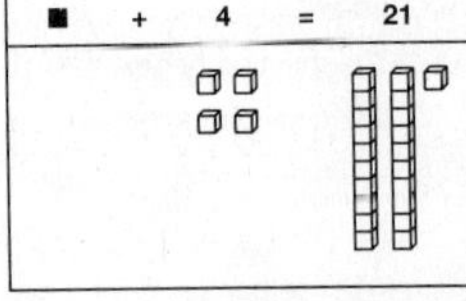

1. Match 4 cubes on one side with 4 on the other. How many more cubes do you need to make 21? **17** + 4 = 21.
2. You already have 4 on one side, so you can count on from 4 until you have 21. You count on **17** more cubes.

Find each missing number. You may use color cubes to help.

3. **16** + 7 = 23
4. **6** + 8 = 14
5. **7** + 5 = 12
6. **15** + 6 = 21
7. 4 + **6** = 10
8. 9 + **19** = 28
9. 11 + **8** = 19
10. **9** + 13 = 22
11. **4** + 19 = 23
12. Is the missing number in ☐ + 4 = 16 the same as the missing number in 4 + ☐ = 16? Explain. **Yes; Adding numbers in any order gives you the same sum, so they are the same.**

Use patterns to find each missing number.

13. **6** + 7 = 13
14. 6 + **7** = 13
15. **6** + 5 = 11
16. 6 + **5** = 11
17. 3 + **9** = 12
18. **3** + 9 = 12

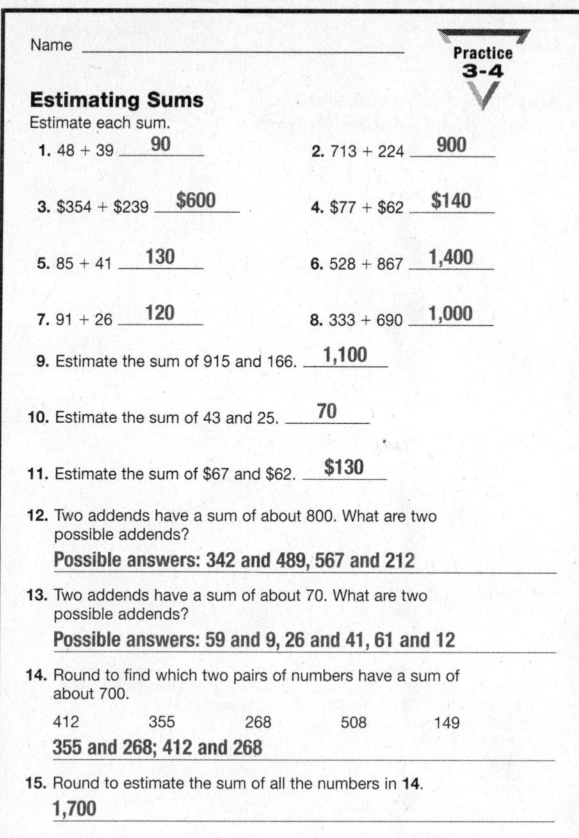

Name ____________________

Practice 3-4

Estimating Sums

Estimate each sum.

1. 48 + 39 **90**
2. 713 + 224 **900**
3. $354 + $239 **$600**
4. $77 + $62 **$140**
5. 85 + 41 **130**
6. 528 + 867 **1,400**
7. 91 + 26 **120**
8. 333 + 690 **1,000**
9. Estimate the sum of 915 and 166. **1,100**
10. Estimate the sum of 43 and 25. **70**
11. Estimate the sum of $67 and $62. **$130**
12. Two addends have a sum of about 800. What are two possible addends?
    Possible answers: 342 and 489, 567 and 212
13. Two addends have a sum of about 70. What are two possible addends?
    Possible answers: 59 and 9, 26 and 41, 61 and 12
14. Round to find which two pairs of numbers have a sum of about 700.
    412 355 268 508 149
    355 and 268; 412 and 268
15. Round to estimate the sum of all the numbers in **14**.
    1,700

Use with pages 102–103. 37

Name ____________________

Practice Chapter 3 Section A

Review and Practice

Vocabulary Match each with its definition.

b 1. estimate — a. the answer obtained when adding numbers

a 2. sum — b. to find an answer that is close to an exact answer

(Lesson 1) Complete.

3. 8 + 8 = **16**
   80 + **80** = 160
   800 + 800 = 1,600
4. $3 + $**9** = $12
   $**30** + $90 = $120
   $300 + $900 = $**1,200**
5. What basic fact can you use to find 300 + 800? **3 + 8 = 11**

(Lesson 2) Find each sum. You may use a hundred chart to help.

6. 36 + 8 = **44**
7. 82 + 12 = **94**
8. 25 + 30 = **55**
9. $64 + $27 = **$91**

(Lesson 3) Find each missing number. You may use color cubes to help.

10. **25** + 7 = 32
11. 8 + **22** = 30
12. I am a 2-digit number. If you add me to 6 you will get a sum of 38. What number am I? **32**

(Lesson 4) Circle the letter that shows the best estimate of each sum.

13. 34 + 55 — a. 80 — b. 100 — **(c.) 90**
14. 522 + 131 — **(a.) 600** — b. 700 — c. 800

(Mixed Review) Use the pictograph to answer each question.

15. How many students does each [cat] represent? **3**
16. How many boys have cats? **12**
17. How many more girls than boys have cats? **3**

Cats Owned

girls	🐱🐱🐱🐱🐱
boys	🐱🐱🐱🐱

Key: 1 [cat] = 3 students

38 Use with page 104.

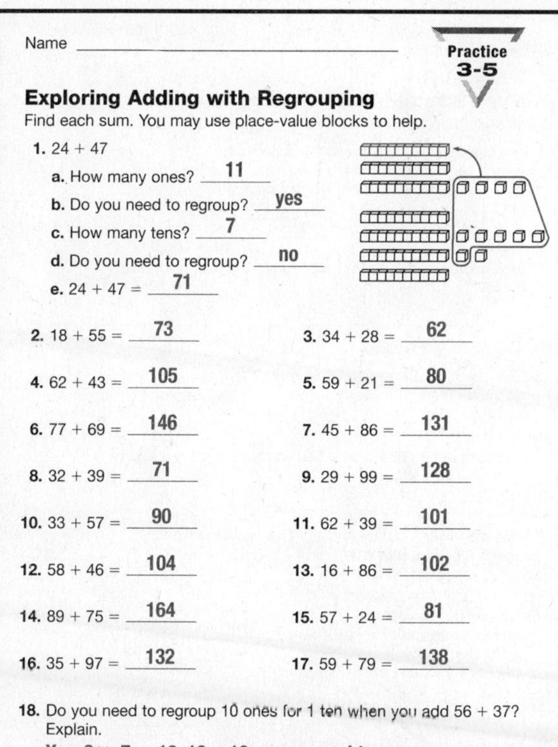

Name ____________________

Practice 3-5

Exploring Adding with Regrouping

Find each sum. You may use place-value blocks to help.

1. 24 + 47
   a. How many ones? **11**
   b. Do you need to regroup? **yes**
   c. How many tens? **7**
   d. Do you need to regroup? **no**
   e. 24 + 47 = **71**
2. 18 + 55 = **73**
3. 34 + 28 = **62**
4. 62 + 43 = **105**
5. 59 + 21 = **80**
6. 77 + 69 = **146**
7. 45 + 86 = **131**
8. 32 + 39 = **71**
9. 29 + 99 = **128**
10. 33 + 57 = **90**
11. 62 + 39 = **101**
12. 58 + 46 = **104**
13. 16 + 86 = **102**
14. 89 + 75 = **164**
15. 57 + 24 = **81**
16. 35 + 97 = **132**
17. 59 + 79 = **138**
18. Do you need to regroup 10 ones for 1 ten when you add 56 + 37? Explain.
    Yes; 6 + 7 = 13, 13 > 10 so you need to regroup.
19. Do you need to regroup 10 ones for 1 ten when you add 56 + 42? Explain.
    No, 6 + 2 = 8, 8 < 10 so you do not need to regroup.

Use with pages 106–107. 39

Name ____________________

Practice 3-6

Adding 2-Digit Numbers

Add. Estimate to check.

1. 43 + 16 = **59**
2. 26 + 72 = **98**
3. $39 + 41 = **$80**
4. 52 + 9 = **61**
5. 85 + 67 = **152**
6. 64 + 89 = **153**
7. 96 + 6 = **102**
8. $58 + 15 = **$73**
9. 22 + 81 = **103**
10. $54 + 7 = **$61**
11. 88 + 99 = **187**
12. 16 + 77 = **93**
13. 91 + 79 = **170**
14. 76 + 37 = **113**
15. 55 + 86 = **141**
16. 47 + 65 = **112**
17. 28 + 54 = **82**
18. $37 + $78 = **$115**
19. 63 + 87 = **150**
20. 92 + 21 = **113**
21. Find the sum of 45 and 37. **82**
22. Add 38 and 19. **57**
23. Write two numbers that add to 70 without regrouping.
    Possible answers: 30 and 40 or 10 and 60
24. When you add 27 + 5 do you start by adding 2 + 5? Explain.
    No; Start by adding 5 and 7.

40 Use with pages 108–109.

Name ______________________

Practice 3-7

Adding 3-Digit Numbers

Complete.

1. 217 + 384 = 601
2. 583 + 74 = 657
3. $357 + 66 = $423
4. 445 + 208 = 653

Add. Estimate to check.

5. $826 + 151 = **$977**
6. 737 + 217 = **954**
7. $42 + 59 = **$101**
8. 431 + 94 = **525**
9. 621 + 377 = **998**
10. 456 + 255 = **711**
11. 388 + 94 = **482**
12. $982 + 635 = **$1,617**

13. 97 + 42 = **139**

14. 358 + 715 = **1,073**

15. $39 + $75 = **$114**

16. 118 + 647 = **765**

17. Find the sum of 380 and 442. **822**

18. Find the sum of 832 and 79. **911**

19. Write two addends with a sum of 258.
Possible answer: 133 and 125

20. Estimate to decide which sum is greater than 1,000:
590 + 462 or 311 + 628.
600 + 500 = 1,100; 300 + 600 = 900; 590 + 462 is greater than 1,000.

Name ______________________

Practice 3-8

Adding 4-Digit Numbers: Choose a Calculation Method

Add.

1. 5,347 + 2,491 = **7,838**
2. 6,200 + 3,500 = **9,700**
3. 4,619 + 1,592 = **6,211**
4. 7,416 + 2,347 = **9,763**
5. $2,400 + 5,500 = **$7,900**
6. 1,348 + 721 = **2,069**
7. 4,827 + 3,164 = **7,991**
8. 6,038 + 831 = **6,869**
9. 6,371 + 2,293 = **8,664**
10. 3,849 + 5,163 = **9,012**
11. 7,345 + 1,681 = **9,026**
12. 4,691 + 5,366 = **10,057**

13. 1,495 + 5,622 = **7,117**

14. 6,400 + 3,500 = **9,900**

15. 9,046 + 716 = **9,762**

16. $5,807 + $2,164 = **$7,971**

17. Find the sum of 648 and 2,115. **2,763**

18. Find the sum of 2,800 and 5,000. **7,800**

19. Estimate to decide if the sum of 6,701 and 2,399 is greater than or less than 10,000.
Less than; 7,000 + 2,000 = 9,000

20. Which two numbers have a sum of 6,000?
1,500 5,000 3,000
2,000 4,500 3,500
1,500 and 4,500

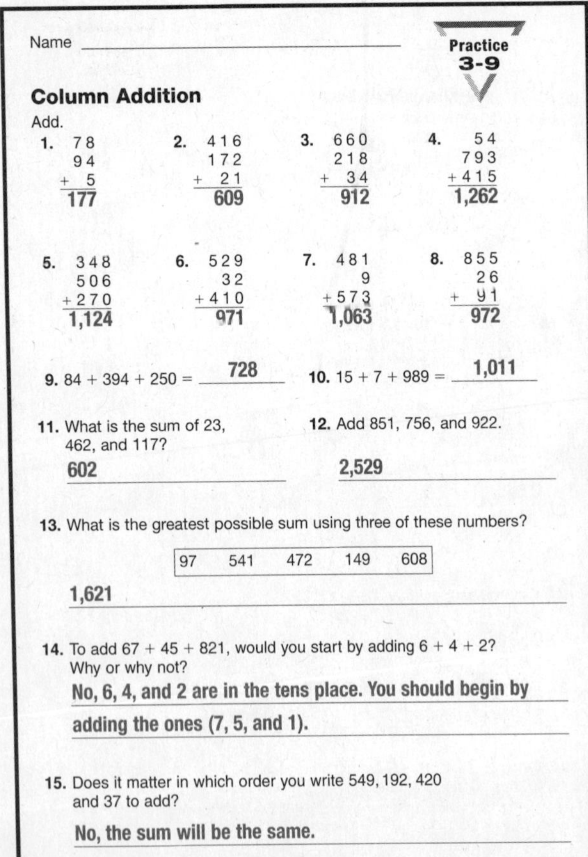

Name ______________________

Practice 3-9

Column Addition

Add.

1. 78 + 94 + 5 = **177**
2. 416 + 172 + 21 = **609**
3. 660 + 218 + 34 = **912**
4. 54 + 793 + 415 = **1,262**
5. 348 + 506 + 270 = **1,124**
6. 529 + 32 + 410 = **971**
7. 481 + 9 + 573 = **1,063**
8. 855 + 26 + 91 = **972**

9. 84 + 394 + 250 = **728**

10. 15 + 7 + 989 = **1,011**

11. What is the sum of 23, 462, and 117? **602**

12. Add 851, 756, and 922. **2,529**

13. What is the greatest possible sum using three of these numbers?

97	541	472	149	608

1,621

14. To add 67 + 45 + 821, would you start by adding 6 + 4 + 2? Why or why not?
No, 6, 4, and 2 are in the tens place. You should begin by adding the ones (7, 5, and 1).

15. Does it matter in which order you write 549, 192, 420 and 37 to add?
No, the sum will be the same.

Name ______________________

Practice 3-10

Analyze Strategies: Guess and Check

Guess and check to solve.

1. The Hawks beat the Jays in a baseball game. The scores were 6 runs apart and there were 22 runs scored in the game. How many runs did each team score?
Hawks scored 14 runs. Jays scored 8 runs.

2. The Hawks lost to the Orioles by 4 runs. There were 18 runs scored in the game. How many runs did the Orioles score?
11 runs

Use any strategy to solve.

3. The Jays beat the Orioles by 8 runs. There were 16 runs scored in the game. How many runs did the Jays score?
12 runs

4. The sum of two numbers is 65. The numbers are 3 apart. What are they?
34 and 31

5. The sum of two numbers is 92. The numbers are 12 apart. What are they?
52 and 40

6. Tim bought three items at the school bookstore. He spent $23. What did Tim buy? Use the prices in the table to solve.
Backpack, dictionary, set of markers

Item	Cost
Backpack	$14
Calculator	$ 9
Dictionary	$ 5
Notebook	$ 3
Set of Markers	$ 4

Name ____________________

Practice Chapter 3 Section B

Review and Practice

(Lesson 5) Find each sum. You may use place-value blocks to help.

1. 68 + 35 = **103**
2. 237 + 125 = **362**
3. 56 + 39 = **95**
4. 53 + 34 = **87**

(Lessons 6 and 7) Add. Estimate to check.

5. 43 + 24 = **67**
6. 651 + 86 = **737**
7. 738 + 339 = **1,077**
8. 49 + 71 = **120**

9. 823 + 119 = **942**
10. 545 + 126 = **671**

11. Do you need to regroup 10 tens for 1 hundred when you add 241 + 387? **Yes**

(Lessons 8 and 9) Add.

12. 2,568 + 812 = **3,380**
13. 355 + 51 + 19 = **425**
14. 402 + 313 + 66 = **781**
15. 7,220 + 867 = **8,087**

(Lesson 10) Guess and check to solve.

16. The Jays beat the Tigers by 5 runs. There were 17 runs scored. How many runs did the Jays score? **11**

(Mixed Review) Circle the letter that answers each question.

17. Which does not tell the correct time?

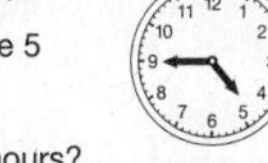

(A) half after 5 B. 15 minutes before 5
C. 4:45 D. 45 minutes after 4

18. What time will it be in 1 and a half hours?
A. 4:15 B. 6:00 **(C)** 6:15 D. 7:30

19. Sal's soccer practice began at 2:45 P.M. and finished at 4:00 P.M. How long was practice?
1 hour 15 minutes

Name ____________________

Practice 3-11

Mental Math

Use mental math to find each sum.

1. 80 + 55 = **135**
2. 62 + 9 = **71**
3. 18 + 40 = **58**
4. 45 + 35 = **80**
5. 59 + 36 = **95**
6. 21 + 18 = **39**
7. 99 + 5 = **104**
8. 73 + 9 = **82**
9. 47 + 29 = **76**
10. 25 + 60 = **85**
11. 88 + 4 = **92**
12. 7 + 43 = **50**
13. 81 + 9 = **90**
14. 27 + 62 = **89**
15. 7 + 19 = **26**
16. 32 + 21 = **53**
17. 55 + 35 = **90**
18. 28 + 83 = **111**
19. 46 + 52 = **98**
20. 67 + 9 = **76**
21. 34 + 28 = **62**
22. 35 + 17 = **52**
23. 8 + 37 = **45**
24. 42 + 17 = **59**

25. Find the sum of 475 and 15. **490**
26. Find the sum of 133 and 7. **140**
27. Add 389 + 4. **393**
28. Add 225 + 25. **250**

29. How does knowing 7 + 3 = 10 help you to add 37 + 13 mentally?
Possible answer: You can add the ones using that fact.

30. How can finding digits that add up to 10 help you to add 64 + 26?
Possible answer: The ones add to 10, so you can just add the tens and the regrouped 1.

Name ____________________

Practice 3-12

Counting Coins

Write the total value in cents.

1. 
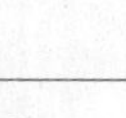
57¢

2. 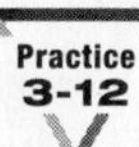

84¢

3. 
51¢

4. 
98¢

5. **85¢**

6. 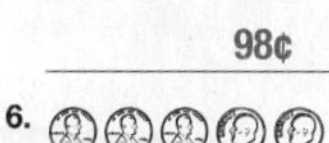
38¢

7. Find three ways to make 67 cents.
Possible answer: 2 quarters, 1 dime, 1 nickel, 2 pennies; 6 dimes, 1 nickel, 2 pennies; 67 pennies

8. Find a way to make 56 cents.
Possible answer: 1 half dollar, 1 nickel, 1 penny

9. Use the fewest coins to make 37 cents.
1 quarter, 1 dime, 2 pennies

Name ____________________

Practice 3-13

Using Dollars and Cents

Write the total value in dollars and cents.

1. 

$2.55

2. 

$7.22

3. Give at least two ways to show $2.65.
Possible answers: 2 dollar bills, 2 quarters, 1 dime, 1 nickel; 2 dollar bills, 2 quarters, 3 nickels; 1 dollar bill, 5 quarters, 3 dimes, 1 nickel, 5 pennies; 10 quarters, 15 pennies

4. Give at least three ways to show $8.57.
Possible answers: 1 five-dollar bill, 3 dollar bills, 2 quarters, 1 nickel, 2 pennies; 8 dollar bills, 1 quarter, 3 dimes, 2 pennies; 1 five-dollar bill, 13 quarters, 2 dimes, 12 pennies; 80 dimes, 57 pennies

5. Alicia said, "I lost a coin! I had $6.96. Now I only have 1 five-dollar bill, 1 one-dollar bill, 3 quarters, 1 dime, 1 nickel, and 1 penny." What coin did Alicia lose?
1 nickel

Name ______________________________

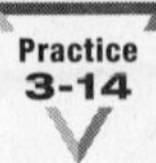

Practice 3-14

Exploring Making Change

Your class is having an art sale to make money for new supplies. You are the cashier.

1. Andy buys a papier-maché mask worth $3.24. He pays with $5.00. How much change will you give him?

   a. Count on by circling the coins and bills you will use to make change. Write the amount.

   1 penny **3 quarters** **1 dollar**

   b. How much change is that? **$1.76**

2. June buys a painting worth $3.31. She pays with $5.00. List which coins and bills you would use to make change. Then write the change in dollars and cents.

   Possible answer: 4 pennies, 1 nickel, 1 dime, 2 quarters, 1 dollar bill; $1.69

3. Sheila's purchases total $2.09. She pays with $3.00.

   a. Write three ways you could make change.

   Possible answers: 1 penny, 1 nickel, 1 dime, 3 quarters; 1 penny, 2 nickels, 3 dimes, 2 quarters; 1 penny, 8 nickels, 5 dimes; 6 pennies, 4 nickels, 4 dimes, 1 quarter.

   b. Which way uses the fewest coins?

   6 coins: 3 quarters, 1 dime, 1 nickel, 1 penny

Name ______________________________

Practice 3-15

Adding Money

Add. Estimate to check.

1. $5.17
+ 4.39
$9.56
2. $8.89
+ 3.14
$12.03
3. $0.52
+ 7.93
$8.45
4. $2.22
+ 3.33
$5.55
5. $4.87
+ 5.14
$10.01
6. $2.06
+ 7.34
$9.40
7. $9.40
+ 1.61
$11.01
8. $6.73
+ 2.99
$9.72
9. $4.34 + $3.71 = **$8.05**
10. $9.49 + $8.84 = **$18.33**
11. $3.25 + $2.96 = **$6.21**
12. $7.69 + $5.91 = **$13.60**
13. Find the sum of $2.41 and $5.57. **$7.98**
14. Add $8.12 + $8.69. **$16.81**

Athletic Equipment	
baseball bat	$7.07
basketball	$6.49
volleyball	$3.34
softball	$2.98
soccer ball	$4.63

15. Will $10.00 be enough to buy a softball and a baseball bat? Explain.

    No; $2.98 + $7.07 = $10.05

16. Which two pieces of equipment together will cost about $11.00?

    The basketball and the soccer ball

17. What two items together would cost less than $7.00? How much would they cost?

    Volleyball and softball; $6.32

Name ______________________________

Practice 3-16

Front-End Estimation

Use front-end estimation to estimate each sum.

1. $6.12
+ 3.77
$9.00
2. 334
865
+ 202
1,300
3. 789
122
+ 960
1,700
4. $2.57
5.16
+ 8.45
$15.00
5. 691
423
+ 606
1,600
6. 928
+ 890
1,700
7. $3.33
5.87
+ 6.63
$14.00
8. 478
150
+ 822
1,300
9. 345 + 312 + 637 **1,200**
10. 841 + 797 + 141 **1,600**
11. Use front-end estimation to estimate the sum of 263, 804, and 469.

    1,400

12. Use front-end estimation to estimate the sum of $7.34, $3.69, and $9.51.

    $19.00

13. Is the sum of $4.32 + $6.90 + $7.86 greater than $17.00? Explain.

    Yes; $4 + $6 + $7 = $17; Cents make sum > $17.00

14. If you buy 2 items that cost $6.32 each, will $11.00 be enough to buy both items? Explain.

    No; $6 + $6 = $12; $12.00 > $11.00

15. If you buy 3 items that cost $5.43 each, will $15.00 be enough to buy all 3 items? Explain.

    No; $5 + $5 + $5 = $15; Cents will make sum > $15.00

16. If you buy 2 items for $6.29 and 1 item for $3.55, will $15.00 be enough? Explain.

    No; $6 + $6 + $3 = $15; Cents will make sum > $15.00

Name ______________________________

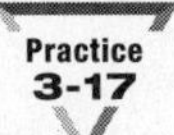

Practice 3-17

Analyze Word Problems: Exact Answer or Estimate?

Ahmed is going shopping for art supplies.

Art Supplies	
crayons	$2.34
marker	$4.98
paintbrush	$1.86
construction paper	$3.15
watercolor paint set	$4.43
frame	$6.71

Write if you need an exact answer or an estimate. Then solve.

1. Ahmed has a $10 bill. Does he have enough money to buy construction paper and a frame? Explain.

   Exact; Estimate is too close to $10.00; Yes, he has enough.

2. How much would it cost to buy crayons, a marker, and construction paper?

   Exact; $10.47

3. If Ahmed has $8.00, and he buys 3 paint brushes, does he have enough money left to buy a watercolor paint set? Explain.

   Possible answers: Estimate is enough; since $10.00 is greater than $8.00; No, Ahmed does not have enough money left to buy watercolor paint. If front-end estimation is used, the exact answer is needed.

4. Ahmed wants to know if $9.00 is enough to buy 2 markers. Does he need to find the exact total? Explain.

   No; The estimate of $10.00 is greater than $9.00.

5. Ahmed began shopping at 11:30 A.M. When he finished it was 12:15 P.M. How long did he spend shopping?

   45 minutes

Name ______________________

Practice
Chapter 3
Section C

Review and Practice

(Lesson 11) Use mental math to find each sum.

1. 75 + 9 **84** **2.** 29 + 43 **72** **3.** 88 + 5 **93**

(Lessons 12 and 13) Write the total value in cents or dollars and cents.

4. 

45¢

5.  

$3.80

(Lesson 14) List which coins and bills you would use to make change. Then write the change in dollars and cents.

6. Metta buys a notebook that costs $1.19. She pays with $2.00.
Possible answer: 1 penny, 1 nickel, 3 quarters; $0.81

(Lesson 15) Add. Estimate to check.

7. $9.15 + $4.82 **$13.97** **8.** $3.56 + $6.89 **$10.45**

9. $1.75 + $9.10 **$10.85** **10.** $7.29 + $0.54 **$7.83**

(Lesson 16) Use front-end estimation to estimate each sum.

11. 325 + 176 + 852 **1,200** **12.** 63 + 55 + 38 **140**

(Lesson 17) Write if you need an exact answer or an estimate. Then solve.

13. Cheryl wants to buy three books that cost $5.95, $2.95, and $3.45. Will $10 be enough money? Explain.
Estimate; The estimate of $12.00 is greater than $10, so $10 is not enough.

(Mixed Review) Write the value of each underlined number.

14. 45,886 **40,000** **15.** 2,846 **6** **16.** 123,654 **100,000**

Name ______________________

Practice
Chapters 1–3

Cumulative Review

(Chapter 1, Lesson 1)

1. Which of the following uses pictures to represent information in a graph?

A. line graph **B.** bar graph **C.** pictograph

C; Pictograph

(Chapter 1, Lesson 3)

2. Which of the following shows changes over time?

A. line graph **B.** bar graph **C.** pictograph

A; Line graph

(Chapter 2, Lesson 4) Write the standard form of each number.

3. four hundred thousand, sixty-seven **400,067**

4. six hundred twenty-one thousand, one hundred ten **621,110**

5. one hundred thirty thousand, six **130,006**

(Chapter 2, Lesson 9) Round each to the nearest hundred.

6. 2,610 **2,600** **7.** 987 **1,000** **8.** 1,651 **1,700** **9.** 705 **700**

(Chapter 3, Lessons 9 and 15) Add.

10. 456 + 238 + 115 = **809** **11.** 321 + 56 + 135 = **512** **12.** $3.15 + 1.49 = **$4.64** **13.** $5.11 + 7.52 = **$12.63**

(Chapter 3, Lesson 12)

14. Dimitrios has a five-dollar bill, 2 one-dollar bills, 3 quarters, 1 dime and 2 nickels. How much money does he have?
$7.95

Name ______________________

Practice
4-1

Reviewing the Meaning of Subtraction

Write a number sentence for each. Then solve.

1. A clown is juggling four bananas. He drops one of them. How many bananas are still in the air?
4 − 1 = 3; 3 bananas

2. Karen invites eight friends to her home for a party. Three people cannot come. How many people are there for the party?
8 − 3 = 5; 5 people

3. Josh had a spelling test today. There were fifteen questions on the test. Josh misspelled six words. How many did he spell correctly?
15 − 6 = 9; 9 words spelled correctly

4. Twelve children attended Melissa's party. There were seven boys. How many girls were there?
12 − 7 = 5; 5 girls

5. The bus stops and six children get on. Now there are thirteen children on the bus. How many children were on the bus before this stop?
13 − 6 = 7; 7 children

6. The cracker box contained eighteen crackers. Now there are only nine. How many crackers were taken?
18 − 9 = 9; 9 crackers

7. Jennifer has read 4 chapters of her book. The book has 16 chapters. How many chapters does she have left to read?
16 − 4 = 12; 12 chapters

8. Phil has $10. He buys a vase for $6. How much money does he have left?
10 − 6 = 4; $4

Name ______________________

Practice
4-2

Exploring Subtraction Patterns

Complete.

1. 8 − 3 = **5**
80 − 30 = 50
800 − **300** = 500

2. 13 − **4** = 9
130 − 40 = **90**
1,300 − 400 = 900

3. $19 − $7 = **$12**
$190 − **$70** = $120
$1,900 − $700 = $1,200

4. 12 − 6 = **6**
120 − 60 = 60
1,200 − 600 = 600

Find each difference using mental math.

5. 90 − 50 = **40** **6.** $100 − $80 = **$20**

7. 1,800 − 400 = **1,400** **8.** $1,200 − $1,100 = **$100**

9. 1,700 − 500 = **1,200** **10.** $1,100 − $600 = **$500**

11. Karima and Rick are playing a game with play money. Rick has $1,100. He lands on a space that makes him pay Karima $400. How much money will he have left? **$700**

12. Marty and Dee live in the same town. Marty's grandparents live 30 miles away. Dee's grandparents live 80 miles away. How much farther away do Dee's grandparents live? **50 miles**

13. Continue the pattern. Then write the rule.

In	70	80	90	100	110	120
Out	40	50	60	**70**	**80**	**90**

Rule: **Subtract 30.**

14. What basic fact could you use to find 1,300 − 500? Solve.
13 − 5 = 8; so 1,300 − 500 = 800

Name ______________________

Practice 4-3

Exploring Subtracting on a Hundred Chart

Find each difference. You may use a hundred chart to help.

1. 92 − 27 = 65
2. 69 − 16 = 53
3. 29 − 12 = 17
4. $77 − $64 = $13
5. 44 − 11 = 33
6. 54 − 37 = 17

Use mental math to find each difference.

7. 71 − 51 = 20
8. $48 − $20 = $28
9. 80 − 40 = 40
10. $45 − $30 = $15
11. 42 − 22 = 20
12. 51 − 21 = 30
13. 31 − 8 = 23
14. 79 − 44 = 35

Find each missing number. You may use a hundred chart to help.

15. 56 − 35 = 21
16. 32 − 25 = 7
17. 61 − 12 = 49
18. 96 − 34 = 62
19. 88 − 17 = 71
20. 89 − 28 = 61

21. On a hundred chart, Lesley begins with her finger on 89. She moves back 5 rows and back 7 spaces.
    a. On what number does she land? 32
    b. What number did she subtract? 57

22. Victor has 40¢. He wants to buy 3 postcards. Each postcard costs 20¢. How much more money will he need to buy the postcards? 20¢

Name ______________________

Practice 4-4

Estimating Differences

Estimate each difference.

1. 988 − 112 = 900
2. 992 − 400 = 600
3. 25 − 14 = 10 or 20
4. 98 − 22 = 80
5. 112 − 56 = 50
6. 506 − 210 = 300
7. 279 − 126 = 200
8. 767 − 547 = 300
9. $4.99 − $3.67 = $1.00
10. $8.22 − $4.83 = $3.00
11. $6.49 − $1.25 = $5.00
12. $5.81 − $2.84 = $3.00
13. 432 − 121 = 300
14. 890 − 160 = 700
15. 62 − 19 = 40
16. 81 − 76 = 0

17. Suppose the length of a movie you plan to watch is 98 minutes. You have been watching it for 50 minutes. Would it make sense to say that you have watched about half of the movie? Explain.
    Yes; 98 − 50 = 48; 98 is close to 100, half of 100 is 50 minutes.

18. Suppose the book that you're reading has 126 pages. You've read 62 pages. Would it make sense to say that you have read about half of the book? Explain.
    Yes; half of 126 is 63

19. The estimated difference of the cost of two games is $2.00. Give two examples of the exact amounts that would make the estimate reasonable.
    Possible answers: $7.95 and $5.99; $21.95 and $19.80

20. The estimated difference of the weight of two elephants is 100 pounds. Give two examples of the exact amounts that would make the estimate reasonable.
    Possible answers: 596 and 480; 930 and 788

Name ______________________

Exploring Regrouping

Regroup 1 ten for 10 ones. You may use place-value blocks or draw a picture to help.

1. 64 is the same as **5 tens and 14 ones**

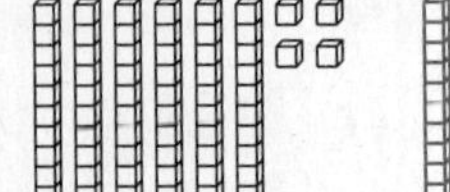

2. 42 = 3 tens, 12 ones
3. 95 = 8 tens, 15 ones
4. 63 = 5 tens, 13 ones
5. 57 = 4 tens, 17 ones
6. 53 = 4 tens, 13 ones
7. 67 = 5 tens, 17 ones
8. 32 = 2 tens, 12 ones
9. 90 = 8 tens, 10 ones
10. 41 = 3 tens, 11 ones
11. 88 = 7 tens, 18 ones

Regroup 1 hundred for 10 tens. You may use place-value blocks or draw a picture to help.

12. 215 = 1 hundred, 11 tens, 5 ones
13. 829 = 7 hundreds, 12 tens, 9 ones
14. 982 = 8 hundreds, 18 tens, 2 ones
15. 302 = 2 hundreds, 10 tens, 2 ones
16. 786 = 6 hundreds, 18 tens, 6 ones
17. 614 = 5 hundreds, 11 tens, 4 ones

18. Regroup 1 ten for 10 ones in the number 567.
    5 hundreds, 5 tens, 17 ones

19. Regroup 1 hundred for 10 tens in the number 412.
    3 hundreds, 11 tens, 2 ones

Name ______________________

Practice Chapter 4 Section A

Review and Practice

(Lesson 1) Write a number sentence for each. Then solve.

1. Harold bought 5 souvenirs in Maine and 3 in Massachusetts. How many more souvenirs did he buy in Maine than Massachusetts? **5 − 3 = 2**

2. Phylis took 18 pictures. 9 are of the Grand Canyon. How many pictures are not of the Grand Canyon? **18 − 9 = 9**

(Lesson 2) Look for a pattern. Complete.

3. 6 − 2 = 4; 60 − 20 = 40; 600 − 200 = 400
4. 13 − 9 = 4; 130 − 90 = 40; 1,300 − 900 = 400
5. 17 − 8 = 9; 170 − 80 = 90; 1,700 − 800 = 900

(Lesson 3) Solve. You may use a hundred chart to help.

6. 35 − 5 = 30
7. $73 − $30 = $43
8. 83 − 64 = 19
9. 59 − 17 = 42
10. 100 − 45 = 55
11. 44 − 28 = 16

(Lesson 4) Estimate each difference.

12. 623 − 455 100
13. $3.75 − $2.29 $2.00

14. Suppose a movie lasts 100 minutes. Does it make sense to say you have about 30 minutes of the show to watch when you've been watching for 47 minutes? Explain.
    No; 100 minutes − 50 minutes = 50 minutes

(Lesson 5) Regroup 1 ten as 10 ones or 1 hundred as 10 tens. You may use place-value blocks or draw a picture to help.

15. 5 [5][14] / 5 6̸ 4
16. [7][18] 2 / 8̸ 8 2
17. [3][19] 0 / 4̸ 9 0

(Mixed Review) Find each sum.

18. 30 + 60 = 90
19. 400 + 300 = 700
20. 90 + 20 = 110

Name ______________________

Exploring Subtracting 2-Digit Numbers

1. Find 86 − 48. You may use place-value blocks or draw a picture to help.
   a. Regroup 1 ten for 10 ones in the number 86. **7** tens and **16** ones.
   b. Subtract the ones. **8** ones
   c. Subtract the tens. **3** tens
   d. The difference is **38**.

Find each difference. You may use place-value blocks or draw a picture to help.

2. 28 − 17 = **11**
3. 41 − 6 = **35**
4. $97 − $16 = **$81**
5. 87 − 68 = **19**
6. 33 − 25 = **8**
7. $55 − $7 = **$48**
8. 19 − 11 = **8**
9. 63 − 6 = **57**
10. $77 − $48 = **$29**
11. 23 − 15 = **8**
12. Subtract 23 from 81. **58**
13. Find the difference of 63 and 47. **16**
14. Find 91 − 52. **39**
15. Your class needs to sell 50 tickets to the school show in order to win a prize. So far the class has sold 22 tickets. How many more tickets need to be sold? **28 tickets**
16. Suppose you had a quarter, 2 dimes, and 7 pennies. If you lost 3 of your pennies, how much money would you have? **$0.49**
17. Genevieve has 60 minutes of homework to do. She has done 44 minutes. How many more minutes of homework does she have to do? **16 minutes**
18. Yuki has read 14 pages of his 51-page book. How many more pages does he have left to read? **37 pages**

Name ______________________

Practice 4-7

Subtracting 2-Digit Numbers

Subtract. Check each answer.

1. 76 − 42 = **34**
2. 63 − 24 = **39**
3. 34 − 7 = **27**
4. $55 − 13 = **$42**
5. 82 − 54 = **28**
6. 29 − 18 = **11**
7. $21 − 9 = **$12**
8. 70 − 15 = **55**
9. 32 − 8 = **24**
10. 97 − 69 = **28**
11. 60 − 31 = **29**
12. 42 − 11 = **31**
13. 37 − 28 = **9**
14. 53 − 15 = **38**
15. $24 − $6 = **$18**
16. 85 − 44 = **41**
17. 66 − 39 = **27**
18. 41 − 14 = **27**
19. Find the difference of 50 and 18. **32**
20. Subtract 27 from 42. **15**
21. Write two numbers you could subtract from 25 with regrouping. **Possible answers: 16, 17, 18, 19, 6, 8, 7, 9**
22. Write two numbers you could subtract from 83 without regrouping. **Possible answers: 80, 81, 82, 70, 71, 72**
23. To subtract 22 from 74 do you need to regroup? Explain. **No; You can subtract the 2 in 22 from the 4 in 74.**

Name ______________________

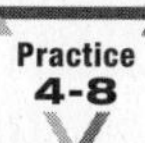

Exploring Subtracting 3-Digit Numbers

Use place-value blocks to help you subtract.

Find 236 − 141.

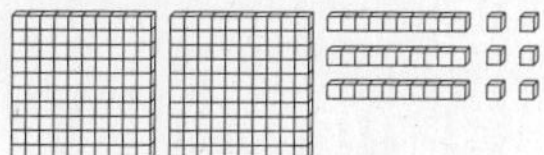

1. Do you need to regroup to subtract the ones? Explain. **No; 6 − 1 = 5**
2. Do you need to regroup to subtract the tens? Explain. **Yes; I need to regroup 1 hundred as 10 tens.**
3. Find the difference. 236 − 141 = **95** (regrouped: **1 13**)

Find each difference. You may use place-value blocks or draw a picture to help.

4. 176 − 119 = **57**
5. 218 − 54 = **164**
6. 343 − 161 = **182**
7. 135 − 72 = **63**
8. 282 − 137 = **145**
9. 329 − 258 = **71**
10. 191 − 78 = **113**
11. 245 − 195 = **50**
12. Subtract 37 from 129. **92**
13. Subtract 274 from 388. **114**
14. Suppose you had 193 baseball cards and your brother had 249. How many more does your brother have? **56**

Name ______________________

Practice 4-9

Subtracting 3-Digit Numbers

Subtract. Check each answer.

1. 342 − 138 = **204**
2. 184 − 123 = **61**
3. 569 − 298 = **271**
4. 257 − 75 = **182**
5. 85 − 29 = **56**
6. 614 − 433 = **181**
7. $232 − 225 = **$7**
8. 94 − 38 = **56**
9. 427 − 164 = **263**
10. $394 − 126 = **$268**
11. 235 − 81 = **154**
12. 522 − 332 = **190**
13. 154 − 119 = **35**
14. 244 − 51 = **193**
15. 363 − 147 = **216**
16. $878 − $56 = **$822**
17. 568 − 284 = **284**
18. 216 − 162 = **54**
19. Find the difference of 426 and 301. **125**
20. Subtract 356 from 637. **281**
21. Explain how to regroup to find 224 − 153. **You need to regroup 1 hundred for 10 tens because you cannot subtract 5 tens from 2 tens.**
22. Kim says, "To subtract 164 from 573, I began by subtracting 3 ones from 4 ones." What did she do wrong? **She must subtract 4 in the ones place from 3 in the ones place, so she must regroup tens to get 13 ones.**

Name ______________________

Practice 4-10

Subtracting with 2 Regroupings

Subtract. Check each answer.

1. 346 − 167 = 179
2. 182 − 95 = 87
3. 225 − 48 = 177
4. 814 − 526 = 288
5. 751 − 383 = 368
6. 427 − 148 = 279
7. $83 − 59 = $24
8. 520 − 451 = 69
9. 442 − 86 = 356
10. 653 − 275 = 378
11. 237 − 179 = 58
12. 866 − 77 = 789

13. 413 − 166 = 247
14. 243 − 59 = 184
15. $961 − $585 = $376
16. 92 − 36 = 56
17. 286 − 197 = 89
18. 354 − 188 = 166
19. Find the difference of 365 and 187. 178
20. Subtract 45 from 219. 174
21. Andrea subtracted 736 − 108 and found 628. She then added 736 and 108 to check her answer. Did she check her answer correctly? Explain.
    No; She should add the difference to the number she subtracted: 628 + 108 = 736.
22. To find 415 − 136, would you need to regroup hundreds? Explain.
    Yes; You need to subtract a 3 in the tens place from a 0 in the tens place, so you must regroup hundreds.

Name ______________________

Practice 4-11

Subtracting Across 0

Subtract. Check each answer.

1. 207 − 82 = 125
2. $403 − 235 = $168
3. 800 − 38 = 762
4. 520 − 359 = 161
5. 309 − 151 = 158
6. 705 − 467 = 238
7. 631 − 206 = 425
8. $104 − 59 = $45
9. 240 − 198 = 42
10. 501 − 164 = 337
11. 408 − 311 = 97
12. 202 − 28 = 174

13. 306 − 147 = 159
14. 500 − 279 = 221
15. 940 − 458 = 482
16. 409 − 45 = 364
17. 604 − 335 = 269
18. 201 − 142 = 59
19. 703 − 497 = 206
20. 506 − 249 = 257
21. What is 703 minus 216? 487
22. Subtract 127 from 400. 273
23. Antonio said, "To solve 506 − 288, I can think of 5 hundreds as 50 tens." How might this help him subtract?
    He can regroup 50 tens and 6 ones as 49 tens and 16 ones.
24. Write a number you could subtract from 202 without regrouping.
    Possible answers: 1, 2, 100, 101, 102, 200, 201, 202

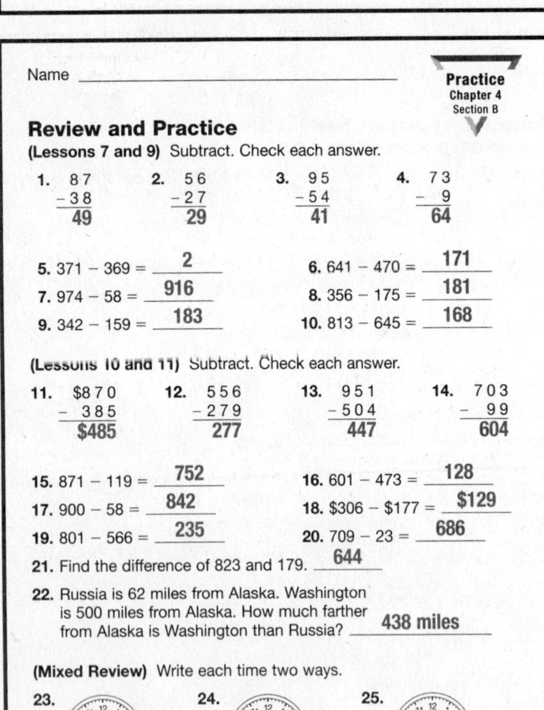

Name ______________________

Practice Chapter 4 Section B

Review and Practice

(Lessons 7 and 9) Subtract. Check each answer.

1. 87 − 38 = 49
2. 56 − 27 = 29
3. 95 − 54 = 41
4. 73 − 9 = 64
5. 371 − 369 = 2
6. 641 − 470 = 171
7. 974 − 58 = 916
8. 356 − 175 = 181
9. 342 − 159 = 183
10. 813 − 645 = 168

(Lessons 10 and 11) Subtract. Check each answer.

11. $870 − 385 = $485
12. 556 − 279 = 277
13. 951 − 504 = 447
14. 703 − 99 = 604
15. 871 − 119 = 752
16. 601 − 473 = 128
17. 900 − 58 = 842
18. $306 − $177 = $129
19. 801 − 566 = 235
20. 709 − 23 = 686
21. Find the difference of 823 and 179. 644
22. Russia is 62 miles from Alaska. Washington is 500 miles from Alaska. How much farther from Alaska is Washington than Russia? 438 miles

(Mixed Review) Write each time two ways.

23. **1:35; 35 minutes after 1**
24. **4:50; 10 minutes before 5**
25. **2:25; 25 minutes after 2**

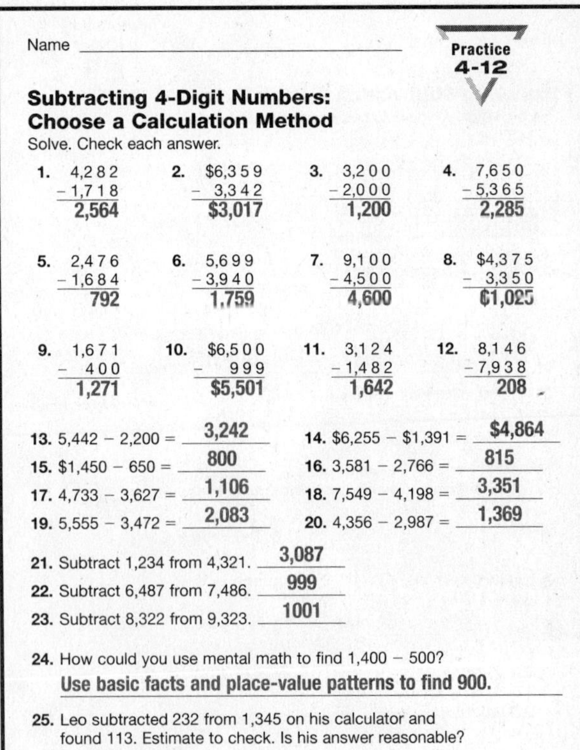

Name ______________________

Practice 4-12

Subtracting 4-Digit Numbers: Choose a Calculation Method

Solve. Check each answer.

1. 4,282 − 1,718 = 2,564
2. $6,359 − 3,342 = $3,017
3. 3,200 − 2,000 = 1,200
4. 7,650 − 5,365 = 2,285
5. 2,476 − 1,684 = 792
6. 5,699 − 3,940 = 1,759
7. 9,100 − 4,500 = 4,600
8. $4,375 − 3,350 = $1,025
9. 1,671 − 400 = 1,271
10. $6,500 − 999 = $5,501
11. 3,124 − 1,482 = 1,642
12. 8,146 − 7,938 = 208

13. 5,442 − 2,200 = 3,242
14. $6,255 − $1,391 = $4,864
15. $1,450 − 650 = 800
16. 3,581 − 2,766 = 815
17. 4,733 − 3,627 = 1,106
18. 7,549 − 4,198 = 3,351
19. 5,555 − 3,472 = 2,083
20. 4,356 − 2,987 = 1,369
21. Subtract 1,234 from 4,321. 3,087
22. Subtract 6,487 from 7,486. 999
23. Subtract 8,322 from 9,323. 1001
24. How could you use mental math to find 1,400 − 500?
    Use basic facts and place-value patterns to find 900.
25. Leo subtracted 232 from 1,345 on his calculator and found 113. Estimate to check. Is his answer reasonable?
    No; His answer should be close to 1,100.

Name ______________________

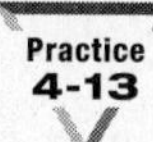

Practice 4-13

Analyze Word Problems: Multiple-Step Problems

Solve each problem.

Movie Admission Prices	
Before 6 P.M.	
Children under 12	$2
Adults	$5
After 6 P.M.	
Children under 12	$3
Adults	$8

1. Mr. and Mrs. Riley want to take their 2 children to the movies. Their children are 5 and 9 years old.
   a. How much will it cost for them to see a movie before 6:00 P.M.? **$14**
   b. How much more will it cost for them to see a movie after 6:00 P.M.? **$8 more**
2. Mr. Ramirez told his 9-year old son that he could have $20 to take his friends to the movies. He wants to invite 4 friends from his class and his 14-year-old brother. How much more money does he need to take everyone to see a movie at 7:00 P.M.? **$3 more**
3. A scout troop leader is taking 14 scouts to the movies. Three scouts canceled and 5 more decided to go. How many scouts are going to the movies ? **16 scouts**
4. The manager sold 55 adult tickets and 20 children's tickets for an afternoon movie. How many more adult tickets were sold than children's tickets? **35 more**

Name ______________________

Practice 4-14

Mental Math

Write what number you would add to each in order to subtract mentally. Subtract.

1. 34 − 19 = **15** I added **1**.
2. 63 − 28 = **35** I added **2**.
3. 62 − 36 = **26** I added **4**.
4. 188 − 9 = **179** I added **1**.
5. 154 − 37 = **117** I added **3**.
6. 156 − 39 = **117** I added **1**.
7. 87 − 28 = **59** I added **2**.
8. 71 − 37 = **34** I added **3**.
9. 92 − 45 = **47** I added **5**.
10. 109 − 69 = **40** I added **1**.
11. 168 − 49 = **119** I added **1**.
12. 144 − 67 = **77** I added **3**.
13. What could you add to each number to find 730 − 260? Explain.
    Possible answer: Add 40 because 770 − 300 can be subtracted mentally.
14. Would you add on to help you find 58 − 20? Explain.
    Possible answer: No; Because 58 − 20 can be subtracted without regrouping.

Name ______________________

Practice 4-15

Subtracting Money

Subtract.

1. $5.86 − 2.55 = **$3.31**
2. $20.00 − 7.05 = **$12.95**
3. $7.00 − 5.76 = **$1.24**
4. $6.25 − 2.98 = **$3.27**
5. $10.00 − 5.87 = **$4.13**
6. $8.75 − 4.35 = **$4.40**
7. $8.28 − 4.99 = **$3.29**
8. $15.00 − 3.89 = **$11.11**
9. $8.98 − 2.79 = **$6.19**
10. $17.00 − 6.72 = **$10.28**
11. $6.87 − 1.98 = **$4.89**
12. $5.24 − 4.25 = **$0.99**
13. $6.50 − $2.17 = **$4.33**
14. $11.50 − $6.75 = **$4.75**
15. $13.85 − $5.98 = **$7.87**
16. $20.00 − $8.88 = **$11.12**
17. $9.89 − $3.57 = **$6.32**
18. $15.00 − $7.99 = **$7.01**
19. Rachel bought a puzzle for $4.89. She gave the clerk $10.00. How much change did she receive? **$5.11**
20. Diego bought a toy and paid with $5.00. He received $3.29 in change. How much did the toy cost? **$1.71**
21. Sophie is buying toothpaste. Superclean costs $4.89 and Sparkles cost $3.24. How much will Sophie save if she buys Sparkles? **$1.65**
22. Sophie pays for Sparkles toothpaste with a $5 bill. How much change will she receive? **$1.76**

Name ______________________

Practice 4-16

Analyze Strategies: Use Objects

Use objects to help solve each problem.

1. Kendra is going to a hockey game at the arena. She climbs 2 steps at a time to get to the door faster. Her little brother climbs 1 step at a time.
   a. When Kendra has climbed 6 steps, how many steps has her brother taken? **3 steps**
   b. When Kendra has climbed 12 steps, how many steps has her brother taken? **6 steps**
2. Keith is waiting in line to buy snacks. There are 8 people ahead of him. Two people leave the line without buying anything. Four people buy their snacks and go to their seats. How many people are ahead of him now? **2 people**
3. Doug counts the pennies in his piggy bank. His sister has two pennies for every one penny Doug has. Doug has 9 pennies. How many pennies does his sister have? **18 pennies**
4. Sheila lives 3 times as far from the school as Julia. If it takes Julia 5 minutes to walk to school, how long will it take Sheila? **15 minutes**
5. From school, Kathy walks 2 blocks, then 1 block to mail a letter. She walks on 4 more blocks toward home. How many blocks does she walk in all? **7 blocks**

Use any strategy to help you solve this problem.

6. Shandra rode her bike 1 mile to school. It took her 15 minutes. How long should it take Shandra to ride her bike 3 miles to the bookstore? **45 minutes**

Name ______________________

Practice Chapter 4 Section C

Review and Practice

(Lesson 12) Solve. Check each answer.

1. 5,738 − 2,667 = **3,071**
2. 6,300 − 4,000 = **2,300**
3. 7,856 − 2,133 = **5,723**
4. 5,000 − 4,025 = **975**

(Lesson 13) Solve.

5. It cost $3 for a child's ticket and $5 for an adult's ticket at the museum. Peter is going to the museum with his two sisters, Uncle Joe, and his mother. Peter and his 2 sisters can each get child's tickets. How much will it cost? **$19**

(Lesson 14) Write what number you would add to each in order to subtract mentally. Subtract.

6. 64 − 45 = **19** Add: **5**
7. 372 − 68 = **304** Add: **2**
8. 134 − 29 = **105** Add: **1**

(Lesson 15) Subtract.

9. $4.56 − 1.38 = **$3.18**
10. $3.89 − 2.99 = **$0.90**
11. $9.00 − 3.46 = **$5.54**
12. $15.89 − 9.69 = **$6.20**

(Lesson 16) Use objects or any strategy to solve.

13. Tippy woke up at 7:00 A.M. She played for 1 hour. Then she napped. She woke up to play for another hour. Then she slept until Maggie came home from school at 3:00 P.M. How many hours did Tippy sleep? **6 hours**

(Mixed Review) Write each time.

14. Elizabeth did her homework at 4:30 P.M. and ate dinner 1 hour and 20 minutes later. What time did she eat? **5:50 P.M.**
15. Jerome got dressed for school at 7:15 A.M. Eight and a half hours later he returned home. What time was it when Jerome got home? **3:45 P.M.**

Name ______________________

Practice Chapters 1–4

Cumulative Review

(Chapter 2 Lesson 13)

1. Brooke starts school at 8:10 A.M. School lets out at 3:25 P.M. How long is Brooke's school day? **C**

   A. 8 hours C. 7 hours, 15 minutes
   B. 7 hours, 35 minutes D. 5 hours, 15 minutes

(Chapter 3 Lesson 14)

2. Clark bought a sandwich for a total of $2.35. He gave the sales person a $5 bill. What is the amount of change he should receive? **B**

   A. $3, 6 dimes, and 1 nickel
   B. $2, 6 dimes, and 1 nickel
   C. $2, 5 dimes, and 5 pennies

(Chapter 3 Lesson 15)

3. $2.19 + 1.97 = **$4.16**
4. $3.05 + 1.50 = **$4.55**
5. $6.89 + 3.27 = **$10.16**
6. Find the sum of $8.78 and $3.29. **$12.07**
7. What is the sum of $12.15 and $8.29? **C**

   A. $10.44 B. $20.14 C. $20.44 D. not here

(Chapter 4 Lessons 7–9)

Find each difference.

8. 56 − 12 = **44**
9. 27 − 9 = **18**
10. 342 − 116 = **226**
11. 2,892 − 1,451 = **1,441**
12. Find the difference of 517 and 230. **287**
13. Subtract 338 from 522. **184**

Name ______________________

Practice 5-1

Exploring Equal Groups

Complete.

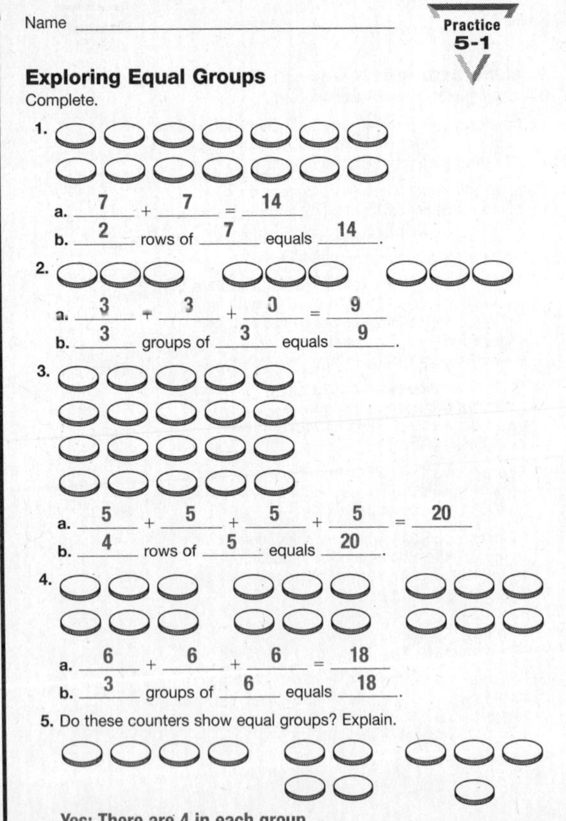

1. a. **7** + **7** = **14**
   b. **2** rows of **7** equals **14**.
2. a. **3** + **3** + **3** = **9**
   b. **3** groups of **3** equals **9**.
3. a. **5** + **5** + **5** + **5** = **20**
   b. **4** rows of **5** equals **20**.
4. a. **6** + **6** + **6** = **18**
   b. **3** groups of **6** equals **18**.
5. Do these counters show equal groups? Explain.

   Yes; There are 4 in each group.

Name ______________________

Practice 5-2

Writing Multiplication Sentences

Complete each number sentence.

1. 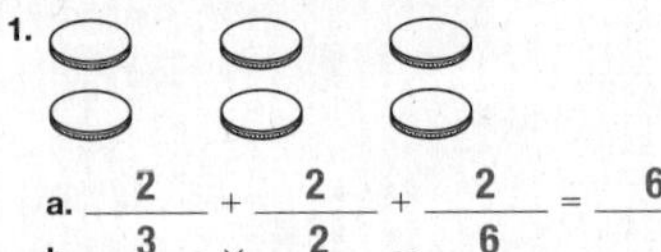

   a. **2** + **2** + **2** = **6**
   b. **3** × **2** = **6**
2. 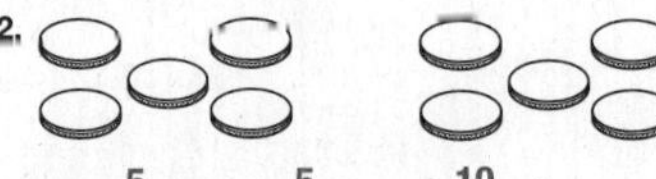

   a. **5** + **5** = **10**
   b. **2** × **5** = **10**
3. 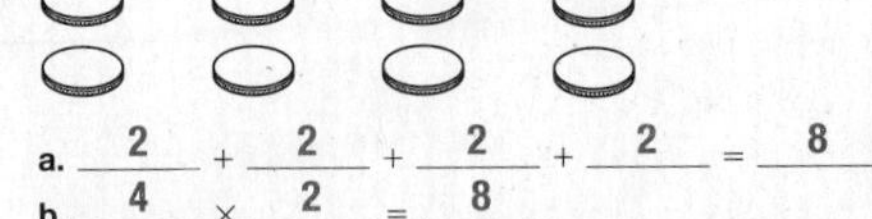

   a. **2** + **2** + **2** + **2** = **8**
   b. **4** × **2** = **8**
4. Draw a picture that shows 3 × 4. Find the product.

   Drawings should show 3 groups of 4 objects or 3 rows of 4 objects; 12
5. Can you multiply to find the total of 9 + 9 + 9? Explain.

   Yes; There are 3 equal groups of 9.
6. Can you multiply to find the total of 3 + 4 + 5? Explain.

   No; The groups are not equal.

Name ______________________

Practice 5-3

Exploring Multiplication Stories

1. Is this a multiplication story? Explain.

   Sam makes shirts. He sold 3 shirts one day, and 4 the next day. How many shirts did Sam sell?

   No, the groups are not equal. (It is an addition story.)

Write a multiplication story for **2–6**.
You may use counters to solve.

2. 2×5
   Look for 2 groups of 5; 10
3. 3×6
   Look for 3 groups of 6; 18
4. 4×4
   Look for 4 groups of 4; 16
5. 6×2
   Look for 6 groups of 2; 12
6. 6×4
   Look for 6 groups of 4; 24

Solve.

7. There are 6 cars in the parking lot. Each car has 4 tires. How many tires are there?
   24 tires

Name ______________________

Practice Chapter 5 Section A

Review and Practice

Vocabulary Match each with its definition.

c	1. product	a. one of the numbers multiplied
a	2. factor	b. an arrangement of rows and columns
b	3. array	c. the number obtained by multiplying numbers

(Lessons 1 and 2) Complete.

4. a. 3 + 3 + 3 + 3 = 12
   b. 4 groups of 3 equals 12.
   c. $4 \times 3 = 12$

5. a. 6 + 6 = 12
   b. 2 rows of 6 equals 12.
   c. $2 \times 6 = 12$

6. Idaho has 2 representatives in the House of Representatives. Minnesota has 4 times as many. How many representatives does Minnesota have?
   8 representatives

7. Is the product of 7×3 the same as the product of 3×7? Explain.
   Yes; The product of 2 numbers is the same no matter the order in which you multiply them.

(Lesson 3) Write a multiplication story for each.
You may use counters to solve.

8. $4 \times 5 =$ **20**
   Look for 4 groups of 5 or 5 groups of 4.
9. $3 \times 7 =$ **21**
   Look for 3 groups of 7 or 7 groups of 3.

(Mixed Review) Add or subtract.

10. 23 + 17 = **40** 11. 45 − 20 = **25** 12. 58 + 26 = **84**

Name ______________________

Practice 5-4

2 as a Factor

Find each product.

1. $3 \times 2 =$ **6**
2. $5 \times 2 =$ **10**
3. $2 \times 1 =$ **2**
4. $2 \times 10 =$ **20**
5. $2 \times 9 =$ **18**
6. $8 \times 2 =$ **16**
7. $4 \times 2 =$ **8**
8. $6 \times 2 =$ **12**
9. $2 \times 2 =$ **4**
10. $2 \times 7 =$ **14**

11. $4 \times 2 =$ **8**
12. $2 \times 5 =$ **10**
13. $6 \times 2 =$ **12**
14. $8 \times 2 =$ **16**
15. $9 \times 2 =$ **18**
16. $10 \times 2 =$ **20**
17. $7 \times 2 =$ **14**
18. $2 \times 1 =$ **2**
19. $2 \times 3 =$ **6**
20. $10 \times 2 =$ **20**

21. Find the product of 5 and 2. **10**
22. Find the product of 2 and 8. **16**
23. Find the product of 10 and 2. **20**
24. Find the product of 6 and 2. **12**
25. Find the product of 7 and 2. **14**
26. Find the product of 3 and 2. **6**
27. Is the product of 5 and 2 the same as the sum of 5 and 2? Explain.
    No; The sum of 5 and 2 is 7 and the product of 5 and 2 is 10.
28. Draw a picture to show that 7×2 is the same as 2×7.
    Drawings should show 2 groups/rows of 7 objects and 7 groups/rows of 2 objects.

Name ______________________

Practice 5-5

5 as a Factor

Find each product.

1. $2 \times 5 =$ **10**
2. $5 \times 5 =$ **25**
3. $5 \times 1 =$ **5**
4. $5 \times 8 =$ **40**
5. $2 \times 9 =$ **18**
6. $3 \times 5 =$ **15**
7. $5 \times 4 =$ **20**
8. $5 \times 6 =$ **30**
9. $5 \times 7 =$ **35**
10. $2 \times 8 =$ **16**

11. $4 \times 5 =$ **20**
12. $5 \times 5 =$ **25**
13. $6 \times 2 =$ **12**
14. $5 \times 8 =$ **40**
15. $9 \times 5 =$ **45**
16. $8 \times 2 =$ **16**
17. $7 \times 2 =$ **14**
18. $2 \times 1 =$ **2**
19. $2 \times 3 =$ **6**
20. $8 \times 5 =$ **40**
21. $5 \times 2 =$ **10**
22. $7 \times 5 =$ **35**
23. $8 \times 5 =$ **40**
24. $6 \times 5 =$ **30**
25. $3 \times 5 =$ **15**

26. Find the product of 5 and 7. **35**
27. Multiply 8 by 5. **40**
28. If you know the product of 8 and 5, how can you use it to find 9×5?
    $8 \times 5 = 40$, $40 + 5 = 45$, so $9 \times 5 = 45$
29. Is 7×5 greater or less than 8×5? Explain.
    Less than; 7 groups of 5 is less than 8 groups of 5.

Name ______________________

Practice 5-6

Exploring Patterns on a Hundred Chart: 2s and 5s

Finish these sentences.

1. a. Multiples of 2 always end in **0, 2, 4, 6 or 8**.
   b. Write some multiplication sentences to show the pattern:
   Possible answer: 2 × 2 = 4; 2 × 4 = 8
2. a. Multiples of 5 always end in **0 or 5**.
   b. Write some multiplication sentences to show the pattern:
   Possible answer: 5 × 1 = 5; 5 × 2 = 10

Find each product.

3. 8 × 2 = **16** 4. 8 × 5 = **40** 5. 2 × 2 = **4**
6. 7 × 5 = **35** 7. 2 × 7 = **14** 8. 5 × 4 = **20**
9. 6 × 5 = **30** 10. 2 × 9 = **18** 11. 2 × 10 = **20**

12. 4 × 2 = **8** 13. 6 × 2 = **12** 14. 9 × 5 = **45** 15. 2 × 1 = **2**

16. 5 × 6 = **30** 17. 3 × 2 = **6** 18. 5 × 1 = **5** 19. 2 × 5 = **10**

20. Find the product of 5 and 3. **15**
21. Multiply 6 by 2. **12**
22. What numbers are shaded twice when you shade multiples of 2s and multiples of 5s on a hundred chart?
    10, 20, 30, 40, 50, 60, 70, 80, 90, 100

Use with pages 216–217. 81

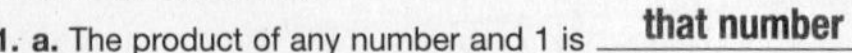

Name ______________________

Practice 5-7

Exploring 0 and 1 as Factors

Finish these sentences.

1. a. The product of any number and 1 is **that number**.
   b. Write a multiplication sentence to show this.
   Possible answer: 100 × 1 = 100
2. a. The product of any number and 0 is **0**.
   b. Write a multiplication sentence to show this.
   Possible answer: 100 × 0 = 0

Find each product.

3. 8 × 0 = **0** 4. 8 × 1 = **8** 5. 0 × 2 = **0**
6. 1 × 5 = **5** 7. 2 × 1 = **2** 8. 5 × 4 = **20**
9. 5 × 5 = **25** 10. 2 × 9 = **18**

11. 4 × 2 = **8** 12. 6 × 1 = **6** 13. 9 × 0 = **0** 14. 2 × 1 = **2**

15. 1 × 6 = **6** 16. 3 × 2 = **6** 17. 5 × 1 = **5** 18. 1 × 5 = **5**

19. 0 × 3 = **0** 20. 1 × 3 = **3** 21. 0 × 1 = **0** 22. 0 × 0 = **0**

23. Find the product of 1 and 1. **1**
24. Multiply 0 by 1. **0**

Complete. Write × or +.

25. 8 **+** 1 = 9 26. 9 **×** 1 = 9 27. 0 **+** 5 = 5
28. 2 **×** 10 = 20 29. 2 **×** 0 = 0 30. 5 **+** 5 = 10

82 Use with pages 218–219.

Name ______________________

Practice 5-8

9 as a Factor

Find each product.

1. 9 × 8 = **72** 2. 4 × 9 = **36** 3. 9 × 7 = **63**
4. 9 × 6 = **54** 5. 5 × 9 = **45** 6. 0 × 5 = **0**
7. 9 × 3 = **27** 8. 3 × 5 = **15** 9. 2 × 6 = **12**

10. 9 × 9 = **81** 11. 8 × 5 = **40** 12. 2 × 7 = **14** 13. 9 × 8 = **72**

14. 5 × 4 = **20** 15. 1 × 9 = **9** 16. 7 × 5 = **35** 17. 9 × 0 = **0**

18. Find the product of 8 and 9. **72**
19. Multiply 9 by 2. **18**
20. If you forget the product of 9 and 9, what can you do to figure it out?
    Possible answer: Find the product of 9 and 5 then add 4 more 9s.
21. Is 6 × 9 the same as 9 × 7? Explain.
    No; 6 × 9 = 54, 9 × 7 = 63
22. Is 5 × 9 the same as 6 × 9? Explain.
    No; 5 × 9 = 45, 6 × 9 = 54
23. Write a number sentence that shows the same product as the product of 9 and 2.
    Possible answers: 2 × 9 = 18, 6 × 3 = 18, 3 × 6 = 18

Use with pages 220–221. 83

Name ______________________

Practice 5-9

Analyze Word Problems: Too Much or Too Little Information

Decide if the problem has too much or too little information. Then solve. If there is not enough information, tell what information is needed.

1. It takes about 3 months to grow tomatoes. The vines should be planted about 2 feet apart and get a lot of sun. If Taylor wants to plant 6 tomato vines in a row, how long should the row be?
   Too much or too little information? **Too much**
   How do you solve it? **Multiply, 6 × 2 = 12, 12 feet long**
2. Each tomato vine can grow about 25 tomatoes. Taylor wants to make 3 gallons of spaghetti sauce with his tomatoes. Will 6 vines be enough?
   Too much or too little information? **Too little**
   How do you solve it? **Need to know how many tomatoes are needed to make 1 gallon of sauce**
3. Kathryn is going to knit a sweater that is red and yellow. She needs 6 skeins of red yarn. If each skein is 100 meters long, how many meters of yarn will she need all together?
   Too much or too little information? **Too little**
   How do you solve it? **Need to know how much yellow yarn Kathryn needs**
4. A piano keyboard has a total of 88 black and white keys. 36 of these are black. It takes 13 keys to play an octave. How many keys are white?
   Too much or too little information? **Too much**
   How do you solve it? **Subtract; 88 − 36 = 52; 52 white keys**

84 Use with pages 224–225.

Name ______________________

Practice 5-10

Analyze Strategies: Draw a Picture

Draw a picture to help you solve.

1. How many bricks will Julia need to build a garden wall 9 bricks long and 8 bricks high? **72**

Drawings should show 9 × 8 = 72.

2. Julia wants to build another garden wall, 10 bricks long and 3 bricks high. Can she build it with red and white bricks, so that no two bricks of the same color are next to each other? **Yes**

Drawings should show alternating red and white bricks.

Draw a picture or use any strategy to solve the problems.

3. Ray is setting the table for a birthday dinner. He needs to set 12 places at a round table. He has 3 different kinds of plates: white plates; blue plates; and gold plates. How can he set the table so that no two of the same kind of plates are next to each other? **Possible answer: White, blue, gold, white, blue, gold, and so on**

4. Ray has 13 forks, 15 spoons, and 11 dinner knives. If 12 people are coming to dinner does he have enough silverware so that each person can have a fork, spoon and dinner knife? **No, he needs 1 more dinner knife.**

Name ______________________

Practice Chapter 5 Section B

Review and Practice

(Lessons 4–8) Find each product.

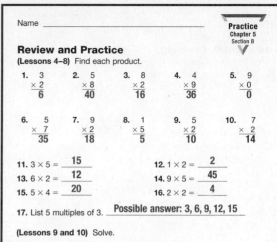

1. 3 × 2 = **6**
2. 5 × 8 = **40**
3. 8 × 2 = **16**
4. 4 × 9 = **36**
5. 9 × 0 = **0**
6. 5 × 7 = **35**
7. 9 × 2 = **18**
8. 1 × 5 = **5**
9. 5 × 2 = **10**
10. 7 × 2 = **14**

11. 3 × 5 = **15**
12. 1 × 2 = **2**
13. 6 × 2 = **12**
14. 9 × 5 = **45**
15. 5 × 4 = **20**
16. 2 × 2 = **4**

17. List 5 multiples of 3. **Possible answer: 3, 6, 9, 12, 15**

(Lessons 9 and 10) Solve.

18. Harold gave each of his nine friends three stickers. Four of the stickers were red. How many stickers did he give away? **27 stickers**

19. Pamela has 2 boxes of crayons. Each box has 48 crayons in it. 8 of the crayons are sharpened. How many crayons does she have? **96**

20. Michele and 2 friends each live on a different floor of a three-story apartment building. Shaun lives above Barb and below Michele. Who lives on the first floor? **Barb**

(Mixed Review) Continue each pattern.

21. 7, 14, 21, 28, **35**, **42**, **49**
22. 18, 27, 36, 45, **54**, **63**, **72**
23. 10, 12, 14, 16, **18**, **20**, **22**

Name ______________________

Cumulative Review

(Chapter 1, Lesson 6) Solve.

1. Sue Ann has $3.50 in quarters and $1.15 in nickels. How many quarters does she have? How many nickels? How much money does she have in all? **14; 23; $4.65**

(Chapter 2, Lesson 7) Write each set of numbers in order from greatest to least.

2. 470, 704, 740, 407 **740, 704, 470, 407**
3. 400,100; 410,000; 401,700; 407,100 **410,000; 407,100; 401,700; 400,100**

(Chapter 3, Lesson 7) Find each sum.

4. 326 + 719 = **1,045**
5. 412 + 811 = **1,223**
6. 319 + 324 = **643**
7. 828 + 124 = **952**

(Chapter 4, Lesson 10) Find each difference.

8. 314 − 126 = **188**
9. 427 − 189 = **238**
10. 516 − 427 = **89**
11. 644 − 356 = **288**

12. 818 − 529 = **289**
13. 745 − 266 = **479**

(Chapter 5, Lessons 4 and 5) Find each product.

14. 3 × 5 = **15**
15. 4 × 2 = **8**
16. 5 × 8 = **40**
17. 2 × 9 = **18**
18. 6 × 5 = **30**

19. 7 × 5 = **35**
20. 2 × 6 = **12**
21. 7 × 2 = **14**

Name ______________________

Practice 6-1

3 as a Factor: Using Known Facts

Find each product.

1. 8 × 3 = **24**
2. 3 × 1 = **3**
3. 6 × 3 = **18**
4. 7 × 3 = **21**
5. 3 × 2 = **6**
6. 3 × 3 = **9**
7. 4 × 3 = **12**
8. 9 × 3 = **27**
9. 3 × 8 = **24**
10. 5 × 3 = **15**

11. 3 × 2 **6**
12. 6 × 3 **18**
13. 3 × 5 **15**
14. 3 × 9 **27**
15. 8 × 3 **24**
16. 1 × 3 **3**
17. 7 × 3 **21**
18. 4 × 3 **12**

19. What is the product of 9 and 3? **27**
20. What is the product of 6 and 3? **18**
21. Multiply 5 by 3. **15**
22. Multiply 3 by 4. **12**

23. If you know the product of 2 × 6, how can you find the product of 3 × 6? What is it? **Add 6 to the product of 2 × 6; 18**

24. Tim says, "To find 3 × 8, I can find 2 × 8 and add one more group of 3." What's wrong? Explain. **He should add one more group of 8 to get 24.**

Name ______________________

Practice 6-2

4 as a Factor: Doubling

Find each product.

1. $\begin{array}{r} 4 \\ \times 5 \\ \hline 20 \end{array}$ 2. $\begin{array}{r} 6 \\ \times 4 \\ \hline 24 \end{array}$ 3. $\begin{array}{r} 9 \\ \times 4 \\ \hline 36 \end{array}$ 4. $\begin{array}{r} 4 \\ \times 3 \\ \hline 12 \end{array}$ 5. $\begin{array}{r} 1 \\ \times 4 \\ \hline 4 \end{array}$

6. $\begin{array}{r} 8 \\ \times 2 \\ \hline 16 \end{array}$ 7. $\begin{array}{r} 4 \\ \times 8 \\ \hline 32 \end{array}$ 8. $\begin{array}{r} 4 \\ \times 4 \\ \hline 16 \end{array}$ 9. $\begin{array}{r} 2 \\ \times 4 \\ \hline 8 \end{array}$ 10. $\begin{array}{r} 4 \\ \times 7 \\ \hline 28 \end{array}$

11. 5×4 20
12. 4×9 36
13. 4×2 8
14. 4×4 16
15. 1×4 4
16. 6×4 24
17. 3×4 12
18. 7×4 28
19. Multiply 8 by 4. 32
20. Multiply 4 by 7. 28
21. What is the product of 4 and 9? 36
22. What is the product of 4 and 5? 20
23. Draw arrays to show that 4×5 is the same as 5×4.
Arrays should show 4 groups of 5 and 5 groups of 4.
24. Could you use doubling to multiply 7×3? Explain.
No; Neither 7 nor 3 is a multiple of 2.

Name ______________________

Practice 6-3

6 as a Factor: Using Known Facts

Find each product.

1. $\begin{array}{r} 0 \\ \times 6 \\ \hline 0 \end{array}$ 2. $\begin{array}{r} 3 \\ \times 6 \\ \hline 18 \end{array}$ 3. $\begin{array}{r} 6 \\ \times 5 \\ \hline 30 \end{array}$ 4. $\begin{array}{r} 9 \\ \times 6 \\ \hline 54 \end{array}$ 5. $\begin{array}{r} 6 \\ \times 6 \\ \hline 36 \end{array}$

6. $\begin{array}{r} 6 \\ \times 2 \\ \hline 12 \end{array}$ 7. $\begin{array}{r} 1 \\ \times 6 \\ \hline 6 \end{array}$ 8. $\begin{array}{r} 7 \\ \times 6 \\ \hline 42 \end{array}$ 9. $\begin{array}{r} 6 \\ \times 4 \\ \hline 24 \end{array}$ 10. $\begin{array}{r} 6 \\ \times 8 \\ \hline 48 \end{array}$

11. 6×4 24
12. 2×6 12
13. 9×6 54
14. 6×0 0
15. 5×6 30
16. 6×8 48
17. 6×6 36
18. 3×6 18
19. Find the product of 6 and 7. 42
20. What is 9 multiplied by 6? 54
21. Find the product of 6 and 6. 36
22. What is 3 multiplied by 6? 18
23. Which is greater, 6×9 or 9×5? How can you tell without multiplying?
6×9 is greater because $6 > 5$.
24. Can you think of a way to use doubling to multiply 6×7? Explain.
Find 3×7 and double it.

Name ______________________

Practice 6-4

7 and 8 as Factors

Find each product.

1. $\begin{array}{r} 7 \\ \times 8 \\ \hline 56 \end{array}$ 2. $\begin{array}{r} 8 \\ \times 9 \\ \hline 72 \end{array}$ 3. $\begin{array}{r} 9 \\ \times 7 \\ \hline 63 \end{array}$ 4. $\begin{array}{r} 6 \\ \times 8 \\ \hline 48 \end{array}$ 5. $\begin{array}{r} 4 \\ \times 8 \\ \hline 32 \end{array}$

6. $\begin{array}{r} 3 \\ \times 7 \\ \hline 21 \end{array}$ 7. $\begin{array}{r} 7 \\ \times 7 \\ \hline 49 \end{array}$ 8. $\begin{array}{r} 5 \\ \times 8 \\ \hline 40 \end{array}$ 9. $\begin{array}{r} 8 \\ \times 8 \\ \hline 64 \end{array}$ 10. $\begin{array}{r} 4 \\ \times 7 \\ \hline 28 \end{array}$

11. 6×7 42
12. 8×7 56
13. 0×7 0
14. 8×2 16
15. 8×0 0
16. 7×7 49
17. 2×7 14
18. 9×7 63
19. Find the product of 8 and 9. 72
20. Find the product of 7 and 6. 42
21. Find the product of 7 and 8. 56
22. Find the product of 8 and 5. 40
23. How could you find the product of 7×8 if you know the product of 5×8?
Add 2 groups of 8.
24. How can you tell that 7×6 is greater than 6×5 without multiplying?
$7 > 5$

Name ______________________

Practice 6-5

Decision Making

Annie is a party planner. She must plan the menu for 3 dinners; one for 4 people, one for 7 people, and one for 8 people. She needs to make a table to find out how many of each item will be needed for each dinner.

Complete the table.

Number per Serving	4-Person Dinner	7-Person Dinner	8-Person Dinner
6 snack crackers	24	42	48
4 potatoes	16	28	32
2 chicken pieces	8	14	16
7 baby carrots	28	49	56
3 broccoli spears	12	21	24
8 parsley sprigs	32	56	64
7 strawberries	28	49	56
1 mint	4	7	8

1. How many baby carrots will Annie need for the 8-person dinner? 56
2. How many chicken pieces will she need for the 7-person dinner? 14
3. Annie decides she wants to serve cream with the strawberries. She needs 3 spoonfuls for each person. How many spoonfuls does she need for:
   a. the 4-person dinner? **12 spoonfuls**
   b. the 7-person dinner? **21 spoonfuls**
   c. the 8-person dinner? **24 spoonfuls**
4. One of the people at the 7-person dinner can't go. How many chicken pieces will Annie need for that dinner now? 12
5. An extra person will be going to the 4-person dinner. How many strawberries will Annie need for that dinner now? 35

Name ______________________

Practice
Chapter 6
Section A

Review and Practice

(Lesson 1) Find each product.

1. 5 × 3 = **15**
2. 3 × 2 = **6**
3. 6 × 3 = **18**
4. 7 × 3 = **21**
5. Leo wants to make 3 apple pies. The recipe calls for 4 apples per pie. How many apples will he need? **12 apples**

(Lesson 2) Find each product.

6. 5 × 4 = **20**
7. 6 × 4 = **24**
8. 4 × 4 = **16**
9. 4 × 9 = **36**
10. Joel bought 4 boxes of note pads. Each box contained 8 note pads. How many notepads did Joel buy? **32 notepads**

(Lesson 3) Find each product.

11. 9 × 6 = **54**
12. 3 × 6 = **18**
13. 6 × 8 = **48**
14. 6 × 0 = **0**
15. Each actor receives 6 free passes to each show. There are 7 shows. How many free passes does each actor receive? **42 free passes**

(Lesson 4) Find each product.

16. 7 × 6 = **42**
17. 8 × 3 = **24**
18. 9 × 8 = **72**
19. 8 × 7 = **56**
20. 7 × 7 = **49**
21. 8 × 8 = **64**

(Mixed Review) Find each sum or difference.

22. 612 + 839 = **1,451**
23. 948 − 479 = **469**
24. 177 − 91 = **86**
25. 608 + 55 = **663**

Name ______________________

Practice 6-6

Exploring Patterns on a Hundred Chart: 3s and 6s

1	2	3	4	5	6	7	8	9	10
11	12	13	14	15	16	17	18	19	20
21	22	23	24	25	26	27	28	29	30
31	32	33	34	35	36	37	38	39	40
41	42	43	44	45	46	47	48	49	50
51	52	53	54	55	56	57	58	59	60

1	2	3	4	5	6	7	8	9	10
11	12	13	14	15	16	17	18	19	20
21	22	23	24	25	26	27	28	29	30
31	32	33	34	35	36	37	38	39	40
41	42	43	44	45	46	47	48	49	50
51	52	53	54	55	56	57	58	59	60

1. What is the sum of the digits in each multiple of 3?
   3, 6, 9 or another multiple of 3
2. How can you tell if a number is a multiple of 6?
   The digits add up to a multiple of 3, and the number is even.

Find each missing number. You may use a hundred chart to help.

3. 3 × **6** = 18
4. **3** × 3 = 9
5. 6 × **6** = 36
6. **6** × 9 = 54
7. **6** × 8 = 48
8. 3 × **6** = 18

Write true or false. If the answer is false, explain why.

9. 34 is a multiple of 3.
   False; The digits add up to 7, which is not a multiple of 3.
10. 24 is a multiple of 3 and 6.
    True
11. 16 is not a multiple of 6 or 3.
    True

Name ______________________

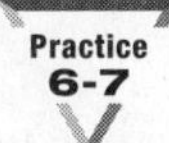

Practice 6-7

Exploring Patterns on a Fact Table

Look for patterns in multiples of greater numbers.

1. What is the pattern for multiples of 10?
   Zero is always in the ones place.
2. What is the pattern for multiples of 11?
   The ones digit increases by 1 each time.
3. What is the pattern for multiples of 12?
   The ones digit increases by 2 each time.

Find each product.

4. 9 × 9 **81**
5. 7 × 8 **56**
6. 6 × 12 **72**
7. 10 × 11 **110**
8. 8 × 5 **40**
9. 7 × 9 **63**
10. 12 × 7 **84**
11. 11 × 11 **121**
12. 12 × 6 **72**
13. 7 × 10 **70**
14. 12 × 9 **108**
15. 11 × 3 **33**

Continue each pattern.

16. 33, 44, 55, **66**, **77**, **88**
17. 72, 60, 48, **36**, **24**, **12**
18. 0, 20, 40, **60**, **80**, **100**
19. 132, 110, 88, **66**, **44**, **22**
20. 48, 60, 72, **84**, **96**, **108**

Name ______________________

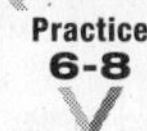

Practice 6-8

Multiplying with 3 Factors

Find each product.

1. (4 × 3) × 2 **24**
2. 1 × (6 × 8) **48**
3. 9 × 1 × 7 **63**
4. 5 × (3 × 3) **45**
5. 2 × 1 × 5 **10**
6. (0 × 1) × 8 **0**
7. 2 × 0 × 9 **0**
8. 3 × (2 × 5) **30**
9. 6 × (6 × 1) **36**
10. (3 × 2) × 7 **42**
11. 1 × 7 × 4 **28**
12. (2 × 0) × 8 **0**
13. (3 × 6) × 0 **0**
14. (2 × 12) × 1 **24**
15. 6 × 3 × 3 **54**
16. Find the product of 1, 7, and 6. **42**
17. Find the product of 9, 4, and 0. **0**
18. Does 6 × 4 have the same product as 3 × 4 × 2? Explain.
    Yes; 3 × 2 = 6 so multiplying 3 × 4 × 2 is the same as multiplying 6 × 4.
19. If you know the product of 5 × 2 × 3, do you also know the product of 3 × 2 × 5? Explain.
    Yes; The three factors have the same product no matter the order you multiply them.

Name ______________________

Practice 6-9

Compare Strategies: Look for a Pattern and Draw a Picture

Use any strategy to solve each problem.

1. Suppose you are planning a picnic for 34 people. You must buy paper plates in packages of 8. How many packages of paper plates will you need? **5 packages**
2. One package of rolls has enough rolls for 8 burgers. How many packages of rolls do you need for 25 burgers? **4 packages**
3. Your softball team has a party. Everyone uses 4 napkins. If there are 13 people at the party, how many napkins were used? **52 napkins**
4. One loaf of bread makes 10 sandwiches. How many loaves do you need to make 54 sandwiches? **6 loaves**
5. You are making pizza for a party. Each pizza has 8 slices.
   a. If 93 people will be at the party, how many pizzas should you make so that each person gets one slice? **12 pizzas**
   b. How many slices will be left over? **3 slices will be left over**
6. Each jug of juice serves 12 people. How many jugs will you need for 60 people? **5 jugs**

Use with pages 262–263. 97

Name ______________________

Practice Chapter 6 Section B

Review and Practice

(Lesson 6) Write true or false. You may use a hundred chart to help.

1. 42 is a multiple of 6. **True**
2. 41 is a multiple of 3. **False**
3. 83 is a multiple of 3 and 6. **False**
4. All multiples of 6 are also multiples of 3. **True**

(Lesson 7) Continue each pattern.

5. 18, 27, 36, **45**, **54**, **63**
6. 36, 48, 60, **72**, **84**, **96**
7. How can you tell without multiplying that 6×10 does not equal 66? **Multiples of 10 end in zero.**

(Lesson 8) Find each product.

8. $5 \times 2 \times 8 =$ **80**
9. $1 \times 9 \times 4 =$ **36**
10. $0 \times 7 \times 1 =$ **0**
11. $3 \times 2 \times 7 =$ **42**
12. $2 \times (2 \times 3) =$ **12**
13. $(6 \times 1) \times 5 =$ **30**

(Lesson 9) Solve. Use any strategy.

14. You want to send cards to 37 people. The cards you want to send come in packages of 6. How many packages will you need? **7 packages**
15. While on vacation Marsha sent 35 postcards. She sent 7 postcards from each city she visited. How many cities did she visit? **5 cities**

(Mixed Review) Continue each pattern.

16. 48, 45, 42, **39**, **36**, **33**
17. 6, 10, 14, 18, **22**, **26**, **30**
18. 12, 24, 36, **48**, **60**, **72**

98 Use with page 266.

Name ______________________

Practice Chapters 1–6

Cumulative Review

(Chapter 3 Lesson 9) Find each sum.

1. $35 + 66 + 88 =$ **189**
2. $84 + 28 + 53 =$ **165**
3. $679 + 44 + 345 =$ **1,068**
4. $71 + 93 + 309 =$ **473**
5. Patricia earned 96, 95, and 87 on three math tests. She needs a total of 279 points to get an A average. Does she have enough points for an A? Explain. **No; 96 + 95 + 87 = 278**

(Chapter 4 Lesson 11) Find each difference.

6. $800 - 58 =$ **742**
7. $907 - 628 =$ **279**
8. $600 - 299 =$ **301**
9. $200 - 184 =$ **16**

(Chapter 5 Lesson 4) Find each product.

10. $8 \times 2 =$ **16**
11. $2 \times 4 =$ **8**
12. $2 \times 5 =$ **10**
13. $7 \times 2 =$ **14**
14. $9 \times 2 =$ **18**

(Chapter 6 Lessons 1–3) Find each product.

15. $3 \times 2 =$ **6**
16. $4 \times 3 =$ **12**
17. $4 \times 5 =$ **20**
18. $7 \times 4 =$ **28**
19. $9 \times 6 =$ **54**
20. $8 \times 3 =$ **24**
21. $6 \times 4 =$ **24**
22. $3 \times 6 =$ **18**
23. $7 \times 6 =$ **42**
24. $9 \times 3 =$ **27**

Use with page 271. 99

Name ______________________

Practice 7-1

Exploring Division as Sharing

Mrs. Robbins and Mrs. Siani are making up flower baskets for a wedding celebration. They have to do 6 baskets in all. They decide to share the work equally. How many baskets will each prepare?

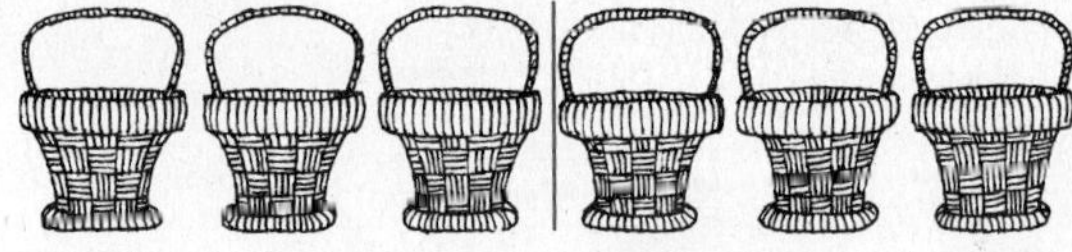

1. Draw a line to divide the baskets into 2 equal groups.
2. 6 flower baskets ÷ 2 women = **3** baskets each.

Complete. You may use counters or draw pictures to help.

3. $8 \div 2 =$ **4**
4. $16 \div 4 =$ **4**

Solve. You may use counters or draw pictures to help.

5. Misha and Angie have volunteered to call 10 people to raise money for their Girl Scout troop. If they divide the calls equally, how many calls will each girl make? **5 calls; 10 ÷ 2 = 5**
6. You are helping the school yearbook editor. There are 24 pictures that will go on 3 pages in the yearbook. How many photos will you put on each page if you divide them evenly? **8 photos; 24 ÷ 3 = 8**

100 Use with pages 276–277.

Name ____________________

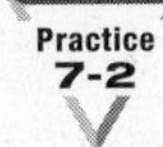

Exploring Division as Repeated Subtraction

Maria is pouring glasses of iced tea. She has 18 ice cubes. If she wants to put 6 ice cubes in each glass, how many glasses can she fill?

1. Draw lines to show 6 ice cubes per glass.
2. 18 ice cubes ÷ 6 per glass = **3** glasses.

Complete. You may use counters or complete the pictures to help.

3. 10 letters
   2 in each mailbox
   10 ÷ 2 = **5**
4. 12 flowers
   3 in each pot
   12 ÷ 3 = **4**
5. Brenda puts 3 cookies on each plate. Can she make 5 plates with 15 cookies? Draw a picture and explain.

   Yes; 15 cookies divided into 5 groups equals 3. Drawing should show 3 cookies on each of 5 plates.

Name ____________________

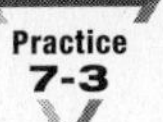

Exploring Division Stories

1. Three friends share a 6-pack of juice equally. How many cans of juice does each one drink?
   6 ÷ 3 = **2** cans
2. Telia made 15 snowflake ornaments. If she gives 3 to each of her friends, how many friends will get ornaments?
   15 ÷ 3 = **5** friends

Write a division story for each. You may use counters to solve.

3. 8 ÷ 4 = **2**
   Look for 2 groups of 4 or 4 groups of 2.
4. 21 ÷ 7 = **3**
   Look for 3 groups of 7 or 7 groups of 3.

Complete each number sentence. You may use counters to solve.

5. 16 ÷ **8** = 2 6. 24 ÷ **3** = 8 7. 36 ÷ **9** = 4

Solve. You may use counters or draw pictures to help.

8. Dana has 10 free show tickets. He can give away 2 to each person in his family. How many people are in his family?
   5 people
9. Beth's book has 28 pages. She reads 4 pages each day. How long will it take her to finish the book? **7 days**
10. Michael used 12 slices of cheese to make 4 equal-sized sandwiches. How many slices of cheese did he put in each sandwich? **3 slices**

Name ____________________

Review and Practice

(Lessons 1 and 2) Use the pictures to help you complete each number sentence.

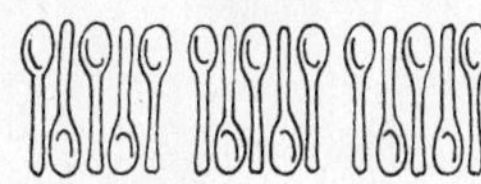

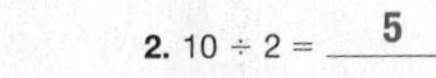

1. 15 ÷ 3 = **5**
2. 10 ÷ 2 = **5**

3. 14 ÷ 7 = **2**
4. 8 ÷ 4 = **2**
5. Natalie and her two brothers have $12 to spend on lunch. One Kid's Meal costs $3. Do they have enough money? Explain how you know.
   Yes; $12 ÷ 3 = $4; They each have $4 to spend.

(Lesson 3) Write a division story for each. You may use counters to solve.

6. 20 ÷ 4 = **5**
   Look for 20 objects divided into 5 groups of 4 or 4 groups of 5.
7. 18 ÷ 9 = **2**
   Look for 18 objects divided into 2 groups of 9 or 9 groups of 2.

(Mixed Review) Complete each number sentence.

8. **5** + 8 = 13 9. **14** − 9 = 5 10. 6 + **5** = 11

Name ____________________

Connecting Multiplication and Division

Complete. You may use counters to help.

1. 7 × **4** = 28; 28 ÷ 7 = **4**
2. 6 × **7** = 42; 42 ÷ 6 = **7**
3. 2 × **6** = 12; 12 ÷ 2 = **6**
4. 2 × **9** = 18; 18 ÷ 2 = **9**
5. 3 × **7** = 21; 21 ÷ 3 = **7**
6. 7 × **5** = 35; 35 ÷ 7 = **5**
7. 2 × **3** = 6; 6 ÷ 2 = **3**
8. 5 × **5** = 25; 25 ÷ 5 = **5**
9. 6 × **2** = 12; 12 ÷ 6 = **2**
10. 4 × **8** = 32; 32 ÷ 4 = **8**
11. 3 × **10** = 30; 30 ÷ 3 = **10**
12. 8 × **3** = 24; 24 ÷ 8 = **3**
13. What multiplication fact could you use to solve 24 ÷ 3?
    3 × 8 = 24, so 24 ÷ 3 = 8
14. What are the number sentences in the fact family with 32 ÷ 4 = 8?
    32 ÷ 8 = 4, 8 × 4 = 32, 4 × 8 = 32
15. What multiplication fact could you use to solve 20 ÷ 2?
    2 × 10 = 20, so 20 ÷ 2 = 10
16. What are the number sentences in the fact family with 24 ÷ 4 = 6?
    24 ÷ 6 = 4, 4 × 6 = 24, 6 × 4 = 24

Name ______________________

Practice 7-5

Dividing by 2

Find each quotient.

1. $2\overline{)10}$ 5
2. $2\overline{)4}$ 2
3. $2\overline{)16}$ 8
4. $2\overline{)18}$ 9

5. 6 ÷ 2 = 3
6. 2 ÷ 2 = 1
7. 8 ÷ 2 = 4
8. 4 ÷ 2 = 2

9. Divide 12 by 2. 6
10. Divide 14 by 2. 7

11. How can you use multiplication to help you find 18 ÷ 2?
Think: 2 × what number is 18? 2 × 9 = 18, so 18 ÷ 2 = 9

12. Nancy says, "I can solve 6 ÷ 2 using the fact 6 × 2 = 12." Do you agree or disagee? Explain.
Disagree; 2 × 3 = 6, so 6 ÷ 2 = 3

13. Ben says, "I can solve 16 ÷ 2 by using the fact 2 × 8 = 16." Do you agree or disagree? Explain.
Agree; Since 2 × 8 = 16, 16 ÷ 2 = 8

14. How can you use multiplication to help you find 8 ÷ 2?
Think: 2 × what number is 8? 2 × 4 = 8, so 8 ÷ 2 = 4

15. How can you use multiplication to help you find 14 ÷ 7?
7 × 2 = 14, so 14 ÷ 7 = 2

16. Use multiplication facts to help you find:
a. 20 ÷ 2 10
b. 16 ÷ 2 8
c. 12 ÷ 2 6

Use with pages 286–287. 105

Name ______________________

Practice 7-6

Dividing by 5

Find each quotient.

1. $5\overline{)15}$ 3
2. $5\overline{)25}$ 5
3. $5\overline{)10}$ 2
4. $5\overline{)30}$ 6
5. $2\overline{)8}$ 4
6. $5\overline{)40}$ 8
7. $5\overline{)35}$ 7
8. $2\overline{)12}$ 6

9. 45 ÷ 5 = 9
10. 20 ÷ 5 = 4
11. 25 ÷ 5 = 5
12. 30 ÷ 5 = 6
13. 16 ÷ 2 = 8
14. 10 ÷ 5 = 2
15. 15 ÷ 5 = 3
16. 45 ÷ 5 = 9

17. Divide 20 by 5. 4

18. What multiplication fact can help you find $5\overline{)40}$?
5 × 8 = 40

19. What multiplication fact can help you find $2\overline{)14}$?
2 × 7 = 14

20. What multiplication fact can help you find 45 ÷ 5?
9 × 5 = 45

21. What multiplication fact can help you find 10 ÷ 2?
2 × 5 = 10

22. How could you take away groups of 5 to find 25 ÷ 5?
25 − 5 = 20; 20 − 5 = 15; 15 − 5 = 10; 10 − 5 = 5; 5 − 5 = 0; You must subtract 5 groups of 5, so 25 ÷ 5 = 5.

106 Use with pages 288–289.

Name ______________________

Practice 7-7

Dividing by 3 and 4

Find each quotient.

1. $3\overline{)15}$ 5
2. $4\overline{)8}$ 2
3. $4\overline{)12}$ 3
4. $5\overline{)30}$ 6
5. $3\overline{)6}$ 2
6. $3\overline{)21}$ 7
7. $4\overline{)28}$ 7
8. $4\overline{)20}$ 5
9. $3\overline{)12}$ 4
10. $2\overline{)10}$ 5
11. $3\overline{)18}$ 6
12. $4\overline{)32}$ 8

13. 27 ÷ 3 = 9
14. 9 ÷ 3 = 3
15. 24 ÷ 4 = 6
16. 24 ÷ 3 = 8
17. 25 ÷ 5 = 5
18. 16 ÷ 4 = 4
19. 14 ÷ 2 = 7
20. 36 ÷ 4 = 9

21. Divide 18 by 3. 6
22. Divide 20 by 4. 5
23. How many 4s are in 28? 7
24. How many 3s are in 15? 5
25. How many 4s are in 40? 10
26. How many 3s are in 30? 10

27. How could you take away equal groups to find $4\overline{)12}$?
12 − 4 = 8; 8 − 4 = 4; 4 − 4 = 0; So, 12 ÷ 4 = 3.

Use with pages 290–291. 107

Name ______________________

Practice 7-8

Exploring Dividing with 0 and 1

Find each quotient. Complete the division rule.

1. a. 3 ÷ 1 = 3
b. Rule: Any number divided by 1 equals **that number**.
2. a. 5 ÷ 5 = 1
b. Rule: Any number (except 0) divided by itself equals 1.
3. a. 0 ÷ 2 = 0
b. Rule: Zero divided by any number (except 0) equals 0.
4. Can you divide by 0? **No**

Find each quotient. Write the division rule that explains the answer.

5. 4 ÷ 4 = 1
Rule: **Any number (except 0) divided by itself equals 1.**

6. 0 ÷ 7 = 0
Rule: **Zero divided by any number (except 0) equals 0.**

7. 8 ÷ 1 = 8
Rule: **Any number divided by 1 equals that number.**

Write >, <, or =.

8. 6 ÷ 6 (=) 3 ÷ 3
9. 12 ÷ 4 (<) 12 ÷ 3
10. 25 ÷ 5 (>) 0 ÷ 5
11. 4 ÷ 1 (<) 6 ÷ 1
12. 6 ÷ 2 (=) 3 ÷ 1
13. 0 ÷ 4 (<) 4 ÷ 2
14. 8 ÷ 4 (=) 4 ÷ 2
15. 10 ÷ 5 (>) 5 ÷ 5

108 Use with pages 292–293.

Name ______________________

Practice 7-9

Analyze Word Problems: Choose an Operation

Which number sentence would you use to solve the problem? Explain.

1. Suppose Blair worked 6 hours a week for 3 weeks. How many hours did she work?
   A. 6 + 3 = 9 B. 6 × 3 = 18 C. 6 − 3 = 3 D. 18 + 6 = 24
   B; Putting together equal groups
2. Marcie sold $8 worth of fruit tarts at a bake sale. Each tart cost $2. How many tarts did she sell?
   A. 8 − 2 = 6 B. 8 ÷ 2 = 4 C. 8 × 2 = 16 D. 8 + 2 = 10
   B; Separating $8 into equal groups of $2
3. Arthur had 6 tickets to a concert. He gave 2 of them to Joe. How many tickets did he have left?
   A. 6 − 2 = 4 B. 6 + 2 = 8 C. 6 × 2 = 12 D. 6 ÷ 2 = 3
   A; Take away 2 tickets

Write which operation you would use. Then solve.

4. Zachary bought 4 bananas and 3 oranges. How many pieces of fruit did he buy?
   Addition; 7 pieces of fruit
5. Lars bought a 2-pound bag of dog food for $2.25 and a 1-pound bag of cat food for $1.54. How much money did he spend?
   Addition; $3.79
6. Isabella earns $4 per hour working at the pet store. If she works for 7 hours, how much money will she earn?
   Multiplication; $28
7. Nick had 16 marbles. He gave an equal number to each of 4 friends. How many marbles did each friend get?
   Division; 4 marbles

Name ______________________

Practice Chapter 7 Section B

Review and Practice

Vocabulary Write true or false for each statement.

1. In the problem 18 ÷ 2 = 9, the divisor is 9. False
2. Fact families are groups of related facts using the same set of digits. True
3. The dividend in the problem 24 ÷ 3 = 8 is 24. True
4. The quotient in the problem 12 ÷ 4 = 3 is 12. False

(Lessons 5–8) Find each quotient.

5. 2 ÷ 2 = 1
6. 16 ÷ 4 = 4
7. 20 ÷ 5 = 4
8. 8 ÷ 2 = 4
9. 12 ÷ 3 = 4
10. 40 ÷ 5 = 8
11. 20 ÷ 4 = 5
12. 18 ÷ 3 = 6
13. 14 ÷ 2 = 7
14. 45 ÷ 5 = 9
15. 54 ÷ 1 = 54
16. 0 ÷ 2 = 0
17. 27 ÷ 3 = 9
18. 36 ÷ 4 = 9
19. 0 ÷ 4 = 0
20. 16 ÷ 2 = 8
21. 2)18 **9**
22. 5)30 **6**
23. 3)21 **7**
24. 4)8 **2**

(Lesson 9) Write which operation you would use. Then solve.

25. Selma wants to build bird houses to give as gifts. It takes 4 boards to make one house. Selma has 24 boards. How many bird houses can she make?
    Division; 24 ÷ 4 = 6
26. Nu has to write 3 reports. Each report must be 2 pages. How many pages must he write?
    Multiplication; 3 × 2 = 6

(Mixed Review) Find each missing factor.

27. 1 × 0 × 8 = 0
28. 3 × 4 × 2 = 24
29. 2 × 5 × 2 = 20
30. 4 × 1 × 5 = 20

Name ______________________

Practice 7-10

Dividing by 6 and 7

Find each quotient.

1. 6)18 **3**
2. 7)14 **2**
3. 6)24 **4**
4. 7)28 **4**
5. 6)6 **1**
6. 1)7 **7**
7. 6)54 **9**
8. 7)49 **7**
9. 7)42 **6**
10. 3)18 **6**
11. 6)12 **2**
12. 6)36 **6**
13. 42 ÷ 6 = 7
14. 7 ÷ 7 = 1
15. 56 ÷ 7 = 8
16. 12 ÷ 6 = 2
17. 63 ÷ 7 = 9
18. 21 ÷ 3 = 7
19. 0 ÷ 6 = 0
20. 30 ÷ 5 = 6
21. 35 ÷ 7 = 5
22. 48 ÷ 6 = 8
23. 24 ÷ 4 = 6
24. 21 ÷ 7 = 3
25. Divide 36 by 6. 6
26. Divide 30 by 6. 5
27. Divide 28 by 4. 7
28. Divide 0 by 7. 0
29. What multiplication fact can help you find 42 ÷ 7?
    7 × 6 = 42
30. What multiplication fact can help you find 24 ÷ 6 ?
    6 × 4 = 24
31. Is the quotient of 48 ÷ 6 greater than or less than the quotient of 42 ÷ 7? Explain.
    Greater; 48 ÷ 6 = 8 and 42 ÷ 7 = 6; 8 is greater than 6.
32. Is the quotient of 63 ÷ 7 greater than or less than the quotient of 54 ÷ 6? Explain.
    Neither; They are equal.

Name ______________________

Practice 7-11

Dividing by 8 and 9

Find each quotient.

1. 8)16 **2**
2. 9)36 **4**
3. 8)40 **5**
4. 9)36 **4**
5. 7)21 **3**
6. 8)8 **1**
7. 9)45 **5**
8. 8)72 **9**
9. 9)0 **0**
10. 4)36 **9**
11. 9)63 **7**
12. 8)56 **7**
13. 81 ÷ 9 = 9
14. 32 ÷ 8 = 4
15. 27 ÷ 9 = 3
16. 9 ÷ 9 = 1
17. 64 ÷ 8 = 8
18. 54 ÷ 9 = 6
19. 72 ÷ 9 = 8
20. 24 ÷ 8 = 3
21. Divide 56 by 8. 7
22. Divide 18 by 9. 2
23. Divide 45 by 9. 5
24. Divide 56 by 7. 8
25. What multiplication fact can help you find 63 ÷ 9?
    9 × 7 = 63
26. What multiplication fact can help you find 48 ÷ 8?
    8 × 6 = 48
27. How does knowing 4 × 9 = 36 help you solve 36 ÷ 9?
    Since you multiply 4 by 9 to get 36, 36 divided by 9 must be 4.
28. Which is greater, 48 ÷ 6 or 48 ÷ 8? Explain.
    48 ÷ 6 = 8; 48 ÷ 8 = 6; 8 > 6
29. Which is greater, 81 ÷ 9 or 36 ÷ 4?
    Neither; They are equal.

Name ______________________

Practice 7-12

Exploring Even and Odd Numbers

1. Even numbers have 0, 2, 4, 6, or 8 in the ones place.
2. Odd numbers have 1, 3, 5, 7, or 9 in the ones place.

Write odd or even for each. You may use color cubes to help.

3. Odd
4. Even

4. 6 Even
5. 19 Odd
6. 9 Odd
7. 24 Even
8. 18 Even
9. 17 Odd
10. 11 Odd
11. 23 Odd

12. Start with 14 and name the next 5 even numbers. Explain how you know which numbers are even.
    14, 16, 18, 20, 22, and 24; Possible answer: They are even because they have a 0, 2, 4, 6, or 8 in the ones place.

13. Add the pairs of odd numbers. Do you get even or odd sums? Even
    a. 7 + 5 12
    b. 3 + 9 12
    c. 11 + 7 18
    d. Can you think of any two odd numbers where the sum of the numbers will be odd? No

14. Add the pairs of even and odd numbers. Do you get even or odd sums? Odd
    a. 5 + 16 21
    b. 8 + 7 15
    c. 14 + 5 19
    d. Can you think of any two numbers, one even and the other odd, in which the sum is an even number? No

15. Tenisha has two pages in her photo album to fill. She puts 7 photos on each page. Did she have an even or odd number of photos? Explain. Even; There are two equal groups of photos.

Name ______________________

Practice 7-13

Compare Strategies: Use Objects and Make an Organized List

Use any strategy to solve.

1. Anita received 12 new stickers and a new sticker album on her birthday. She wants to put an equal number of stickers on each page that she uses.
   a. How many pages could Anita use in her sticker album?
      1, 2, 3, 4, 6, or 12
   b. How many stickers could be on each page?
      12, 6, 4, 3, 2, or 1
   c. List all the ways Anita could put the stickers in her sticker album.
      1 page of 12, 2 pages of 6, 3 pages of 4, 4 pages of 3, 6 pages of 2, or 12 pages of 1

2. Paul has a collection of action figures. He wants to arrange the figures in equal rows. If Paul has 30 action figures, what are all the ways to arrange the figures?
   1 row of 30; 2 rows of 15; 3 rows of 10; 5 rows of 6; 6 rows of 5; 10 rows of 3; 15 rows of 2; 30 rows of 1

3. Juan has 2 pairs of sneakers, one black pair and one white pair. He has 3 baseball caps, one red, one blue and the other orange. What are all the combinations of shoes and caps he could wear?
   Black shoes, red cap; black shoes, blue cap; black shoes, orange cap; white shoes, red cap; white shoes, blue cap; white shoes, orange cap

4. Rosalind must read an 18-page book. She wants to read an equal number of pages every day. List all the possible ways she could divide her reading.
   18 pages on 1 day, 9 pages on 2 days, 6 pages on 3 days; 3 pages on 6 days, 2 pages on 9 days, or 1 page on 18 days

Name ______________________

Practice 7-14

Exploring Algebra: Balancing Scales

Find all the ways to balance each scale. Make a table to record each way. You may use color cubes to help.

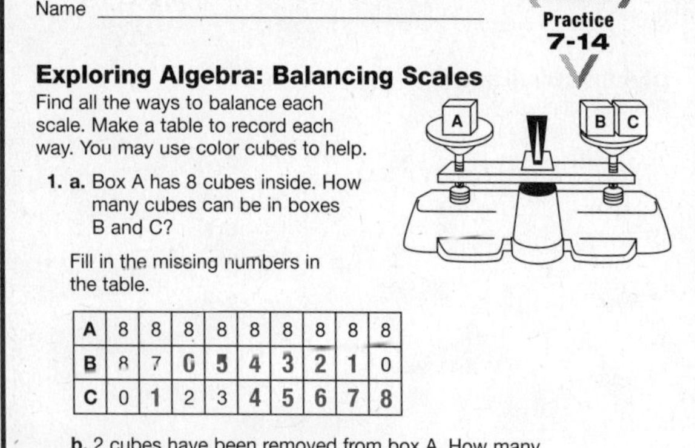

1. a. Box A has 8 cubes inside. How many cubes can be in boxes B and C?

   Fill in the missing numbers in the table.

A	8	8	8	8	8	8	8	8	8
B	8	7	6	5	4	3	2	1	0
C	0	1	2	3	4	5	6	7	8

   b. 2 cubes have been removed from box A. How many cubes are now in the boxes? Fill in the missing numbers in the table.

A	6	6	6	6	6	6	6
B	6	5	4	3	2	1	0
C	0	1	2	3	4	5	6

2. Box B has 7 cubes inside. Box C has 5 cubes inside. How many cubes are in each box A?
   6

3. Box A has 15 cubes inside. How many cubes are in each box B?
   5

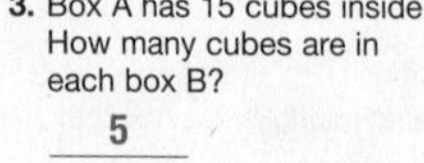

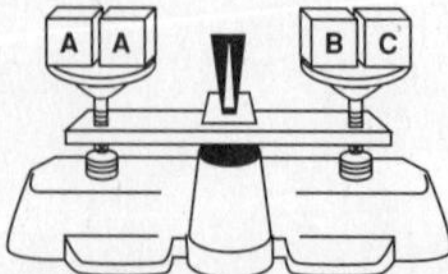

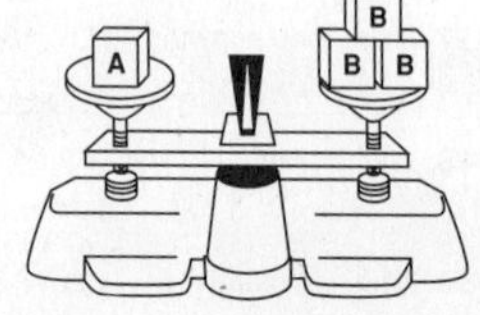

Name ______________________

Practice Chapter 7 Section C

Review and Practice

Vocabulary Match the set of numbers with the word describing it.

1. even a
2. odd b

a. 26, 32, 24, 48
b. 31, 47, 19, 21

(Lessons 10 and 11) Find each quotient.

3. $12 \div 6 =$ 2
4. $16 \div 8 =$ 2
5. $21 \div 7 =$ 3
6. $28 \div 7 =$ 4
7. $18 \div 9 =$ 2
8. $45 \div 9 =$ 5
9. $24 \div 8 =$ 3
10. $18 \div 6 =$ 3
11. Divide 49 by 7. 7
12. Divide 56 by 8. 7

(Lesson 12) Write odd or even. You may use color cubes to help.

13. 17 Odd
14. 36 Even
15. 15 Odd

(Lesson 13) Use any strategy to solve.

16. Hunter wants to take a picture of his class. There are 24 students in his class. He wants them to stand in equal rows. What are all the ways he could arrange them?
    24 rows of 1; 12 rows of 2; 8 rows of 3; 6 rows of 4; 4 rows of 6; 3 rows of 8; 2 rows of 12; 1 row of 24

(Lesson 14) Solve. You may use color cubes to help.

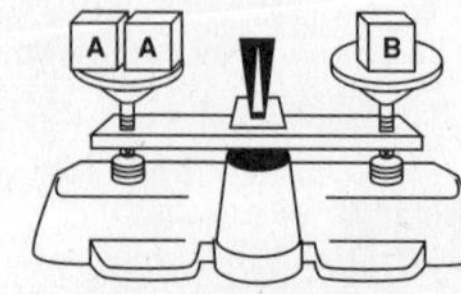

17. Each box A has 4 cubes inside. How many cubes can be in box B?
    8

(Mixed Review) Multiply.

18. $6 \times 8 =$ 48
19. $9 \times 9 =$ 81
20. $5 \times 7 =$ 35
21. $4 \times 8 =$ 32

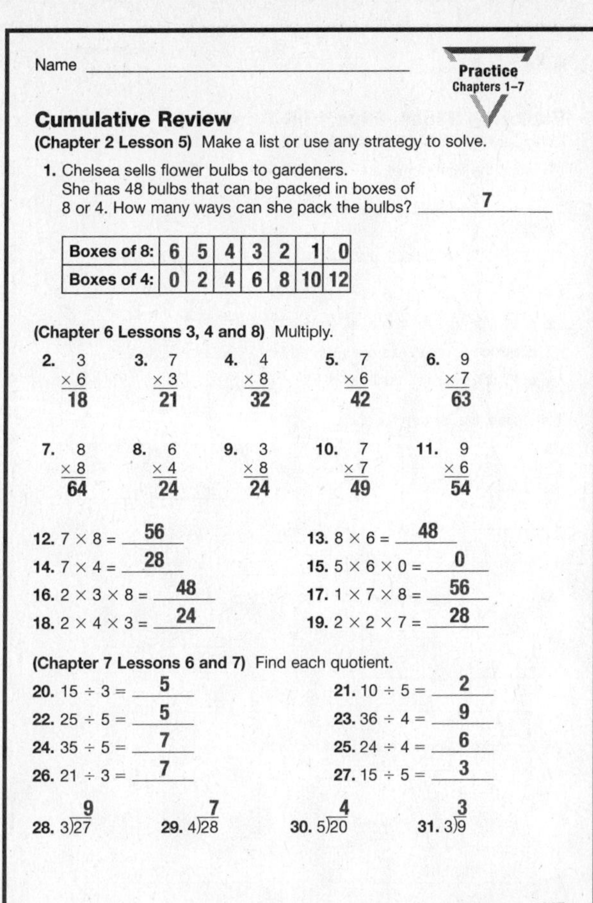

Name ______________________

Practice Chapters 1–7

Cumulative Review

(Chapter 2 Lesson 5) Make a list or use any strategy to solve.

1. Chelsea sells flower bulbs to gardeners. She has 48 bulbs that can be packed in boxes of 8 or 4. How many ways can she pack the bulbs? **7**

Boxes of 8:	6	5	4	3	2	1	0
Boxes of 4:	0	2	4	6	8	10	12

(Chapter 6 Lessons 3, 4 and 8) Multiply.

2. $3 \times 6 = $ **18**
3. $7 \times 3 = $ **21**
4. $4 \times 8 = $ **32**
5. $7 \times 6 = $ **42**
6. $9 \times 7 = $ **63**
7. $8 \times 8 = $ **64**
8. $6 \times 4 = $ **24**
9. $3 \times 8 = $ **24**
10. $7 \times 7 = $ **49**
11. $9 \times 6 = $ **54**
12. $7 \times 8 = $ **56**
13. $8 \times 6 = $ **48**
14. $7 \times 4 = $ **28**
15. $5 \times 6 \times 0 = $ **0**
16. $2 \times 3 \times 8 = $ **48**
17. $1 \times 7 \times 8 = $ **56**
18. $2 \times 4 \times 3 = $ **24**
19. $2 \times 2 \times 7 = $ **28**

(Chapter 7 Lessons 6 and 7) Find each quotient.

20. $15 \div 3 = $ **5**
21. $10 \div 5 = $ **2**
22. $25 \div 5 = $ **5**
23. $36 \div 4 = $ **9**
24. $35 \div 5 = $ **7**
25. $24 \div 4 = $ **6**
26. $21 \div 3 = $ **7**
27. $15 \div 5 = $ **3**
28. $3\overline{)27}$ **9**
29. $4\overline{)28}$ **7**
30. $5\overline{)20}$ **4**
31. $3\overline{)9}$ **3**

Use with page 317. 117

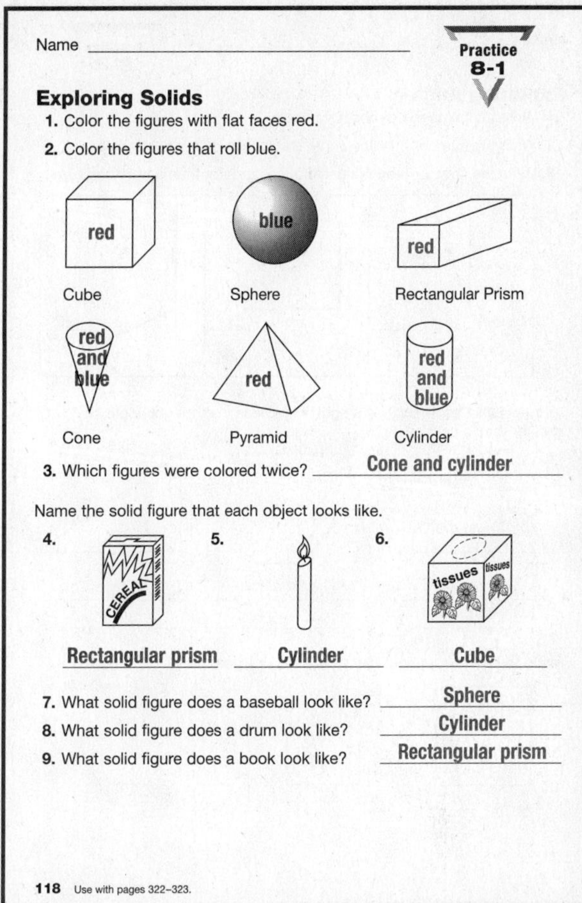

Name ______________________

Practice 8-1

Exploring Solids

1. Color the figures with flat faces red.
2. Color the figures that roll blue.

Cube — Sphere — Rectangular Prism

Cone — Pyramid — Cylinder

3. Which figures were colored twice? **Cone and cylinder**

Name the solid figure that each object looks like.

4. **Rectangular prism**
5. **Cylinder**
6. **Cube**
7. What solid figure does a baseball look like? **Sphere**
8. What solid figure does a drum look like? **Cylinder**
9. What solid figure does a book look like? **Rectangular prism**

118 Use with pages 322–323.

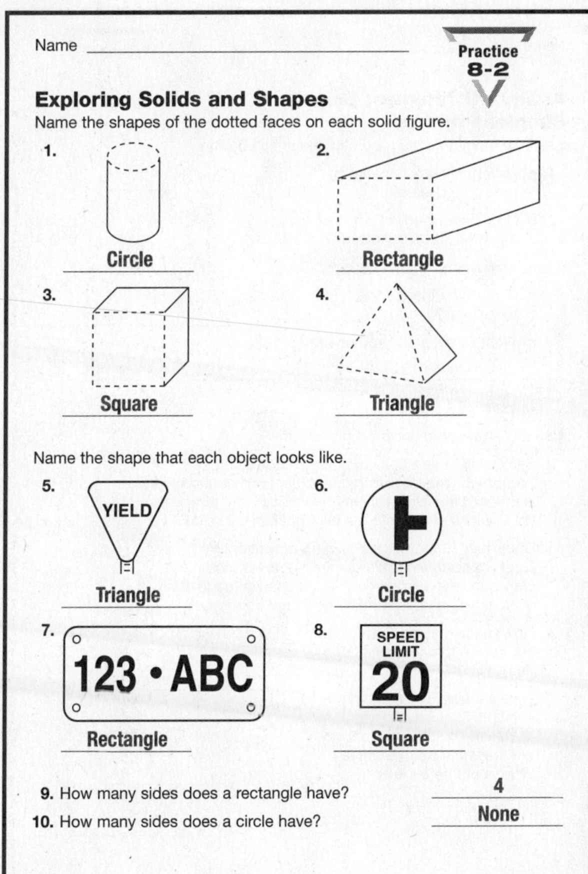

Name ______________________

Practice 8-2

Exploring Solids and Shapes

Name the shapes of the dotted faces on each solid figure.

1. **Circle**
2. **Rectangle**
3. **Square**
4. **Triangle**

Name the shape that each object looks like.

5. **Triangle**
6. **Circle**
7. **Rectangle**
8. **Square**
9. How many sides does a rectangle have? **4**
10. How many sides does a circle have? **None**

Use with pages 324–325. 119

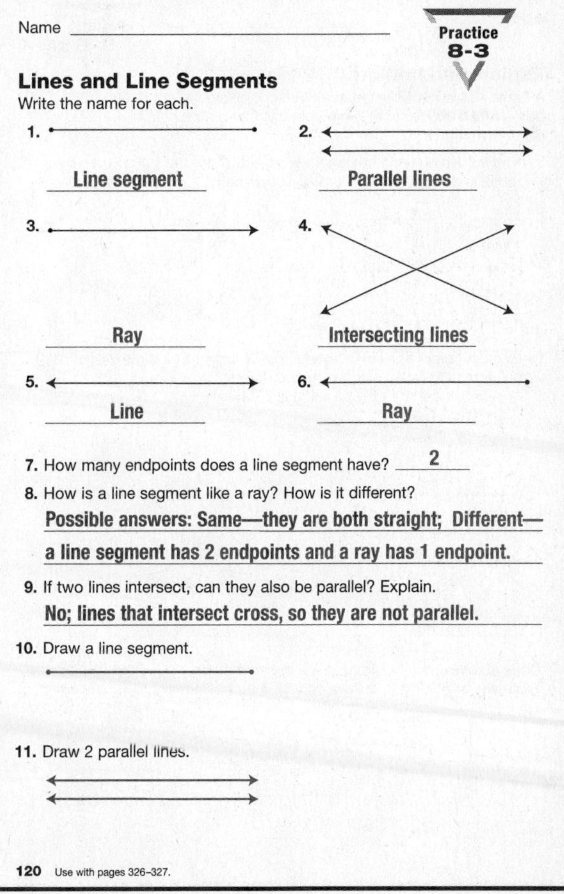

Name ______________________

Practice 8-3

Lines and Line Segments

Write the name for each.

1. **Line segment**
2. **Parallel lines**
3. **Ray**
4. **Intersecting lines**
5. **Line**
6. **Ray**
7. How many endpoints does a line segment have? **2**
8. How is a line segment like a ray? How is it different? **Possible answers: Same—they are both straight; Different—a line segment has 2 endpoints and a ray has 1 endpoint.**
9. If two lines intersect, can they also be parallel? Explain. **No; lines that intersect cross, so they are not parallel.**
10. Draw a line segment.
11. Draw 2 parallel lines.

120 Use with pages 326–327.

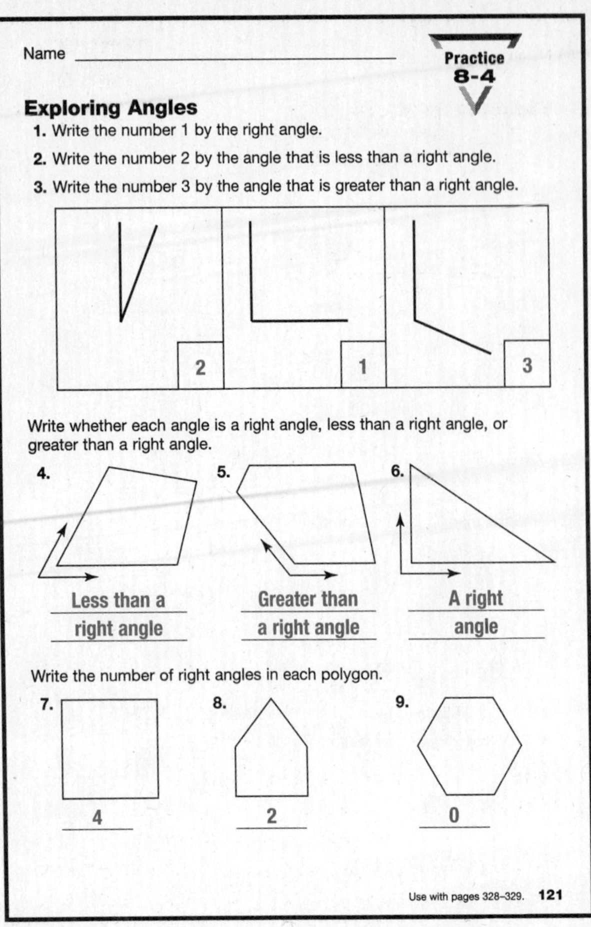

Name ______________________

Practice 8-4

Exploring Angles

1. Write the number 1 by the right angle.
2. Write the number 2 by the angle that is less than a right angle.
3. Write the number 3 by the angle that is greater than a right angle.

Write whether each angle is a right angle, less than a right angle, or greater than a right angle.

4. Less than a right angle
5. Greater than a right angle
6. A right angle

Write the number of right angles in each polygon.

7. 4
8. 2
9. 0

Use with pages 328–329. 121

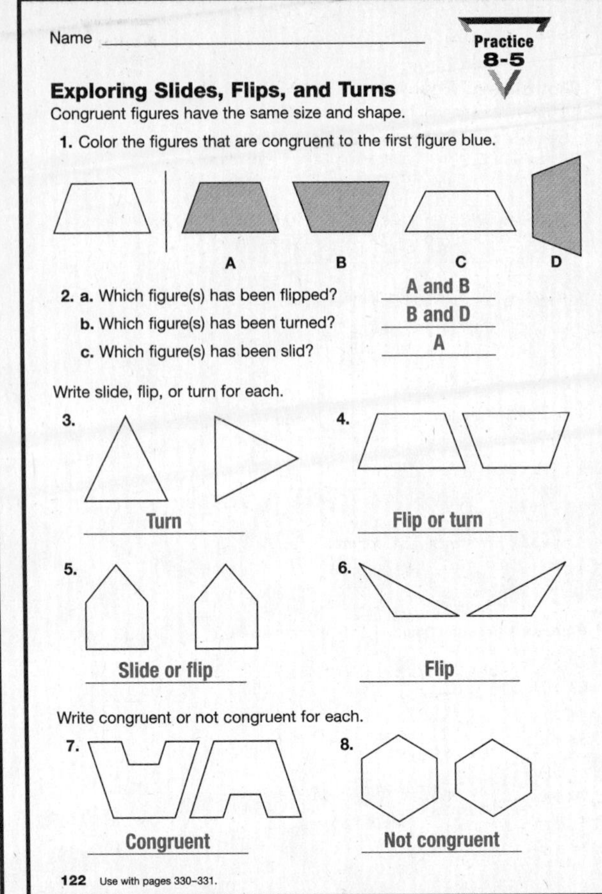

Name ______________________

Practice 8-5

Exploring Slides, Flips, and Turns

Congruent figures have the same size and shape.

1. Color the figures that are congruent to the first figure blue.

2. a. Which figure(s) has been flipped? A and B
   b. Which figure(s) has been turned? B and D
   c. Which figure(s) has been slid? A

Write slide, flip, or turn for each.

3. Turn
4. Flip or turn
5. Slide or flip
6. Flip

Write congruent or not congruent for each.

7. Congruent
8. Not congruent

122 Use with pages 330–331.

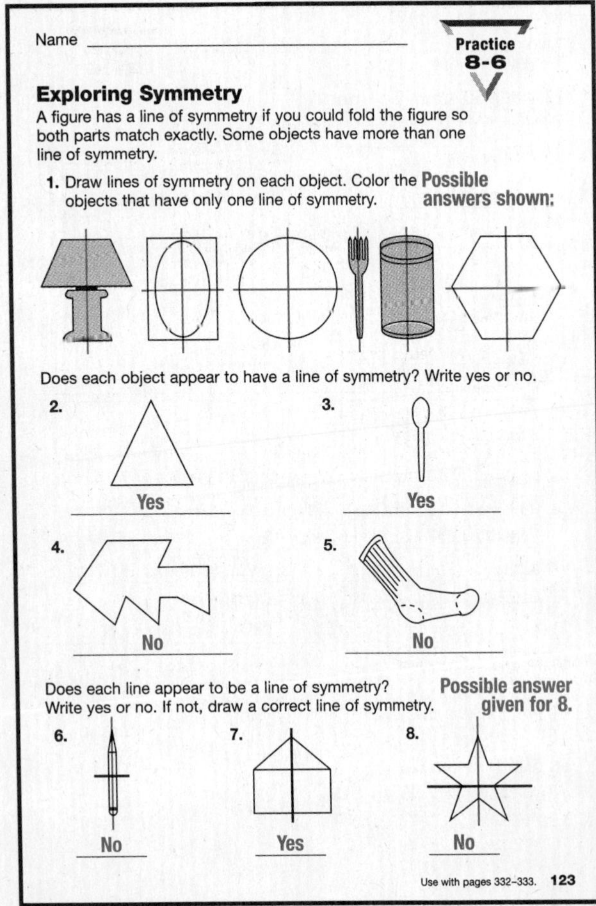

Name ______________________

Practice 8-6

Exploring Symmetry

A figure has a line of symmetry if you could fold the figure so both parts match exactly. Some objects have more than one line of symmetry.

1. Draw lines of symmetry on each object. Color the objects that have only one line of symmetry. Possible answers shown.

Does each object appear to have a line of symmetry? Write yes or no.

2. Yes
3. Yes
4. No
5. No

Does each line appear to be a line of symmetry? Write yes or no. If not, draw a correct line of symmetry. Possible answer given for 8.

6. No
7. Yes
8. No

Use with pages 332–333. 123

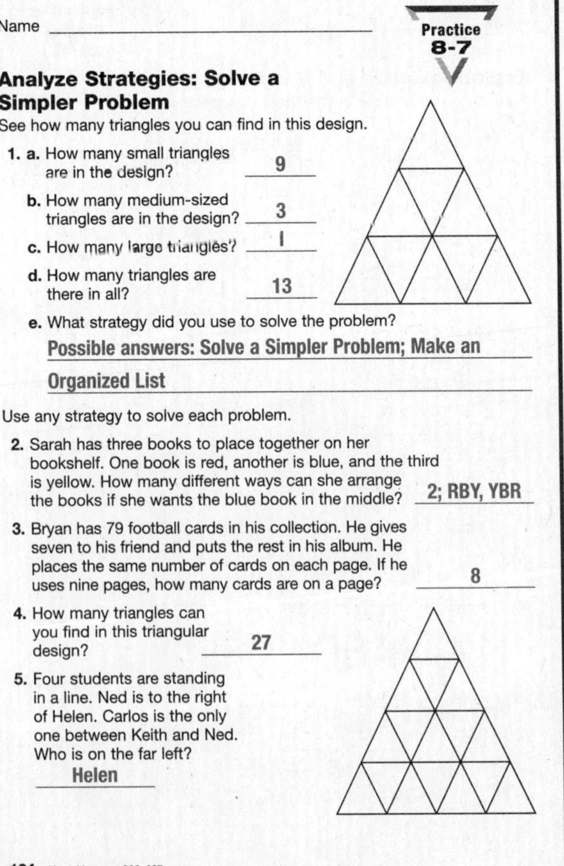

Name ______________________

Practice 8-7

Analyze Strategies: Solve a Simpler Problem

See how many triangles you can find in this design.

1. a. How many small triangles are in the design? 9
   b. How many medium-sized triangles are in the design? 3
   c. How many large triangles? 1
   d. How many triangles are there in all? 13
   e. What strategy did you use to solve the problem? Possible answers: Solve a Simpler Problem; Make an Organized List

Use any strategy to solve each problem.

2. Sarah has three books to place together on her bookshelf. One book is red, another is blue, and the third is yellow. How many different ways can she arrange the books if she wants the blue book in the middle? 2; RBY, YBR
3. Bryan has 79 football cards in his collection. He gives seven to his friend and puts the rest in his album. He places the same number of cards on each page. If he uses nine pages, how many cards are on a page? 8
4. How many triangles can you find in this triangular design? 27
5. Four students are standing in a line. Ned is to the right of Helen. Carlos is the only one between Keith and Ned. Who is on the far left? Helen

124 Use with pages 336–337.

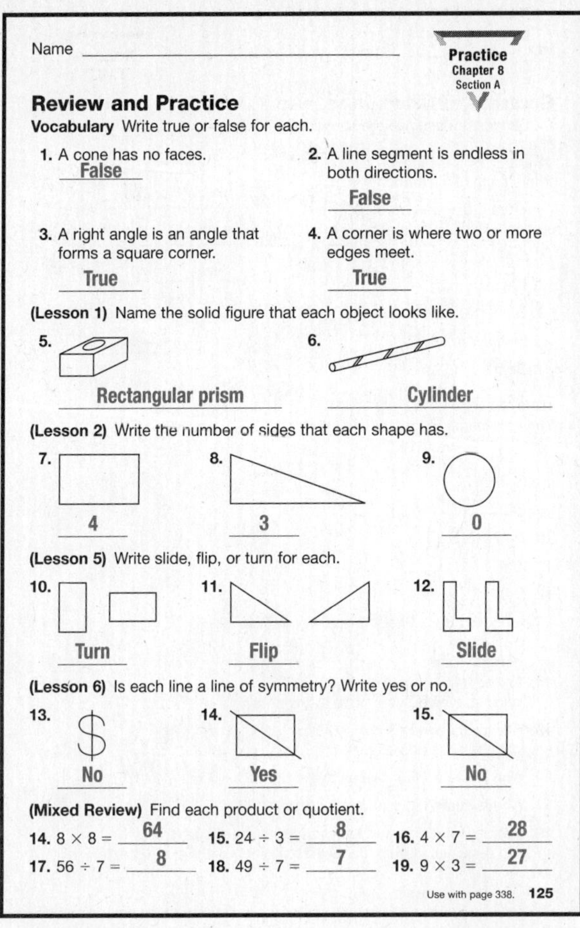

Name ______________________

Practice
Chapter 8
Section A

Review and Practice

Vocabulary Write true or false for each.

1. A cone has no faces. **False**

2. A line segment is endless in both directions. **False**

3. A right angle is an angle that forms a square corner. **True**

4. A corner is where two or more edges meet. **True**

(Lesson 1) Name the solid figure that each object looks like.

5. **Rectangular prism**

6. **Cylinder**

(Lesson 2) Write the number of sides that each shape has.

7. **4**

8. **3**

9. **0**

(Lesson 5) Write slide, flip, or turn for each.

10. **Turn**

11. **Flip**

12. **Slide**

(Lesson 6) Is each line a line of symmetry? Write yes or no.

13. $ **No**

14. **Yes**

15. **No**

(Mixed Review) Find each product or quotient.

14. 8 × 8 = **64** **15.** 24 ÷ 3 = **8** **16.** 4 × 7 = **28**

17. 56 ÷ 7 = **8** **18.** 49 ÷ 7 = **7** **19.** 9 × 3 = **27**

Use with page 338. 125

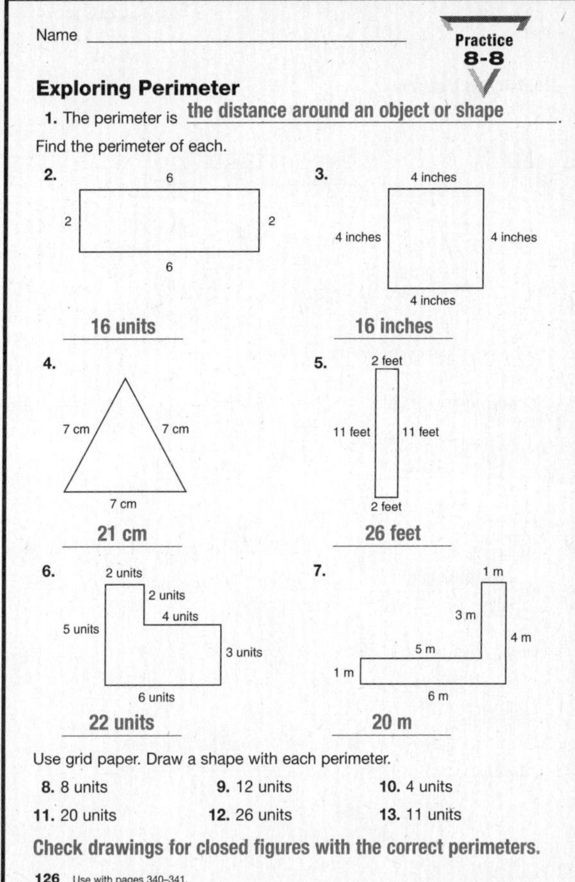

Name ______________________

Practice
8-8

Exploring Perimeter

1. The perimeter is **the distance around an object or shape**.

Find the perimeter of each.

2. **16 units**

3. **16 inches**

4. **21 cm**

5. **26 feet**

6. **22 units**

7. **20 m**

Use grid paper. Draw a shape with each perimeter.

8. 8 units **9.** 12 units **10.** 4 units

11. 20 units **12.** 26 units **13.** 11 units

Check drawings for closed figures with the correct perimeters.

126 Use with pages 340–341.

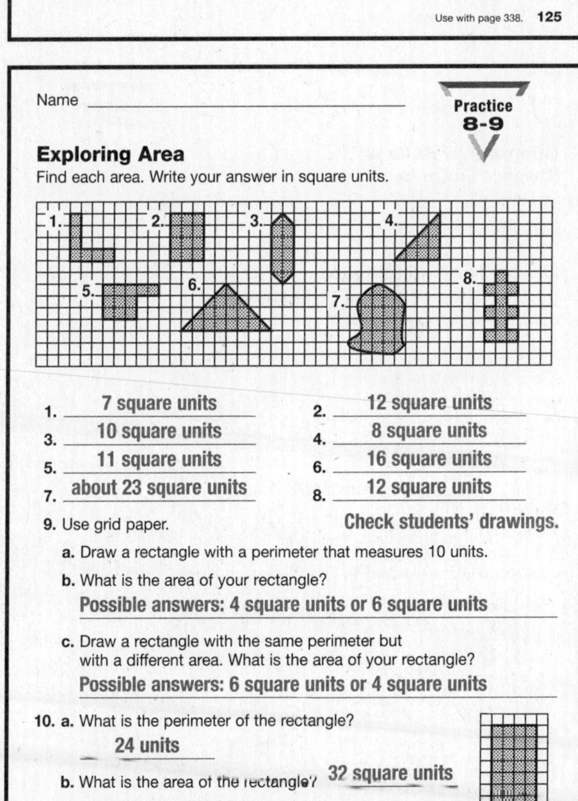

Name ______________________

Practice
8-9

Exploring Area

Find each area. Write your answer in square units.

1. **7 square units** **2.** **12 square units**

3. **10 square units** **4.** **8 square units**

5. **11 square units** **6.** **16 square units**

7. **about 23 square units** **8.** **12 square units**

9. Use grid paper. **Check students' drawings.**

a. Draw a rectangle with a perimeter that measures 10 units.

b. What is the area of your rectangle?

Possible answers: 4 square units or 6 square units

c. Draw a rectangle with the same perimeter but with a different area. What is the area of your rectangle?

Possible answers: 6 square units or 4 square units

10. a. What is the perimeter of the rectangle?

24 units

b. What is the area of the rectangle? **32 square units**

c. What happens to the perimeter if you halve each side?

The new perimeter is half the old perimeter.

d. What happens to the area if you halve each side?

The new area is 8.

Use with pages 342–343. 127

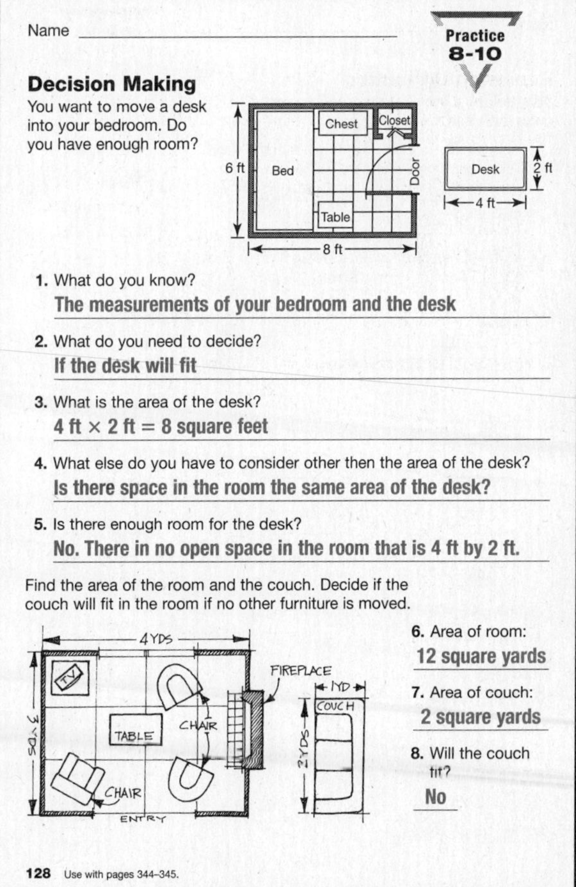

Name ______________________

Practice
8-10

Decision Making

You want to move a desk into your bedroom. Do you have enough room?

1. What do you know?

The measurements of your bedroom and the desk

2. What do you need to decide?

If the desk will fit

3. What is the area of the desk?

4 ft × 2 ft = 8 square feet

4. What else do you have to consider other then the area of the desk?

Is there space in the room the same area of the desk?

5. Is there enough room for the desk?

No. There in no open space in the room that is 4 ft by 2 ft.

Find the area of the room and the couch. Decide if the couch will fit in the room if no other furniture is moved.

6. Area of room: **12 square yards**

7. Area of couch: **2 square yards**

8. Will the couch fit? **No**

128 Use with pages 344–345.

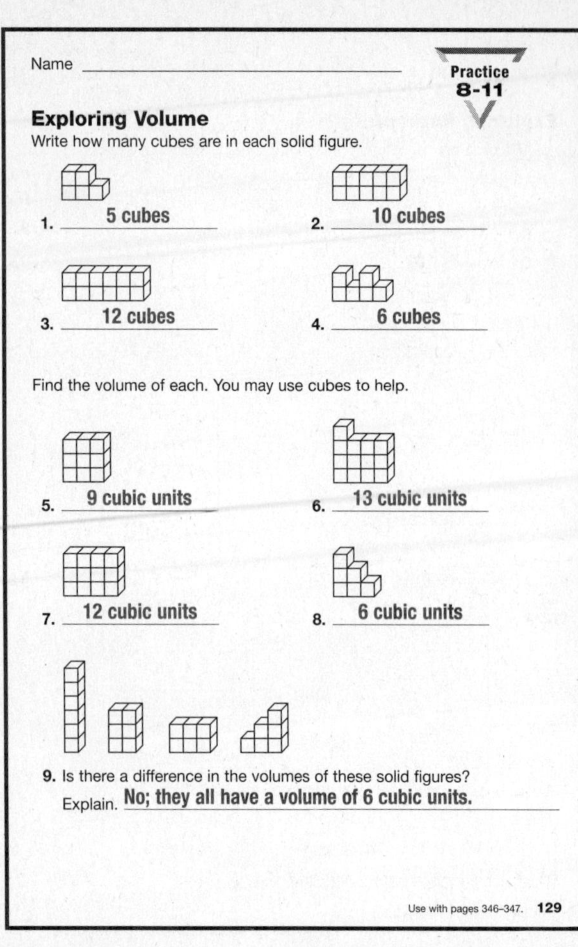

Name ____________

Practice 8-11

Exploring Volume

Write how many cubes are in each solid figure.

1. **5 cubes**
2. **10 cubes**
3. **12 cubes**
4. **6 cubes**

Find the volume of each. You may use cubes to help.

5. **9 cubic units**
6. **13 cubic units**
7. **12 cubic units**
8. **6 cubic units**

9. Is there a difference in the volumes of these solid figures? Explain. **No; they all have a volume of 6 cubic units.**

Use with pages 346–347. 129

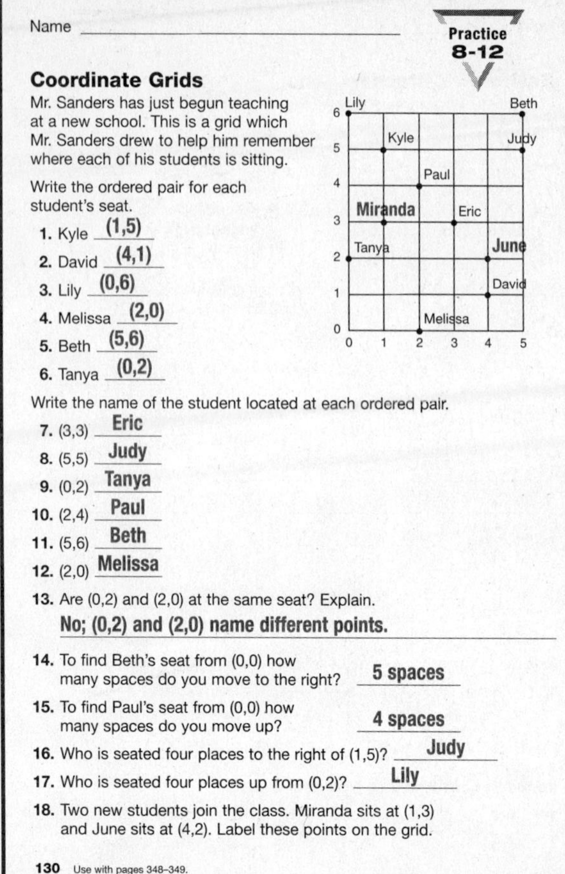

Name ____________

Practice 8-12

Coordinate Grids

Mr. Sanders has just begun teaching at a new school. This is a grid which Mr. Sanders drew to help him remember where each of his students is sitting.

Write the ordered pair for each student's seat.

1. Kyle **(1,5)**
2. David **(4,1)**
3. Lily **(0,6)**
4. Melissa **(2,0)**
5. Beth **(5,6)**
6. Tanya **(0,2)**

Write the name of the student located at each ordered pair.

7. (3,3) **Eric**
8. (5,5) **Judy**
9. (0,2) **Tanya**
10. (2,4) **Paul**
11. (5,6) **Beth**
12. (2,0) **Melissa**
13. Are (0,2) and (2,0) at the same seat? Explain. **No; (0,2) and (2,0) name different points.**
14. To find Beth's seat from (0,0) how many spaces do you move to the right? **5 spaces**
15. To find Paul's seat from (0,0) how many spaces do you move up? **4 spaces**
16. Who is seated four places to the right of (1,5)? **Judy**
17. Who is seated four places up from (0,2)? **Lily**
18. Two new students join the class. Miranda sits at (1,3) and June sits at (4,2). Label these points on the grid.

130 Use with pages 348–349.

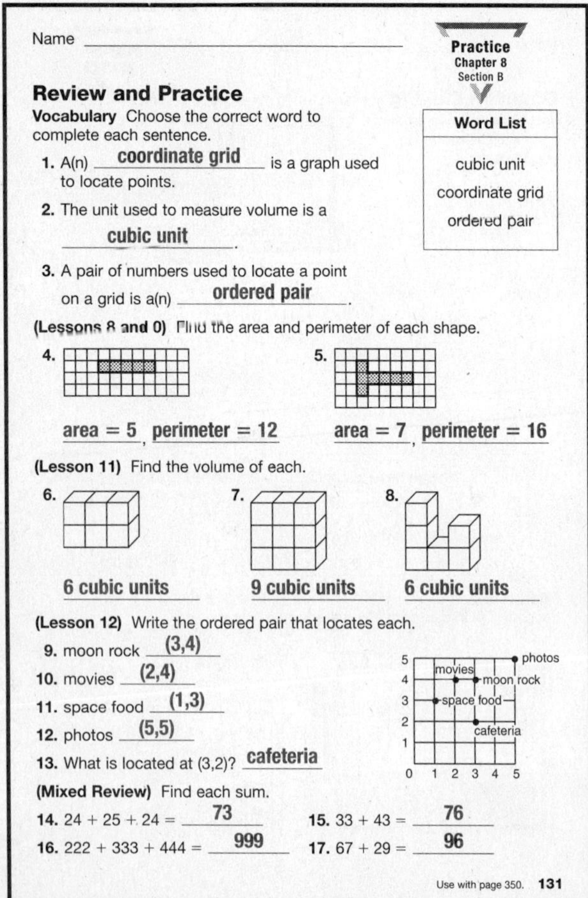

Name ____________

Practice Chapter 8 Section B

Review and Practice

Vocabulary Choose the correct word to complete each sentence.

Word List
cubic unit
coordinate grid
ordered pair

1. A(n) **coordinate grid** is a graph used to locate points.
2. The unit used to measure volume is a **cubic unit**.
3. A pair of numbers used to locate a point on a grid is a(n) **ordered pair**.

(Lessons 8 and 9) Find the area and perimeter of each shape.

4. **area = 5**, **perimeter = 12**
5. **area = 7**, **perimeter = 16**

(Lesson 11) Find the volume of each.

6. **6 cubic units**
7. **9 cubic units**
8. **6 cubic units**

(Lesson 12) Write the ordered pair that locates each.

9. moon rock **(3,4)**
10. movies **(2,4)**
11. space food **(1,3)**
12. photos **(5,5)**
13. What is located at (3,2)? **cafeteria**

(Mixed Review) Find each sum.

14. 24 + 25 + 24 = **73**
15. 33 + 43 = **76**
16. 222 + 333 + 444 = **999**
17. 67 + 29 = **96**

Use with page 350. 131

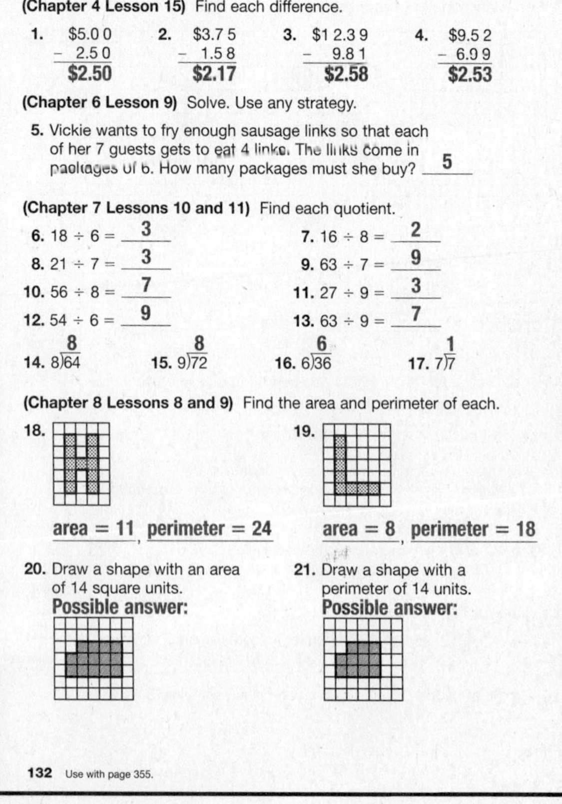

Name ____________

Practice Chapters 1–8

Cumulative Review

(Chapter 4 Lesson 15) Find each difference.

1. \$5.00 − 2.50 = **\$2.50**
2. \$3.75 − 1.58 = **\$2.17**
3. \$12.39 − 9.81 = **\$2.58**
4. \$9.52 − 6.99 = **\$2.53**

(Chapter 6 Lesson 9) Solve. Use any strategy.

5. Vickie wants to fry enough sausage links so that each of her 7 guests gets to eat 4 links. The links come in packages of 6. How many packages must she buy? **5**

(Chapter 7 Lessons 10 and 11) Find each quotient.

6. 18 ÷ 6 = **3**
7. 16 ÷ 8 = **2**
8. 21 ÷ 7 = **3**
9. 63 ÷ 7 = **9**
10. 56 ÷ 8 = **7**
11. 27 ÷ 9 = **3**
12. 54 ÷ 6 = **9**
13. 63 ÷ 9 = **7**
14. 8)64 **8**
15. 9)72 **8**
16. 6)36 **6**
17. 7)7 **1**

(Chapter 8 Lessons 8 and 9) Find the area and perimeter of each.

18. **area = 11**, **perimeter = 24**
19. **area = 8**, **perimeter = 18**
20. Draw a shape with an area of 14 square units. **Possible answer:**
21. Draw a shape with a perimeter of 14 units. **Possible answer:**

132 Use with page 355.

Name ______________________

Practice 9-1

Exploring Multiplying Tens

Complete. You may use place-value blocks to help.

1. 5 groups of 7
   5 × 7 ones = 35 ones
   5 × 7 = 35
2. 5 groups of 70
   5 × 7 tens = 35 tens
   5 × 70 = 350
3. 5 × 1 ten = 5 tens
   5 × 10 = 50
4. 2 × 4 tens = 8 tens
   2 × 40 = 80
5. 3 × 5 tens = 15 tens
   3 × 50 = 150
6. 2 × 5 tens = 10 tens
   2 × 50 = 100
7. 3 × 6 tens = 18 tens
   3 × 60 = 180
8. 4 × 6 tens = 24 tens
   4 × 60 = 240
9. 7 × 1 ten = 7 tens
   7 × 10 = 70
10. 3 × 8 tens = 24 tens
    3 × 80 = 240
11. 4 × 4 tens = 16 tens
    4 × 40 = 160
12. 2 × 7 tens = 14 tens
    2 × 70 = 140
13. How can you use 7 × 6 to help you find 7 × 60?
    Possible answer: Since 7 × 6 = 42, 7 × 6 tens = 42 tens, or 420.

50 PENNIES

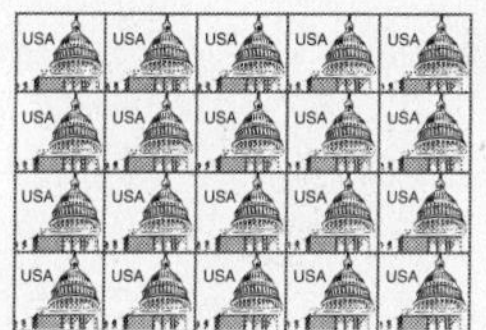

14. How many pennies are in 3 rolls? **150 pennies**
15. How many stamps are on 5 sheets? **100 stamps**

Name ______________________

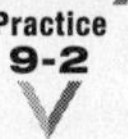

Practice 9-2

Exploring Multiplication Patterns

Complete.

1. 6 × 7 ones = 42 ones
   6 × 7 = 42
2. 6 × 7 tens = 42 tens
   6 × 70 = 420
3. 6 × 7 hundreds = 42 hundreds
   6 × 700 = 4,200
4. 3 × 4 = 12
   3 × 40 = 120
   3 × 400 = 1,200
5. 2 × 4 = 8
   2 × 40 = 80
   2 × 400 = 800
6. 4 × 5 = 20
   4 × 50 = 200
   4 × 500 = 2,000
7. 3 × 6 = 18
   3 × 60 = 180
   3 × 600 = 1,800
8. 7 × 4 = 28
   7 × 40 = 280
   7 × 400 = 2,800
9. 6 × 6 = 36
   6 × 60 = 360
   6 × 600 = 3,600

Find each product using mental math.

10. 3 × 90 = **270**
11. 3 × 800 = **2,400**
12. 4 × 400 = **1,600**
13. 2 × 70 = **140**
14. 5 × 600 = **3,000**
15. 6 × 800 = **4,800**
16. 3 × 300 = **900**
17. 5 × 90 = **450**
18. 6 × 300 = **1,800**
19. 4 × 500 = **2,000**
20. 9 × 200 = **1,800**
21. 7 × 700 = **4,900**
22. 8 × 400 = **3,200**
23. 5 × 800 = **4,000**
24. Can you use the basic fact 3 × 8 to find 3 × 800?
    Yes; 3 × 8 = 24, so 3 × 800 = 2,400
25. Can you use 5 × 7 to find 5 × 700?
    Yes; 5 × 7 = 35, so 5 × 700 = 3,500

Name ______________________

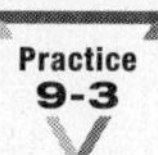

Practice 9-3

Estimating Products

Estimate each product.

1. 3 × 32 **90**
2. 7 × 820 **5,600**
3. 5 × 46 **250**
4. 2 × 350 **800**
5. 8 × 67 **560**
6. 6 × 865 **5,400**
7. 3 × 523 **1,500**
8. 4 × 628 **2,400**
9. 4 × 233 **800**
10. 9 × 58 **540**
11. 5 × 797 **4,000**
12. 6 × 84 **480**
13. 3 × 124 **300**
14. 5 × 99 **500**
15. 7 × 280 **2,100**
16. 8 × 241 **1,600**
17. 6 × 890 **5,400**
18. 2 × 916 **1,800**
19. 9 × 760 **7,200**
20. 4 × 675 **2,800**
21. 3 × 210 **600**
22. 9 × 63 **540**
23. 4 × 334 **1,200**
24. 6 × 912 **5,400**
25. 7 × 489 **3,500**
26. 8 × 38 **320**
27. Estimate the product of 6 and 34. **180**
28. Estimate the product of 7 and 569. **4,200**
29. Estimate the product of 9 and 435. **3,600**
30. Estimate the product of 8 and 750. **6,400**
31. Estimate to decide if 6 × 856 is greater than or less than 7 × 536. Explain.
    greater than; 5,400 > 3,500
32. The product of 6 and another number is about 240. Give two numbers that make this sentence true. Explain.
    Since 6 × 40 = 240, look for numbers from 35 to 44.

Name ______________________

Practice 9-4

Exploring Multiplication with Arrays

Complete the steps to find each product.

1. 3 × 14

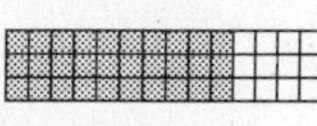

   a. 3 rows of 10
      3 × 10 = 30
   b. 3 rows of 4
      3 × 4 = 12
   c. 30 + 12 = 42
   d. 3 × 14 = 42
2. 2 × 26
   a. 2 rows of 20
      2 × 20 = 40
   b. 2 rows of 6
      2 × 6 = 12
   c. 40 + 12 = 52
   d. 2 × 26 = 52
3. 4 × 23 = **92**
4. 5 × 13 = **65**

Find each product. You may use place-value blocks or grid paper to help.

5. 4 × 12 = **48**
6. 6 × 13 = **78**
7. 3 × 32 = **96**
8. 4 × 17 = **68**
9. 4 × 19 = **76**
10. 2 × 47 = **94**
11. 5 × 18 = **90**
12. 3 × 28 = **84**
13. 3 × 31 = **93**
14. 2 × 39 = **78**

Find the missing number. You may use grid paper or place-value blocks to solve.

15. 18 × **3** = 54
16. 12 × **7** = 84
17. 22 × **4** = 88
18. **3** × 19 = 57
19. 6 × 15 = **90**
20. 5 × **14** = 70

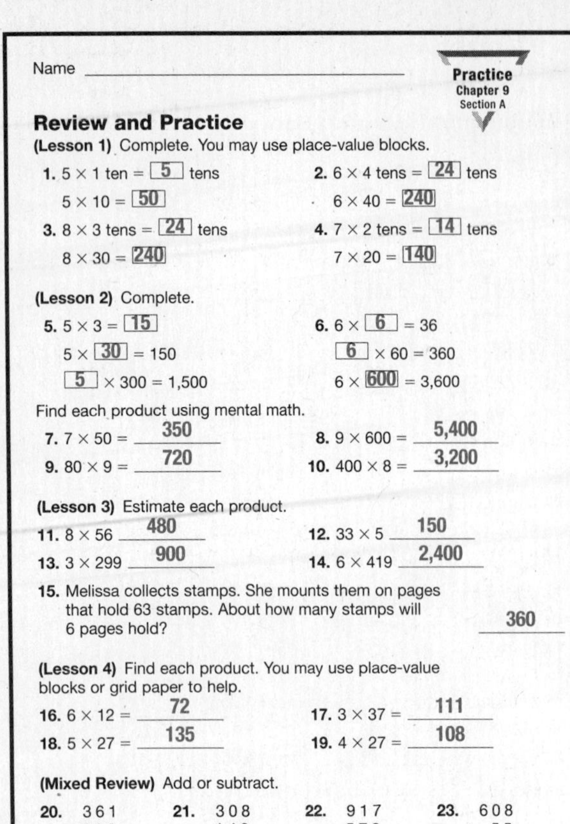

Name ______________________

Practice
Chapter 9
Section A

Review and Practice

(Lesson 1) Complete. You may use place-value blocks.

1. 5 × 1 ten = **5** tens
   5 × 10 = **50**
2. 6 × 4 tens = **24** tens
   6 × 40 = **240**
3. 8 × 3 tens = **24** tens
   8 × 30 = **240**
4. 7 × 2 tens = **14** tens
   7 × 20 = **140**

(Lesson 2) Complete.

5. 5 × 3 = **15**
   5 × **30** = 150
   5 × 300 = 1,500
6. 6 × **6** = 36
   6 × 60 = 360
   6 × **600** = 3,600

Find each product using mental math.

7. 7 × 50 = **350**
8. 9 × 600 = **5,400**
9. 80 × 9 = **720**
10. 400 × 8 = **3,200**

(Lesson 3) Estimate each product.

11. 8 × 56 **480**
12. 33 × 5 **150**
13. 3 × 299 **900**
14. 6 × 419 **2,400**
15. Melissa collects stamps. She mounts them on pages that hold 63 stamps. About how many stamps will 6 pages hold? **360**

(Lesson 4) Find each product. You may use place-value blocks or grid paper to help.

16. 6 × 12 = **72**
17. 3 × 37 = **111**
18. 5 × 27 = **135**
19. 4 × 27 = **108**

(Mixed Review) Add or subtract.

20. 361 + 839 = **1,200**
21. 308 − 149 = **159**
22. 917 − 579 = **338**
23. 608 + 55 = **663**

Use with pages 368. 137

Name ______________________

Practice
9-5

Multiplying: Partial Products

Find each product.

1. 15 × 3: 15, **30**, **45**
2. 72 × 2: **4**, 140, **144**
3. 21 × 7: **7**, **140**, **147**
4. 13 × 6: **18**, **60**, **78**
5. 39 × 7: **63**, **210**, **273**
6. 42 × 6: **12**, **240**, **252**
7. 67 × 7: **49**, **420**, **469**
8. 53 × 5: **15**, **250**, **265**

9. 43 × 5 = **215**
10. 64 × 3 = **192**
11. 88 × 7 = **616**
12. 39 × 4 = **156**
13. 67 × 8 = **536**
14. 37 × 6 = **222**
15. 45 × 4 = **180**
16. 69 × 2 = **138**
17. 36 × 2 = **72**
18. 84 × 5 = **420**
19. 18 × 6 = **108**
20. 23 × 9 = **207**

21. Explain why 9 × 34 is the same as 270 + 36.
    9 × 3 tens = 270 and 9 × 4 ones = 36.
22. How can you tell that 7 × 23 will be at least 3 digits?
    7 × 20 tens is 140, so the product will be more than 140.
23. Alexis says, "The product of 5 and 47 is less than 200." Is she right? Explain.
    No; 5 × 4 tens = 200, so 5 × 47 will be greater than 200.

138 Use with pages 370–371.

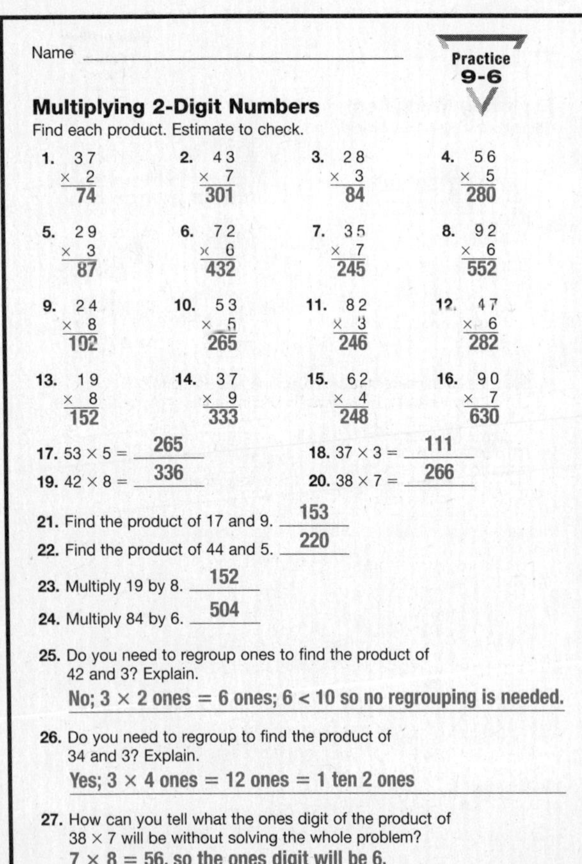

Name ______________________

Practice
9-6

Multiplying 2-Digit Numbers

Find each product. Estimate to check.

1. 37 × 2 = **74**
2. 43 × 7 = **301**
3. 28 × 3 = **84**
4. 56 × 5 = **280**
5. 29 × 3 = **87**
6. 72 × 6 = **432**
7. 35 × 7 = **245**
8. 92 × 6 = **552**
9. 24 × 8 = **192**
10. 53 × 5 = **265**
11. 82 × 3 = **246**
12. 47 × 6 = **282**
13. 19 × 8 = **152**
14. 37 × 9 = **333**
15. 62 × 4 = **248**
16. 90 × 7 = **630**
17. 53 × 5 = **265**
18. 37 × 3 = **111**
19. 42 × 8 = **336**
20. 38 × 7 = **266**
21. Find the product of 17 and 9. **153**
22. Find the product of 44 and 5. **220**
23. Multiply 19 by 8. **152**
24. Multiply 84 by 6. **504**
25. Do you need to regroup ones to find the product of 42 and 3? Explain.
    No; 3 × 2 ones = 6 ones; 6 < 10 so no regrouping is needed.
26. Do you need to regroup to find the product of 34 and 3? Explain.
    Yes; 3 × 4 ones = 12 ones = 1 ten 2 ones
27. How can you tell what the ones digit of the product of 38 × 7 will be without solving the whole problem?
    7 × 8 = 56, so the ones digit will be 6.

Use with pages 372–375. 139

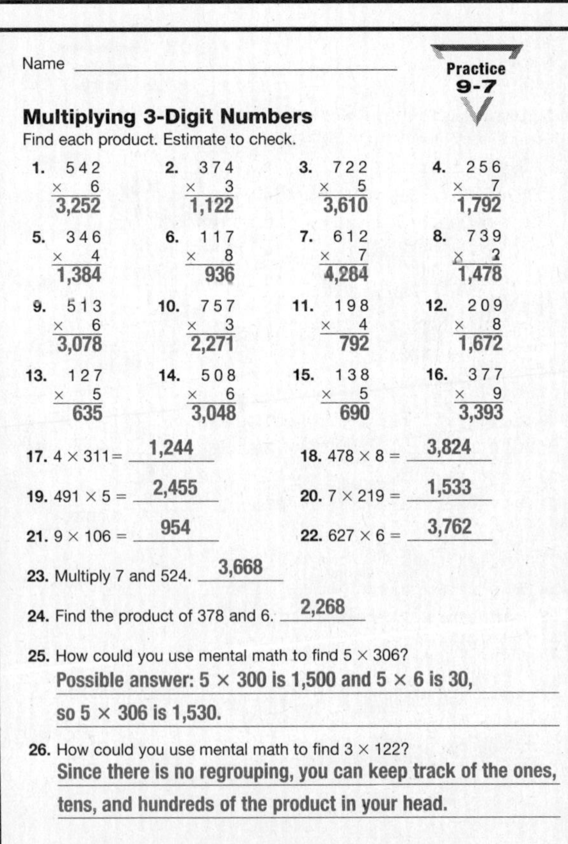

Name ______________________

Practice
9-7

Multiplying 3-Digit Numbers

Find each product. Estimate to check.

1. 542 × 6 = **3,252**
2. 374 × 3 = **1,122**
3. 722 × 5 = **3,610**
4. 256 × 7 = **1,792**
5. 346 × 4 = **1,384**
6. 117 × 8 = **936**
7. 612 × 7 = **4,284**
8. 739 × 2 = **1,478**
9. 513 × 6 = **3,078**
10. 757 × 3 = **2,271**
11. 198 × 4 = **792**
12. 209 × 8 = **1,672**
13. 127 × 5 = **635**
14. 508 × 6 = **3,048**
15. 138 × 5 = **690**
16. 377 × 9 = **3,393**
17. 4 × 311 = **1,244**
18. 478 × 8 = **3,824**
19. 491 × 5 = **2,455**
20. 7 × 219 = **1,533**
21. 9 × 106 = **954**
22. 627 × 6 = **3,762**
23. Multiply 7 and 524. **3,668**
24. Find the product of 378 and 6. **2,268**
25. How could you use mental math to find 5 × 306?
    Possible answer: 5 × 300 is 1,500 and 5 × 6 is 30, so 5 × 306 is 1,530.
26. How could you use mental math to find 3 × 122?
    Since there is no regrouping, you can keep track of the ones, tens, and hundreds of the product in your head.

140 Use with pages 378–379.

Name ______

Practice 9-8

Multiplying Money

Find each product.

1. $1.20 × 5 = **$6.00**
2. $0.65 × 7 = **$4.55**
3. $3.24 × 6 = **$19.44**
4. $1.75 × 5 = **$8.75**
5. $0.49 × 8 = **$3.92**
6. $3.19 × 4 = **$12.76**
7. $2.39 × 3 = **$7.17**
8. $4.12 × 5 = **$20.60**
9. $2.25 × 3 = **$6.75**
10. $1.52 × 6 = **$9.12**
11. $2.22 × 6 = **$13.32**
12. $4.33 × 7 = **$30.31**

13. 6 × $7.41 = **$44.46**
14. $2.29 × 4 = **$9.16**
15. $1.19 × 8 = **$9.52**
16. 9 × $0.79 = **$7.11**
17. $5.25 × 4 = **$21.00**
18. 7 × $3.50 = **$24.50**
19. What is the product of 5 and $7.44? **$37.20**
20. Multiply 6 and $0.72. **$4.32**
21. Is $0.32 the same amount as 32¢? **Yes**
22. Mindy multiplied $1.37 and 4. She recorded $5.48. Is she correct? **Yes**
23. If you bought 9 cans of juice for 72¢ each, would you spend more than $5.00? Explain.
Yes; 9 × 72¢ = 9 × $0.72 = $6.48
24. Ralph multiplied $2.69 and 5. He recorded $1345. Is he correct?
No; He needs to put the decimal point after the 3.

Name ______

Practice 9-9

Mental Math

Find each product using mental math.

1. 42 × 3 **126**
2. 26 × 2 **52**
3. 14 × 6 **84**
4. 23 × 5 **115**
5. 32 × 8 **256**
6. 17 × 9 **153**
7. 37 × 3 **111**
8. 19 × 4 **76**
9. 21 × 6 **126**
10. 44 × 3 **132**
11. 53 × 4 **212**
12. 63 × 2 **126**
13. Multiply 6 and 47. **282**
14. What is the product of 92 and 7. **644**
15. If you know 30 × 4 = 120, how could you solve 36 × 4 mentally?
Add 6 groups of 4 to find 144.
16. If you know 30 × 3 = 90, how could you solve 29 × 3 mentally?
Subtract 1 group of 3 to find 87.
17. What are two ways you could use mental math to find the product of 57 and 2?
50 × 2 plus 7 × 2; 60 × 2, subtract 3 × 2.

Name ______

Practice 9-10

Analyze Strategies: Make a Table

1. This summer, a new 20-story hospital was built downtown. Electricians worked quickly to put in wiring in the building. After one week, 4 floors had wiring. After two weeks, 8 floors had wiring. After three weeks, 12 floors had wiring.

   a. Fill in the table to show what you know.

Week	1	2	3	4	5
Floors Wired	4	**8**	**12**	**16**	**20**

   b. What multiplication pattern can help you complete the table?
   Multiply the number of weeks by 4 to find the number of floors wired.

   c. If the electricians continued to work at the same speed, how many weeks did it take them to put in wire in all 20 floors? **5 weeks**

2. If it takes Ginny 7 minutes to ride 1 mile on her bike, how long would it take her to ride 6 miles? **42 minutes**
3. If Todd can throw 20 curve balls in one minute, how many curve balls could he throw in 4 minutes? **80 curve balls**
4. Shea is decorating a frame. She has 4 rubber stamps she could use. They are a leaf, a ladybug, a flower, and a bee. She wants to make a design with 2 rubber stamps. How many choices does she have? **6 choices**
5. Eduardo has a red shirt, a blue shirt, and a white shirt, black trousers and blue jeans. How many different outfits can he make? **6 outfits**

Name ______

Practice Chapter 9 Section B

Review and Practice

(Lessons 5–8) Find each product.

1. 43 × 7 = **301**
2. 23 × 3 = **69**
3. 93 × 6 = **558**
4. 62 × 4 = **248**
5. 308 × 4 = **1,232**
6. 611 × 8 = **4,888**
7. 980 × 4 = **3,920**
8. 237 × 7 = **1,659**
9. $6.18 × 9 = **$55.62**
10. $1.23 × 6 = **$7.38**
11. $0.11 × 4 = **$0.44**
12. $4.56 × 3 = **$13.68**
13. Sheila has 5 packets of raisins. Each packet contains 214 raisins. About how many raisins does Sheila have in all? **About 1,000**
14. Jack buys 4 tickets to a concert. Each ticket costs $4.89. How much does Jack spend? **$19.56**

(Lesson 9) Use mental math to find each product.

15. 34 × 5 = **170**
16. 82 × 3 = **246**
17. 38 × 4 = **152**
18. 72 × 4 = **288**

(Lesson 10) Use any strategy to solve.

19. Kerim is saving money to buy a present. The first week he saves $1. The next week he saves $3. The third week he saves $5. If this pattern continues, how many more weeks will it be until he saves $25 in all? **2**

(Mixed Review) Find each quotient.

20. 56 ÷ 8 = **7**
21. 48 ÷ 6 = **8**
22. 63 ÷ 9 = **7**
23. 45 ÷ 5 = **9**

Name ______________________

Practice 9-11

Exploring Division Patterns

Find the quotients. Use basic facts and place-value patterns to help you divide mentally.

1. 8 ones ÷ 2 = **4** ones
   8 ÷ 2 = **4**
   8 tens ÷ 2 = **4** tens
   80 ÷ 2 = **40**
   8 hundreds ÷ 2 = **4** hundreds
   800 ÷ 2 = **400**

2. 9 ones ÷ 3 = **3** ones
   9 ÷ 3 = **3**
   9 tens ÷ 3 = **3** tens
   90 ÷ 3 = **30**
   9 hundreds ÷ 3 = **3** hundreds
   900 ÷ 3 = **300**

Complete.

3. 7 ÷ 7 = **1**
   70 ÷ **7** = 10
   700 ÷ 7 = 100

4. 8 ÷ 2 = **4**
   80 ÷ 2 = 40
   800 ÷ 2 = 400

5. 8 ÷ 4 = **2**
   80 ÷ **4** = 20
   800 ÷ 4 = 200

6. 10 ÷ 2 = **5**
   100 ÷ **2** = 50
   1,000 ÷ 2 = 500

Find each quotient using mental math.

7. 800 ÷ 2 = **400**
8. 90 ÷ 9 = **10**
9. 200 ÷ 4 = **50**
10. 270 ÷ 3 = **90**
11. 210 ÷ 7 = **30**
12. 360 ÷ 6 = **60**

13. How can you use 16 ÷ 4 = 4 to help you find 160 ÷ 4?
    Possible answer: 16 tens ÷ 4 = 4 tens or 40

Name ______________________

Practice 9-12

Estimating Quotients

Estimate each quotient.

1. 25 ÷ 6 **5**
2. 35 ÷ 4 **9**
3. 17 ÷ 4 **4**
4. 29 ÷ 4 **7**
5. 31 ÷ 8 **4**
6. 19 ÷ 6 **3**
7. 20 ÷ 3 **7**
8. 14 ÷ 5 **3**
9. 35 ÷ 6 **6**
10. 39 ÷ 8 **5**
11. 13 ÷ 6 **2**
12. 65 ÷ 8 **8**
13. 10 ÷ 3 **3**
14. 11 ÷ 5 **2**
15. 13 ÷ 4 **3**
16. 73 ÷ 9 **8**

17. Estimate the quotient of 25 ÷ 3. **8**
18. Estimate the quotient of 41 ÷ 5. **8**

19. What basic division fact can you use to help you estimate the quotient of 14 ÷ 5? Explain.
    15 ÷ 5 = 3; Possible answer: Since 14 is close to 15, the quotient is about 3.

20. Is the quotient of 49 ÷ 6 greater than or less than 8? Explain.
    Greater than; 48 ÷ 6 = 8, so 49 ÷ 6 is greater than 8.

21. Is the quotient of 53 ÷ 9 greater than or less than 6? Explain.
    Less than; 54 ÷ 9 = 6, so 53 ÷ 9 is less than 6.

Name ______________________

Practice 9-13

Exploring Division with Remainders

Find each quotient and remainder. You may use counters to help you.

1. 2)13 **6 R1**
2. 8)29 **3 R5**
3. 5)33 **6 R3**
4. 4)25 **6 R1**
5. 3)17 **5 R2**
6. 6)21 **3 R3**
7. 7)18 **2 R4**
8. 5)28 **5 R3**
9. 6)55 **9 R1**
10. 5)16 **3 R1**
11. 7)47 **6 R5**
12. 3)26 **8 R2**

13. Catherine says, "If I have 19 strawberries, I can give myself and 3 friends each 5 strawberries." Do you agree or disagree?
    Disagree, she will need 1 more strawberry.

14. Kim says, "If I need 25 granny-squares for a quilt, I can knit 8 squares a week for 3 weeks." Do you agree or disagree?
    Disagree, she will need 1 more square.

15. Stefan was packing books into boxes. He had 8 boxes that would each hold 4 books. Stefan had 33 books. How many would not fit into the boxes?
    1 book

16. Robin is putting photographs into an album. He can fit 7 photographs onto a page. The album has 7 pages and Robin has 53 photographs. How many will not fit in the album?
    4 photographs

Name ______________________

Practice 9-14

Dividing

Find each quotient and remainder.

1. 2)15 **7 R1**
2. 4)23 **5 R3**
3. 8)56 **7**
4. 5)43 **8 R3**
5. 6)25 **4 R1**
6. 9)48 **5 R3**
7. 6)56 **9 R2**
8. 4)33 **8 R1**

9. 42 ÷ 7 = **6**
10. 70 ÷ 8 = **8 R6**
11. 51 ÷ 8 = **6 R3**
12. 26 ÷ 3 = **8 R2**
13. 22 ÷ 8 = **2 R6**
14. 61 ÷ 7 = **8 R5**
15. 35 ÷ 9 = **3 R8**
16. 48 ÷ 6 = **8**
17. 47 ÷ 5 = **9 R2**
18. 34 ÷ 8 = **4 R2**

19. Divide 55 by 7. **7 R6**
20. Divide 66 by 8. **8 R2**
21. Divide 44 by 6. **7 R2**
22. Divide 33 by 4. **8 R1**
23. Divide 22 by 5. **4 R2**
24. Divide 88 by 9. **9 R7**

25. 12 volunteers will paint 4 walls. How many volunteers should work on each wall? **3 volunteers**

26. Suppose you want at least 15 rolls of film for your vacation. How many 4-roll packages should you buy? **4 packages**

27. How many traffic lights can you fill with a case of 24 light bulbs? (There are 3 lights on each traffic light.) **8 traffic lights**

28. How many take-out boxes can you fill from a crate of 50 muffins if there are 6 muffins per take-out box? **8 take-out boxes**

29. Suppose 1 bottle of juice serves 5 people. How many bottles will you need for 27 people? **6 bottles**

Name ____________________

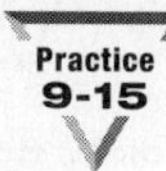

Decision Making

You are planning a race. You need a water station every 3 miles. How many water stations will you need if the race is:

1. 12 miles long? **12 ÷ 3 = 4 stations**
2. 21 miles long? **21 ÷ 3 = 7 stations**
3. 15 miles long? **15 ÷ 3 = 5 stations**
4. 18 miles long? **18 ÷ 3 = 6 stations**
5. 24 miles long? **24 ÷ 3 = 8 stations**
6. 30 miles long? **30 ÷ 3 = 10 stations**
7. 26 miles long? **26 ÷ 3 = 8 stations (R2)**
8. 20 miles long? **20 ÷ 3 = 6 stations (R2)**
9. There are 36 runners in your race. They must be divided into equal starting groups. Find 3 different ways to divide 36 runners into equal groups.
   a. ____ groups of ____ = 36
   b. ____ groups of ____ = 36
   c. ____ groups of ____ = 36
   Possible answers: 3 groups of 12, 9 groups of 4, 4 groups of 9, 6 groups of 6, 2 groups of 18.
10. What if there are only 12 runners? Find 3 different ways to divide 12 runners into equal groups.
   a. ____ groups of ____ = 12
   b. ____ groups of ____ = 12
   c. ____ groups of ____ = 12
   Possible answers: 4 groups of 3, 3 groups of 4, 2 groups of 6, 6 groups of 2

Name ____________________

Practice
Chapter 3
Section C

Review and Practice

Vocabulary Underline the term that will complete the sentence correctly.

1. The (quotient, product) is the answer to a division problem.
2. The (quotient, remainder) is the number left over after dividing.

(Lesson 11) Use mental math to find each quotient.

3. 300 ÷ 6 = **50**
4. 320 ÷ 8 = **40**
5. 630 ÷ 7 = **90**
6. 160 ÷ 4 = **40**
7. Sarah's family is going on a 120-minute walk. They stop to rest 3 times. How often to they stop to rest? **every 40 minutes**

(Lesson 12) Estimate each quotient.

8. 31 ÷ 5 = **6**
9. 46 ÷ 9 = **5**
10. 19 ÷ 3 = **6**
11. 52 ÷ 7 = **7**

(Lessons 13 and 14) Find each quotient and remainder.

12. 2)9 **4 R1**
13. 6)43 **7 R1**
14. 4)29 **7 R1**
15. 5)47 **9 R2**
16. 69 ÷ 9 = **7 R6**
17. 58 ÷ 7 = **8 R2**
18. A bottle holds 9 ounces. How many bottles are needed to hold 57 ounces? Will all the bottles be full? Explain.
   7; no; there will be 6 full bottles and 1 bottle with only 3 ounces in it.

(Mixed Review) Add or subtract.

19. 135 + 222 = **357**
20. 504 − 243 = **261**
21. 379 − 84 = **295**
22. 803 + 59 = **862**

Name ____________________

Cumulative Review

(Chapter 7 Lesson 9) Write which operation you would use. Then solve.

1. Mickey bought a dog collar for $5.95. He also bought a 4-pound bag of dog food for $6.19. How much money did he spend? **Addition; $12.14**

(Chapter 8 Lesson 4) Write whether each angle is a right angle, less than a right angle, or greater than a right angle.

2. 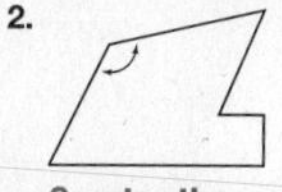 **Greater than a right angle**
3. 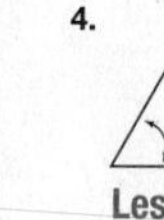 **Equal to a right angle**
4. 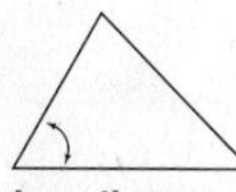 **Less than a right angle**

(Chapter 8 Lesson 11) Find the volume of each shape. You may use cubes to help.

5. 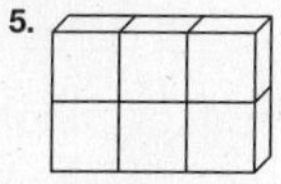 **6**
6. 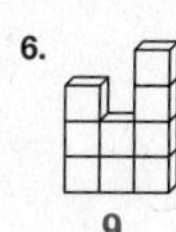 **9**

(Chapter 9 Lessons 6 and 7) Multiply.

7. 37 × 6 = **222**
8. 21 × 8 = **168**
9. 75 × 7 = **525**
10. 63 × 4 = **252**
11. 465 × 5 = **2,325**
12. 307 × 9 = **2,763**
13. 243 × 4 = **972**
14. 500 × 3 = **1,500**

(Chapter 9 Lesson 14)

15. 4)29 **7 R1**
16. 9)71 **7 R8**
17. 3)28 **9 R1**
18. 6)23 **3 R5**

Name ____________________

Practice
10-1

Exploring Equal Parts

Tell how many equal parts.

1. 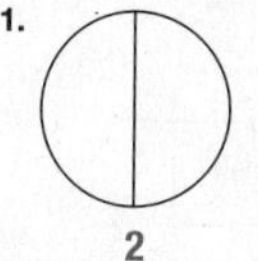 **2**
2. 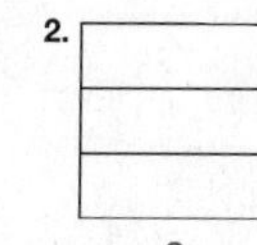 **3**
3. 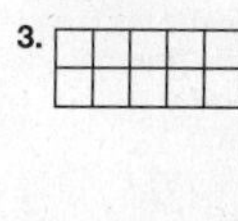 **10**

Write whether each has equal parts or unequal parts.

4. 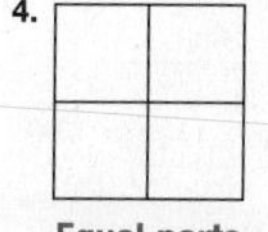 **Equal parts**
5. 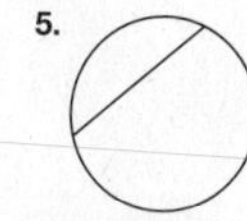 **Unequal parts**
6. 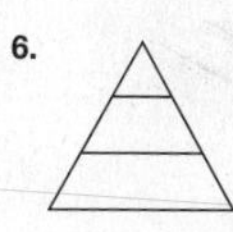 **Unequal parts**

Name the equal parts of each whole.

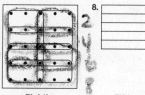

7. **Eighths**
8. **Fifths**
9. 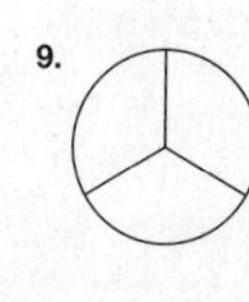 **Thirds**

Draw a picture to show each. You may use grid paper to help.

10. thirds **Look for a whole with 3 equal parts.**
11. fourths **Look for a whole with 4 equal parts.**
12. tenths **Look for a whole with 10 equal parts.**

Name ______________________

Practice 10-2

Naming and Writing Fractions

Write the fraction of each figure that is shaded.

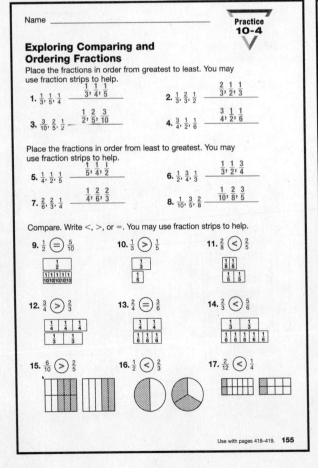

1. 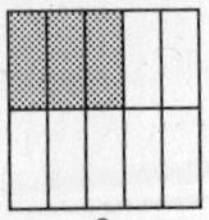 $\frac{3}{10}$
2. 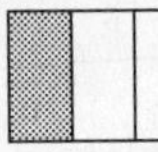 $\frac{1}{3}$
3. 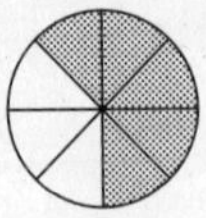 $\frac{5}{8}$
4. 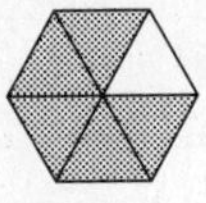 $\frac{5}{6}$
5. 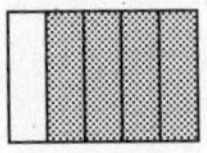 $\frac{4}{5}$
6. 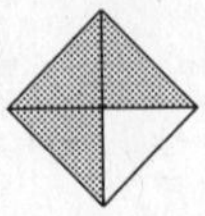 $\frac{3}{4}$

Draw a picture to show each fraction.

7. $\frac{3}{6}$ shaded 8. $\frac{1}{10}$ shaded 9. $\frac{7}{12}$ shaded

Look for pictures with the correct number of equal parts shaded.

10. $\frac{1}{6}$ shaded 11. $\frac{3}{5}$ shaded 12. $\frac{2}{4}$ shaded

Look for pictures with the correct number of equal parts shaded.

13. Khalifa says "$\frac{2}{4}$ of the Maryland flag has one design, and $\frac{2}{4}$ has another design." Do you agree or disagree? Explain.

Agree; it's divided into 4 equal parts, and 2 of the parts have one design, 2 have another.

Name ______________________

Practice 10-3

Exploring Equivalent Fractions

Complete. You may use fraction strips to help.

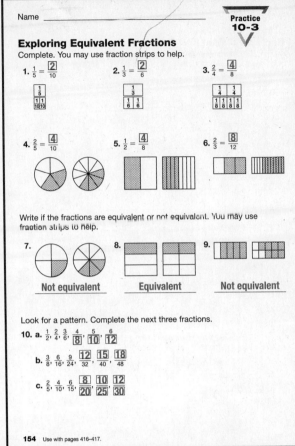

1. $\frac{1}{5} = \frac{2}{10}$ 
2. $\frac{1}{3} = \frac{2}{6}$ 
3. $\frac{2}{4} = \frac{4}{8}$ 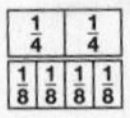
4. $\frac{2}{5} = \frac{4}{10}$ 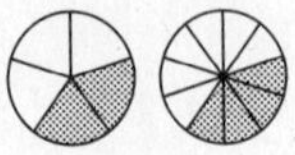
5. $\frac{1}{2} = \frac{4}{8}$ 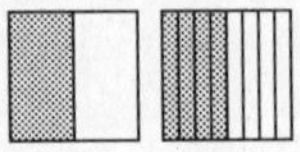
6. $\frac{2}{3} = \frac{8}{12}$

Write if the fractions are equivalent or not equivalent. You may use fraction strips to help.

7. 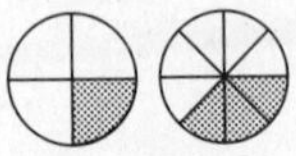 **Not equivalent**
8. 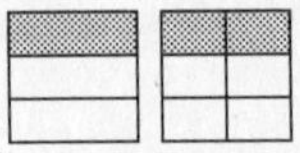 **Equivalent**
9.  **Not equivalent**

Look for a pattern. Complete the next three fractions.

10. a. $\frac{1}{2}, \frac{2}{4}, \frac{3}{6}, \frac{4}{8}, \frac{5}{10}, \frac{6}{12}$

b. $\frac{3}{8}, \frac{6}{16}, \frac{9}{24}, \frac{12}{32}, \frac{15}{40}, \frac{18}{48}$

c. $\frac{2}{5}, \frac{4}{10}, \frac{6}{15}, \frac{8}{20}, \frac{10}{25}, \frac{12}{30}$

Name ______________________

Practice 10-4

Exploring Comparing and Ordering Fractions

Place the fractions in order from greatest to least. You may use fraction strips to help.

1. $\frac{1}{3}, \frac{1}{5}, \frac{1}{4}$ — $\frac{1}{3}, \frac{1}{4}, \frac{1}{5}$
2. $\frac{1}{3}, \frac{2}{3}, \frac{1}{2}$ — $\frac{2}{3}, \frac{1}{2}, \frac{1}{3}$
3. $\frac{3}{10}, \frac{2}{5}, \frac{1}{2}$ — $\frac{1}{2}, \frac{2}{5}, \frac{3}{10}$
4. $\frac{3}{4}, \frac{1}{2}, \frac{1}{6}$ — $\frac{3}{4}, \frac{1}{2}, \frac{1}{6}$

Place the fractions in order from least to greatest. You may use fraction strips to help.

5. $\frac{1}{4}, \frac{1}{2}, \frac{1}{5}$ — $\frac{1}{5}, \frac{1}{4}, \frac{1}{2}$
6. $\frac{1}{2}, \frac{3}{4}, \frac{1}{3}$ — $\frac{1}{3}, \frac{1}{2}, \frac{3}{4}$
7. $\frac{2}{6}, \frac{2}{3}, \frac{1}{4}$ — $\frac{1}{4}, \frac{2}{6}, \frac{2}{3}$
8. $\frac{1}{10}, \frac{3}{5}, \frac{2}{8}$ — $\frac{1}{10}, \frac{2}{8}, \frac{3}{5}$

Compare. Write <, >, or =. You may use fraction strips to help.

9. $\frac{1}{2} = \frac{5}{10}$ 
10. $\frac{1}{3} > \frac{1}{5}$ 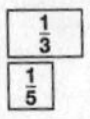
11. $\frac{2}{8} < \frac{2}{5}$
12. $\frac{3}{4} > \frac{2}{3}$ 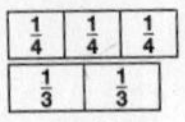
13. $\frac{2}{4} = \frac{3}{6}$ 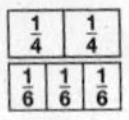
14. $\frac{2}{3} < \frac{5}{6}$
15. $\frac{6}{10} > \frac{2}{5}$ 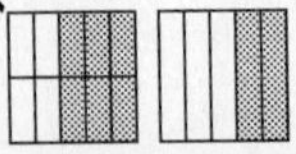
16. $\frac{1}{2} < \frac{2}{3}$
17. $\frac{2}{12} < \frac{1}{4}$

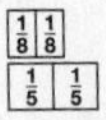

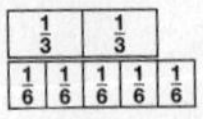

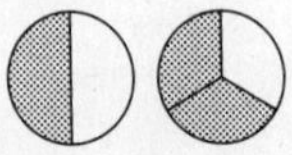

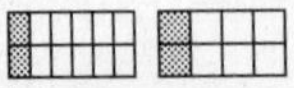

Name ______________________

Practice 10-5

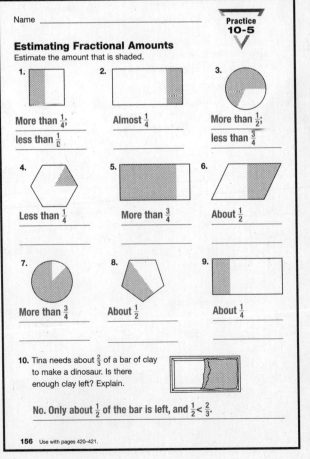

Estimating Fractional Amounts

Estimate the amount that is shaded.

1. **More than $\frac{1}{4}$; less than $\frac{1}{2}$**
2. 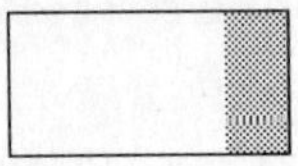 **Almost $\frac{1}{4}$**
3. 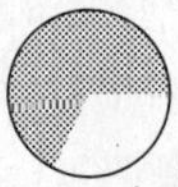 **More than $\frac{1}{2}$; less than $\frac{3}{4}$**
4. 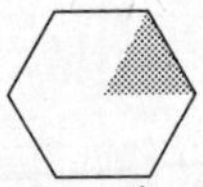 **Less than $\frac{1}{4}$**
5. 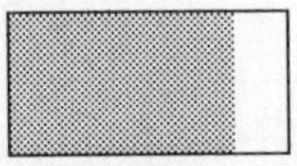 **More than $\frac{3}{4}$**
6. 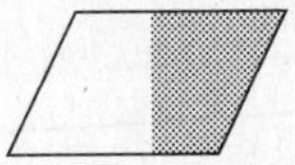 **About $\frac{1}{2}$**
7. 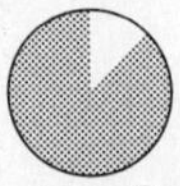 **More than $\frac{3}{4}$**
8. 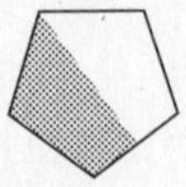 **About $\frac{1}{2}$**
9. 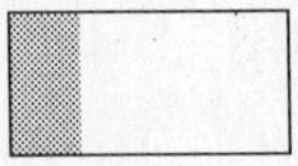 **About $\frac{1}{4}$**

10. Tina needs about $\frac{2}{3}$ of a bar of clay to make a dinosaur. Is there enough clay left? Explain.

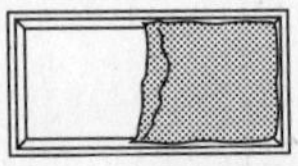

No. Only about $\frac{1}{2}$ of the bar is left, and $\frac{1}{2} < \frac{2}{3}$.

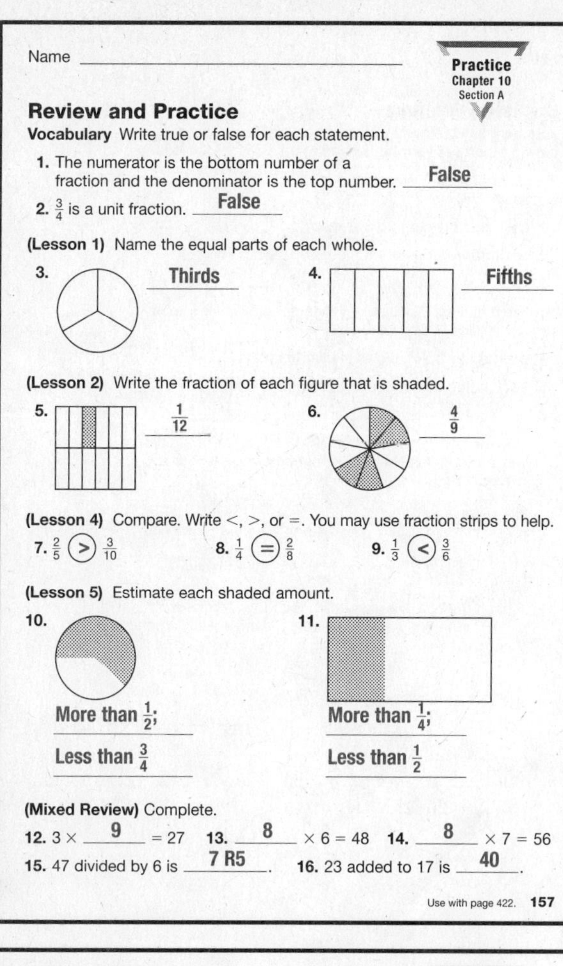

Name ____________________

Practice
Chapter 10
Section A

Review and Practice

Vocabulary Write true or false for each statement.

1. The numerator is the bottom number of a fraction and the denominator is the top number. **False**
2. $\frac{3}{4}$ is a unit fraction. **False**

(Lesson 1) Name the equal parts of each whole.

3. **Thirds** 4. **Fifths**

(Lesson 2) Write the fraction of each figure that is shaded.

5. $\frac{1}{12}$ 6. $\frac{4}{9}$

(Lesson 4) Compare. Write <, >, or =. You may use fraction strips to help.

7. $\frac{2}{5}$ (>) $\frac{3}{10}$ 8. $\frac{1}{4}$ (=) $\frac{2}{8}$ 9. $\frac{1}{3}$ (<) $\frac{3}{6}$

(Lesson 5) Estimate each shaded amount.

10. **More than $\frac{1}{2}$; Less than $\frac{3}{4}$**
11. **More than $\frac{1}{4}$; Less than $\frac{1}{2}$**

(Mixed Review) Complete.

12. 3 × **9** = 27 13. **8** × 6 = 48 14. **8** × 7 = 56
15. 47 divided by 6 is **7 R5**. 16. 23 added to 17 is **40**.

Use with page 422. 157

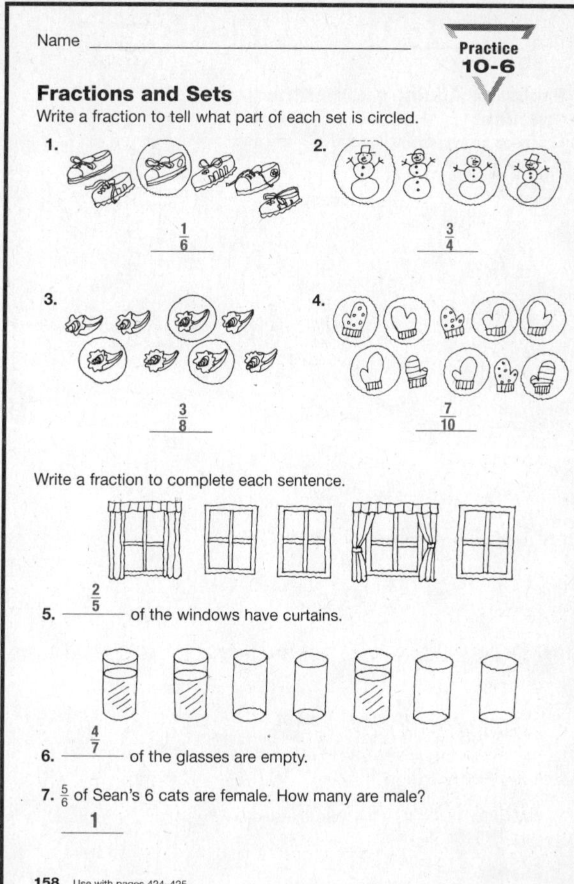

Name ____________________

Practice
10-6

Fractions and Sets

Write a fraction to tell what part of each set is circled.

1. $\frac{1}{6}$ 2. $\frac{3}{4}$
3. $\frac{3}{8}$ 4. $\frac{7}{10}$

Write a fraction to complete each sentence.

5. $\frac{2}{5}$ of the windows have curtains.

6. $\frac{4}{7}$ of the glasses are empty.

7. $\frac{5}{6}$ of Sean's 6 cats are female. How many are male? **1**

158 Use with pages 424–425.

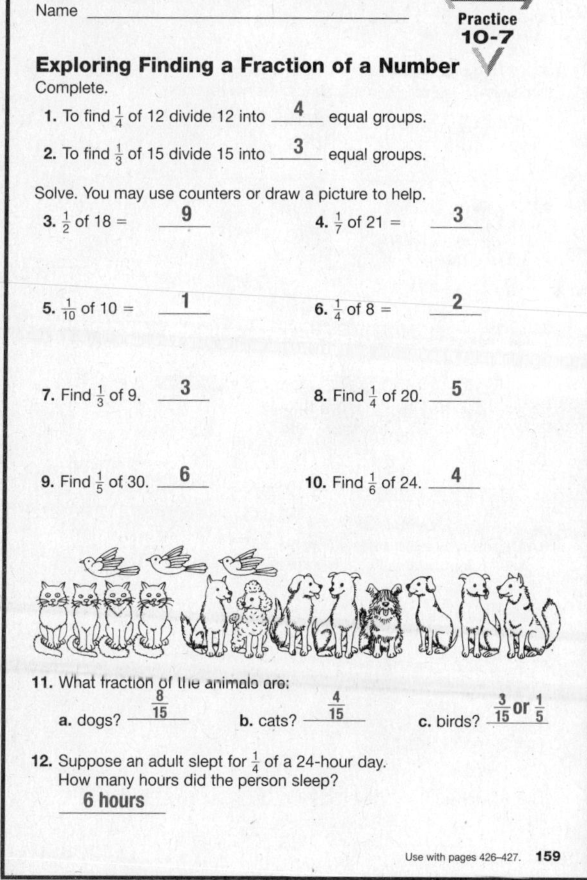

Name ____________________

Practice
10-7

Exploring Finding a Fraction of a Number

Complete.

1. To find $\frac{1}{4}$ of 12 divide 12 into **4** equal groups.
2. To find $\frac{1}{3}$ of 15 divide 15 into **3** equal groups.

Solve. You may use counters or draw a picture to help.

3. $\frac{1}{2}$ of 18 = **9** 4. $\frac{1}{7}$ of 21 = **3**
5. $\frac{1}{10}$ of 10 = **1** 6. $\frac{1}{4}$ of 8 = **2**
7. Find $\frac{1}{3}$ of 9. **3** 8. Find $\frac{1}{4}$ of 20. **5**
9. Find $\frac{1}{5}$ of 30. **6** 10. Find $\frac{1}{6}$ of 24. **4**

11. What fraction of the animals are:
a. dogs? $\frac{8}{15}$ b. cats? $\frac{4}{15}$ c. birds? $\frac{3}{15}$ or $\frac{1}{5}$

12. Suppose an adult slept for $\frac{1}{4}$ of a 24-hour day. How many hours did the person sleep? **6 hours**

Use with pages 426–427. 159

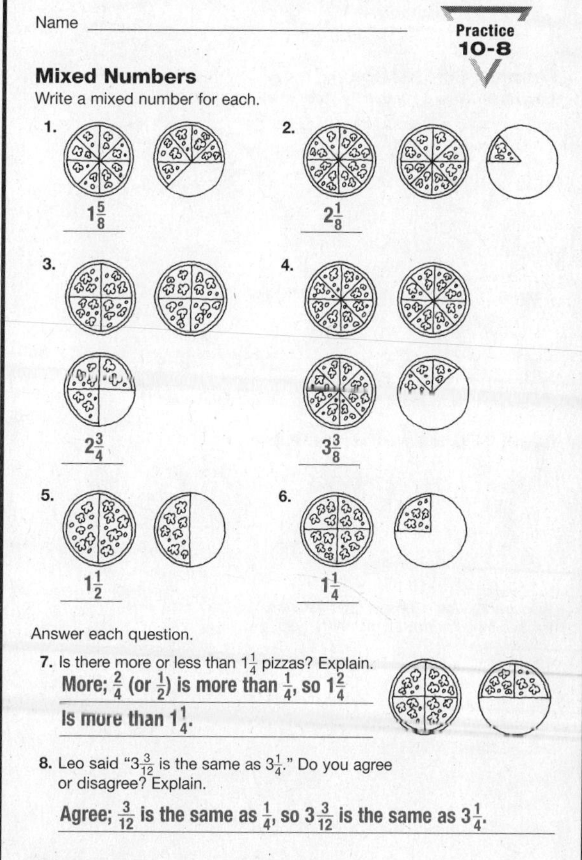

Name ____________________

Practice
10-8

Mixed Numbers

Write a mixed number for each.

1. $1\frac{5}{8}$ 2. $2\frac{1}{8}$
3. $2\frac{3}{4}$ 4. $3\frac{3}{8}$
5. $1\frac{1}{2}$ 6. $1\frac{1}{4}$

Answer each question.

7. Is there more or less than $1\frac{1}{4}$ pizzas? Explain.
More; $\frac{2}{4}$ (or $\frac{1}{2}$) is more than $\frac{1}{4}$, so $1\frac{2}{4}$ is more than $1\frac{1}{4}$.

8. Leo said "$3\frac{3}{12}$ is the same as $3\frac{1}{4}$." Do you agree or disagree? Explain.
Agree; $\frac{3}{12}$ is the same as $\frac{1}{4}$, so $3\frac{3}{12}$ is the same as $3\frac{1}{4}$.

160 Use with pages 428–429.

Name ______________________

Practice 10-9

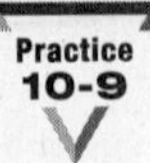

Exploring Adding and Subtracting Fractions

Find each sum or difference. You may use fraction strips or draw a picture to help.

1. $\frac{3}{5} + \frac{1}{5} = \frac{4}{5}$
2. $\frac{1}{4} + \frac{2}{4} = \frac{3}{4}$
3. $\frac{3}{5} - \frac{1}{5} = \frac{2}{5}$
4. $\frac{3}{4} - \frac{2}{4} = \frac{1}{4}$
5. $\frac{2}{6} + \frac{3}{6} = \frac{5}{6}$
6. $\frac{1}{5} + \frac{1}{5} = \frac{2}{5}$
7. $\frac{9}{12} - \frac{4}{12} = \frac{5}{12}$
8. $\frac{2}{9} - \frac{1}{9} = \frac{1}{9}$
9. $\frac{9}{10} - \frac{4}{10} = \frac{5}{10}$ or $\frac{1}{2}$
10. $\frac{9}{16} + \frac{2}{16} = \frac{11}{16}$
11. $\frac{1}{4} + \frac{1}{4} = \frac{2}{4}$ or $\frac{1}{2}$
12. $\frac{4}{7} - \frac{1}{7} = \frac{3}{7}$
13. $\frac{1}{3} + \frac{1}{3} = \frac{2}{3}$
14. $\frac{2}{6} - \frac{1}{6} = \frac{1}{6}$
15. $\frac{5}{8} - \frac{3}{8} = \frac{2}{8}$ or $\frac{1}{4}$
16. $\frac{9}{12} - \frac{7}{12} = \frac{2}{12}$ or $\frac{1}{6}$
17. Suppose you knocked over 9 out of 10 bowling pins. What fraction of the pins would still be standing? $\frac{1}{10}$
18. Suppose 5 out of 10 bowling pins were still standing. What fraction of the pins were knocked over? $\frac{5}{10}$

Name ______________________

Practice 10-10

Decision Making

Your school won the city chess championship! Your team is having a party at your house and there are 8 players to feed.

You want at least 3 pieces of pizza per player. How many pizzas will you need if . . .

1. each pizza is cut into 6 pieces? 4
2. each pizza is cut into 8 pieces? 3
3. each pizza is cut into 10 pieces? 3

You want at least 2 glasses of juice per player. How many bottles of juice will you need if . . .

4. each bottle holds 6 glasses worth of juice? 3
5. each bottle holds 10 glasses worth of juice? 2
6. each bottle holds 4 glasses worth of juice? 4
7. Don't forget the victory cake! Can you think of 2 different ways to cut it so everyone gets the same number of pieces?
   a. 8 pieces
   b. 16 pieces

8. What if the coach wants cake, too? Draw pictures to show 2 different ways to divide the cake equally among 9 people.

Possible answers:

a. 

b. 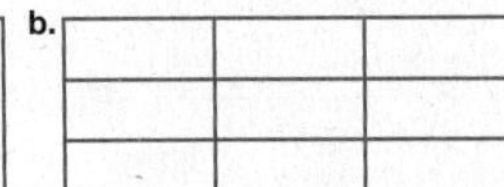

Name ______________________

Practice Chapter 10 Section B

Review and Practice

(Lesson 6) Write a fraction that tells what part of the set is circled.

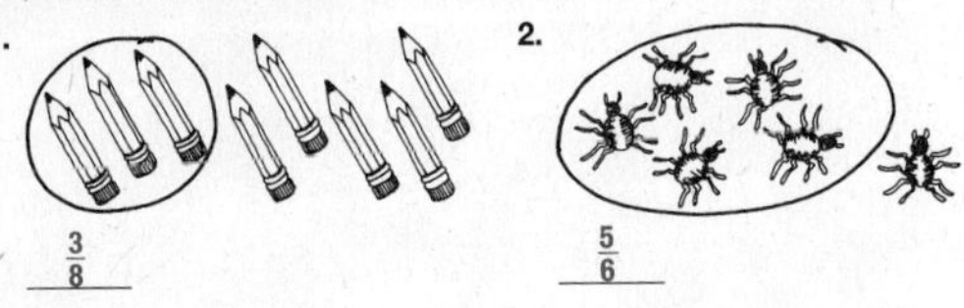

1. $\frac{3}{8}$
2. $\frac{5}{6}$

(Lesson 7) Solve. You may use counters or draw a picture to help.

3. Find $\frac{1}{4}$ of 24. 6
4. Find $\frac{1}{3}$ of 12. 4
5. Find $\frac{1}{5}$ of 20. 4
6. Find $\frac{1}{2}$ of 14. 7
7. Mitch has $18. He did put $\frac{1}{3}$ of the money in his savings account. How much did he put in his savings account? $6

(Lesson 8) Write a mixed number for each.

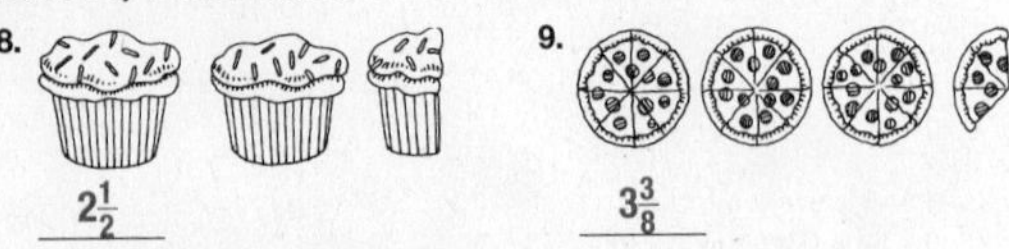

8. $2\frac{1}{2}$
9. $3\frac{3}{8}$

(Lesson 9) Find each sum or difference. You may use fraction strips or draw a picture to help.

10. $\frac{1}{6} + \frac{4}{6} = \frac{5}{6}$
11. $\frac{4}{5} - \frac{1}{5} = \frac{3}{5}$
12. $\frac{7}{9} - \frac{3}{9} = \frac{4}{9}$
13. $\frac{3}{8} + \frac{2}{8} = \frac{5}{8}$

(Mixed Review) Add or subtract.

14. $62 + 33 = 95$
15. $98 - 19 = 79$
16. $80 + 73 = 153$
17. $82 - 45 = 37$

Name ______________________

Practice 10-11

Exploring Length

Estimate each length. Then measure to the nearest inch.

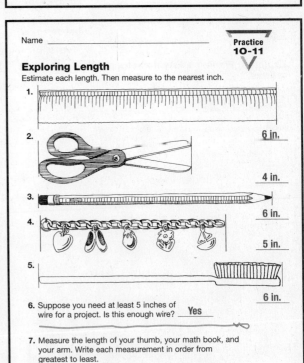

1. 6 in.
2. 4 in.
3. 6 in.
4. 5 in.
5. 6 in.
6. Suppose you need at least 5 inches of wire for a project. Is this enough wire? Yes
7. Measure the length of your thumb, your math book, and your arm. Write each measurement in order from greatest to least.
   Measurements will vary; arm, math book, thumb
8. Use a ruler. Draw a line to show each length.
   a. $2\frac{1}{2}$ inches
   b. 5 inches
   c. $6\frac{1}{4}$ inches

   Check lengths for accuracy.

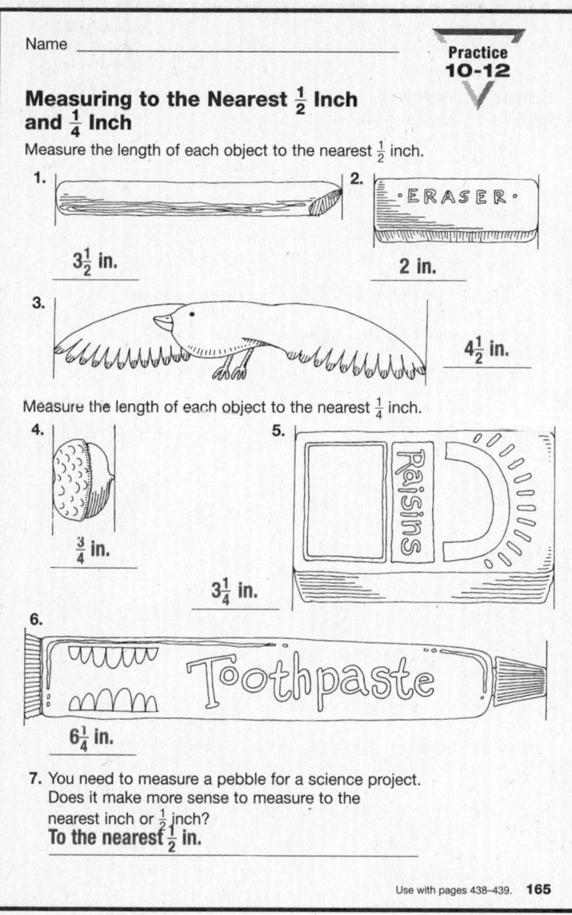

Name ______

Practice 10-12

Measuring to the Nearest $\frac{1}{2}$ Inch and $\frac{1}{4}$ Inch

Measure the length of each object to the nearest $\frac{1}{2}$ inch.

1. $3\frac{1}{2}$ in.
2. 2 in.
3. $4\frac{1}{2}$ in.

Measure the length of each object to the nearest $\frac{1}{4}$ inch.

4. $\frac{3}{4}$ in.
5. $3\frac{1}{4}$ in.
6. $6\frac{1}{4}$ in.

7. You need to measure a pebble for a science project. Does it make more sense to measure to the nearest inch or $\frac{1}{2}$ inch?
To the nearest $\frac{1}{2}$ in.

Use with pages 438–439. 165

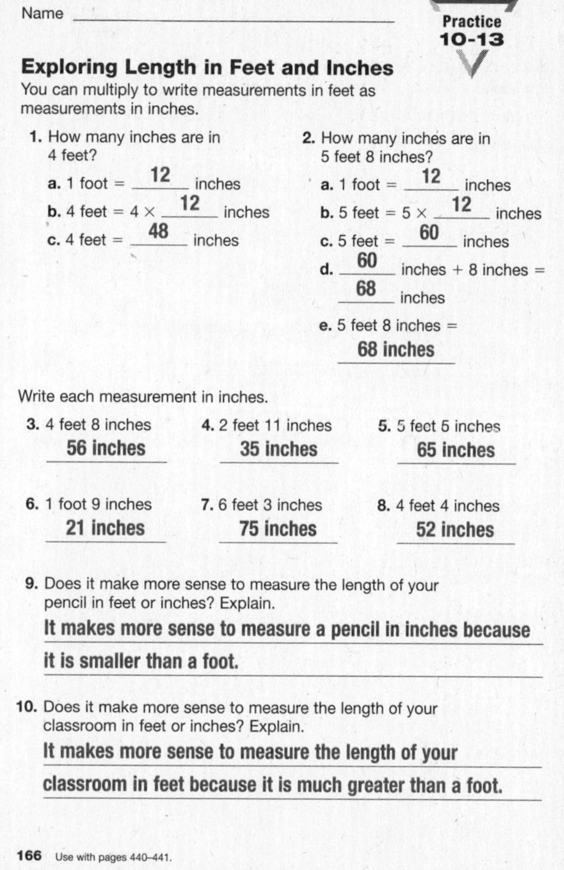

Name ______

Practice 10-13

Exploring Length in Feet and Inches

You can multiply to write measurements in feet as measurements in inches.

1. How many inches are in 4 feet?
   a. 1 foot = **12** inches
   b. 4 feet = 4 × **12** inches
   c. 4 feet = **48** inches
2. How many inches are in 5 feet 8 inches?
   a. 1 foot = **12** inches
   b. 5 feet = 5 × **12** inches
   c. 5 feet = **60** inches
   d. **60** inches + 8 inches = **68** inches
   e. 5 feet 8 inches = **68 inches**

Write each measurement in inches.

3. 4 feet 8 inches **56 inches**
4. 2 feet 11 inches **35 inches**
5. 5 feet 5 inches **65 inches**
6. 1 foot 9 inches **21 inches**
7. 6 feet 3 inches **75 inches**
8. 4 feet 4 inches **52 inches**
9. Does it make more sense to measure the length of your pencil in feet or inches? Explain.
It makes more sense to measure a pencil in inches because it is smaller than a foot.
10. Does it make more sense to measure the length of your classroom in feet or inches? Explain.
It makes more sense to measure the length of your classroom in feet because it is much greater than a foot.

166 Use with pages 440–441.

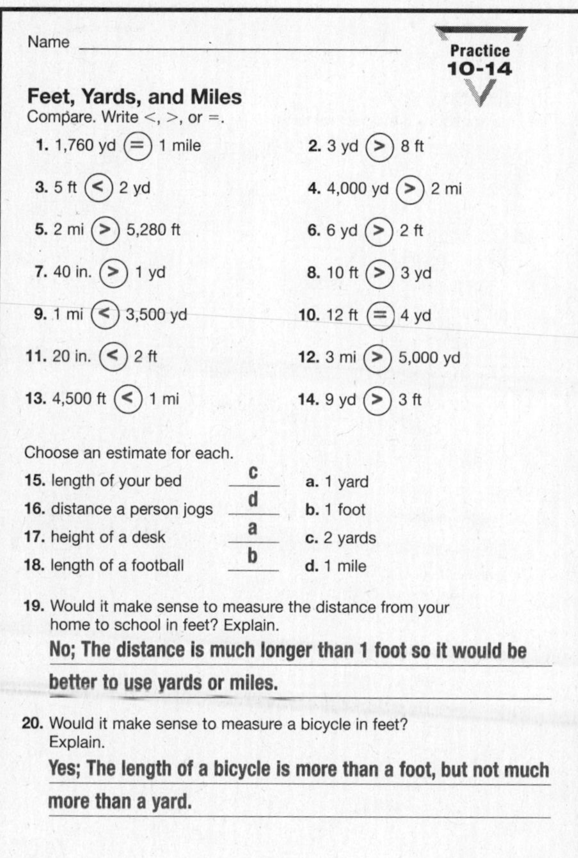

Name ______

Practice 10-14

Feet, Yards, and Miles

Compare. Write <, >, or =.

1. 1,760 yd (=) 1 mile
2. 3 yd (>) 8 ft
3. 5 ft (<) 2 yd
4. 4,000 yd (>) 2 mi
5. 2 mi (>) 5,280 ft
6. 6 yd (>) 2 ft
7. 40 in. (>) 1 yd
8. 10 ft (>) 3 yd
9. 1 mi (<) 3,500 yd
10. 12 ft (=) 4 yd
11. 20 in. (<) 2 ft
12. 3 mi (>) 5,000 yd
13. 4,500 ft (<) 1 mi
14. 9 yd (>) 3 ft

Choose an estimate for each.

15. length of your bed **c** — a. 1 yard
16. distance a person jogs **d** — b. 1 foot
17. height of a desk **a** — c. 2 yards
18. length of a football **b** — d. 1 mile
19. Would it make sense to measure the distance from your home to school in feet? Explain.
No; The distance is much longer than 1 foot so it would be better to use yards or miles.
20. Would it make sense to measure a bicycle in feet? Explain.
Yes; The length of a bicycle is more than a foot, but not much more than a yard.

Use with pages 442–443. 167

Name ______

Practice 10-15

Analyze Strategies: Use Logical Reasoning

Use logical reasoning to solve.

1. Help Peter figure out which soccer teams finished in first, second, third, and fourth place. The Wings finished in third place. The Hawks beat the Eagles and the Wings. The Tigers finished in last place.
Hawks, Eagles, Wings, Tigers
2. Ramon, Max, Jenna, and Maya are all on the same soccer team. Max is the youngest. Maya is older than Ramon. Jenna is 10 years old. If each player is either 9, 10, 11, or 12 years old, how old is each person?
Max is 9, Jenna is 10, Ramon is 11, and Maya is 12.

Use any strategy to solve.

3. Sean, Sharon, Ali, and Marie all have scored goals this season. Sharon has scored more goals than Ali and Sean. Sean has scored fewer goals than the three other players. Sharon has scored fewer goals than Marie. Order the players from greatest number of goals scored to fewest.
Marie, Sharon, Ali, Sean
4. I am an even number between 20 and 30. The sum of my tens digit and my ones digit is 6. What number am I? **24**
5. I am an odd number between 50 and 60. The sum of my tens digit and my ones digit is 10. What number am I? **55**
6. Mickey has 5 coins. The total value of the coins is \$0.60. He doesn't have any pennies and only has 1 nickel. What coins does Mickey have?
1 quarter, 1 nickel, 3 dimes
7. I am a number between 10 and 20. The difference between my digits is 0. What number am I? **11**

168 Use with pages 444–445.

Name ______________________

Practice Chapter 10 Section C

Review and Practice

Vocabulary Write true or false for each statement.

1. Kevin can walk 1 mile in 1 second. **False**
2. This paper is about 1 foot in length. **True**

(Lesson 11) Measure the length of the object to the nearest inch.

3. **3 inches**

(Lesson 12) Measure the length of the object to the nearest $\frac{1}{4}$ inch.

4. **$2\frac{3}{4}$ inches**

(Lesson 13) Write each measurement in inches.

5. 8 feet **96**
6. 3 feet **36**
7. 2 feet **24**

(Lesson 14) Compare. Write <, >, or =.

8. 2 feet **(>)** 22 inches
9. 2 yards **(=)** 6 feet
10. 5 yards **(>)** 140 inches
11. 3 miles **(<)** 21,120 feet

(Lesson 15) Use any strategy to solve.

12. Freda has 9 coins worth $1. Two are quarters. None are pennies. There is 1 more nickel than there are dimes. What coins does Freda have?

2 quarters, 3 dimes, 4 nickels

(Mixed Review) Multiply or divide.

13. $6 \times 2 =$ **12**
14. $32 \div 8 =$ **4**

Name ______________________

Practice Chapters 1–10

Cumulative Review

(Chapter 4 Lesson 10) Subtract.

1. $673 - 425 =$ **248**
2. $315 - 99 =$ **216**
3. $830 - 609 =$ **221**
4. $749 - 73 =$ **676**

(Chapter 9 Lesson 8) Multiply.

5. $3.29 × 3 = **$9.87**
6. $3.10 × 4 = **$12.40**
7. $9.01 × 5 = **$45.05**

(Chapter 9 Lesson 13) Find each quotient and remainder. You may use counters to help.

8. $3\overline{)13}$ **4 R1**
9. $5\overline{)48}$ **9 R3**
10. $7\overline{)59}$ **8 R3**
11. $2\overline{)19}$ **9 R1**

(Chapter 10 Lesson 2) Write the fraction of each figure that is shaded.

12. 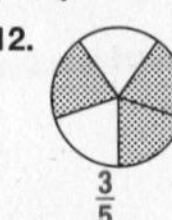 $\frac{3}{5}$

13. 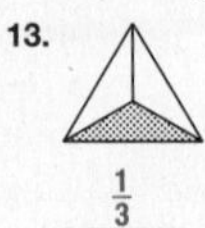 $\frac{1}{3}$

(Chapter 10 Lesson 4) Compare. Write <, >, or =. You may use fraction strips to help.

14. $\frac{1}{4}$ **(<)** $\frac{5}{8}$
15. $\frac{3}{6}$ **(>)** $\frac{5}{12}$
16. $\frac{2}{4}$ **(=)** $\frac{4}{8}$
17. $\frac{4}{5}$ **(>)** $\frac{5}{10}$
18. $\frac{1}{2}$ **(<)** $\frac{2}{3}$
19. $\frac{3}{4}$ **(>)** $\frac{8}{12}$

(Chapter 10 Lesson 9) Find each sum or difference. You may use fraction strips or draw a picture to help.

20. $\frac{6}{8} + \frac{1}{8} =$ **$\frac{7}{8}$**
21. $\frac{2}{5} + \frac{3}{5} =$ **$\frac{5}{5}$ or 1**
22. $\frac{6}{9} - \frac{3}{9} =$ **$\frac{3}{9}$ or $\frac{1}{3}$**
23. $\frac{7}{8} - \frac{5}{8} =$ **$\frac{2}{8}$ or $\frac{1}{4}$**

Name ______________________

Practice 11-1

Exploring Tenths

Any number in tenths can be written as a fraction or as a decimal.

Complete the table.

	Grids	Fraction or Mixed Number	Decimal	Word Name
1.		$\frac{3}{10}$	0.3	**three tenths**
2.		$1\frac{1}{10}$	**1.1**	one and one tenth

Write the fraction and the decimal to name each shaded part.

3. 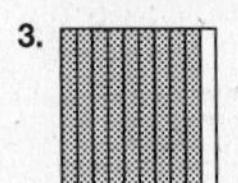 **$\frac{9}{10}$; 0.9**

4. 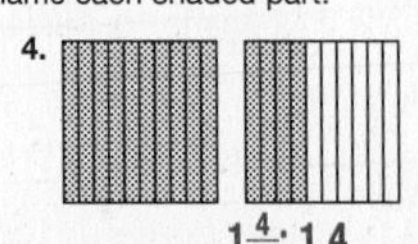 **$1\frac{4}{10}$; 1.4**

Write each as a decimal.

5. eight tenths **0.8**
6. $\frac{5}{10}$ **0.5**
7. two and two tenths **2.2**
8. $1\frac{6}{10}$ **1.6**

9. Write each part of the circle as a fraction and a decimal.

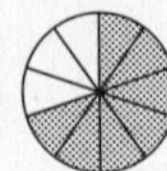

		Fraction	Decimal
a.	Shaded	$\frac{7}{10}$	**0.7**
b.	Not shaded	$\frac{3}{10}$	**0.3**

Name ______________________

Practice 11-2

Hundredths

Write the fraction and the decimal to name each shaded part.

1. 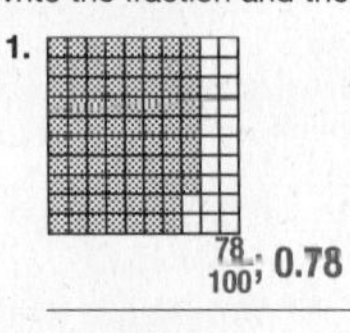 **$\frac{78}{100}$; 0.78**

2. 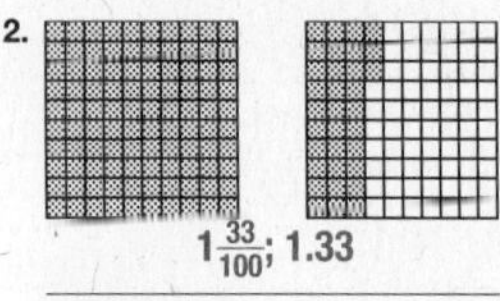 **$1\frac{33}{100}$; 1.33**

3. 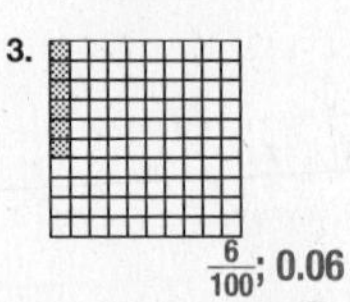 **$\frac{6}{100}$; 0.06**

4. 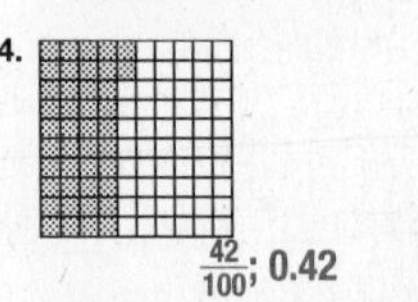 **$\frac{42}{100}$; 0.42**

Write each as a decimal.

5. seventeen hundredths **0.17**
6. nine hundredths **0.09**
7. one and three hundredths **1.03**
8. $\frac{22}{100}$ **0.22**
9. fifty-one hundredths **0.51**
10. $\frac{1}{100}$ **0.01**
11. $2\frac{65}{100}$ **2.65**
12. $1\frac{99}{100}$ **1.99**

13. Is 0.70 greater than, less than, or equal to 0.7? Explain.

Equal to; 70 hundredths is equal to 7 tenths.

14. What is the value of each bold digit?

a. 0.**8**4 **8 tenths**
b. 1.3**2** **2 hundredths**
c. **3**.59 **3 ones**

Name ______________________

Practice 11-3

Exploring Adding and Subtracting Decimals

You can add and subtract decimals using pencil and paper. You may use tenths grids to help.

1. Add 1.4 and 0.8.

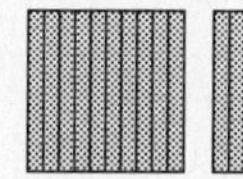

a. Write the equation vertically in the space below. Line up the decimal points.

  1.4
+ 0.8

b. Add tenths. Regroup if needed. Then add ones. What is the sum? **2.2**

2. Subtract 1.6 from 2.5.

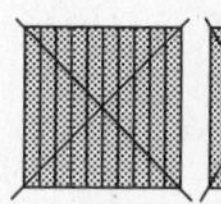
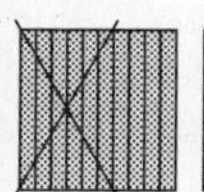

a. Write the equation vertically in the space below. Line up the decimal points.

  2.5
− 1.6

b. Subtract tenths. Regroup if needed. Then subtract ones. What is the difference? **0.9**

Find each sum or difference. You may use tenths grids to help.

3. 3.3 + 2.2 = **5.5**
4. 1.9 + 4.5 = **6.4**
5. 8.6 − 3.4 = **5.2**
6. 6.2 − 4.8 = **1.4**
7. 0.7 + 0.3 = **1.0**
8. 2.2 − 1.9 = **0.3**
9. 5.8 − 0.7 = **5.1**
10. 1.5 + 1.6 = **3.1**

Name ______________________

Practice 11-4

Connecting Decimals and Money

Write each as a money amount.

1. $\frac{73}{100}$ of \$1.00 **\$0.73**
2. $\frac{39}{100}$ of \$1.00 **\$0.39**
3. $1\frac{15}{100}$ of \$1.00 **\$1.15**
4. $\frac{51}{100}$ of \$1.00 **\$0.51**
5. $2\frac{27}{100}$ of \$1.00 **\$2.27**
6. $\frac{98}{100}$ of \$1.00 **\$0.98**
7. sixty-six cents **\$0.66**
8. forty-two cents **\$0.42**
9. one dollar and ninety-one cents **\$1.91**
10. three dollars and three cents **\$3.03**
11. five dollars and twelve cents **\$5.12**
12. two dollars and eighty-eight cents **\$2.88**
13. fifty-four hundredths of \$1.00 **\$0.54**
14. three and thirty-seven hundredths of \$1.00 **\$3.37**
15. Complete the table.

		Fraction of \$1.00	Decimal Part of \$1.00
a.	\$0.74	$\frac{74}{100}$	0.74
b.	\$0.02	$\frac{2}{100}$	0.02
c.	\$0.19	$\frac{19}{100}$	0.19

Name ______________________

Practice 11-5

Decision Making

You've decided to purchase a get-well gift for a friend who is ill. You want to go to the local mall to shop for the gift. Your goal is to find the perfect present and to be home by 5:00 P.M. You are bringing \$10.00 with you. Below is a copy of the bus schedule for the bus which will take you to the mall. The bus stops on Carey Ave. right outside your house.

Leave Carey Ave.	Arrive Milford Mall	Leave Milford Mall	Arrive Carey Ave.
2:00 P.M.	2:15 P.M.	3:15 P.M.	4:00 P.M.
4:00 P.M.	4:15 P.M.	4:30 P.M.	4:45 P.M.

1. What information does the schedule give you?
When the bus leaves the bus stop, when it arrives at the mall, when it leaves the mall, and when it returns to Carey Ave.

2. When is the latest time you could leave the mall in order to get home on time?
4:30 P.M. (will arrive at Carey Ave. bus stop at 4:45 P.M., 15 minutes before 5:00 P.M.)

3. How long does it take the bus to get to the mall from your bus stop on Carey Ave.? **15 minutes**

4. If the one-way bus fare is \$0.50, how much spending money do you actually have?
\$9.00. (\$0.50 + \$0.50 = \$1.00. \$10.00 − \$1.00 = \$9.00)

5. You buy a shirt for your friend. It costs \$8.00. How much money do you have left over to buy a snack? (Don't forget about the bus fare!)
\$1.00. (\$9.00 − \$8.00 = \$1.00)

6. A muffin costs \$0.60. Do you have enough money to buy one for your snack? **Yes**
Could you buy two muffins?
No; \$0.60 × 2 = \$1.20. I only have \$1.00 for a snack.

Name ______________________

Practice Chapter 11 Section A

Review and Practice

Vocabulary Write true or false for each.

1. 85 cents is 85 tenths of a dollar. **false**
2. A decimal uses place value and a decimal point to show tenths, hundredths, and so on. **true**
3. The symbol used to separate ones from tenths in decimals is a comma. **false**

(Lessons 1 and 2) Write the fraction and the decimal to name each shaded part.

4. 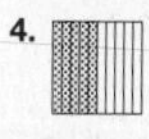 **0.5**; **$\frac{5}{10}$**
5. 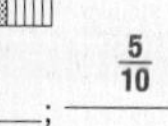 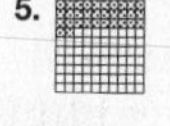 **0.32**; **$\frac{32}{100}$**
6. 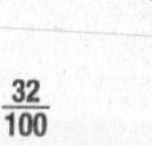 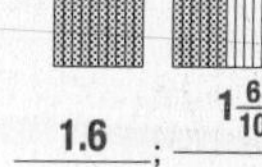 **1.6**; **$1\frac{6}{10}$**

Write each as a decimal.

7. twenty-nine hundredths **0.29**
8. $5\frac{3}{100}$ **5.03**
9. two and four tenths **2.4**
10. $\frac{8}{10}$ **0.8**

(Lesson 3) Find each sum or difference. You may use tenths grids to help.

11. 3.8 + 5.4 = **9.2**
12. 8.3 − 6.5 = **1.8**
13. 2.6 + 3.4 = **6.0**
14. 8.5 − 5.8 = **2.7**
15. 4.7 + 8.6 = **13.3**

(Lesson 4) Write each as a money amount.

16. $\frac{16}{100}$ of \$1.00 **\$0.16**
17. $3\frac{29}{100}$ of \$1.00 **\$3.29**

(Mixed Review) Complete each number sentence.

18. 18 + **11** = 29
19. 57 − **36** = 21
20. **9** × 6 = 54
21. 56 ÷ **8** = 7

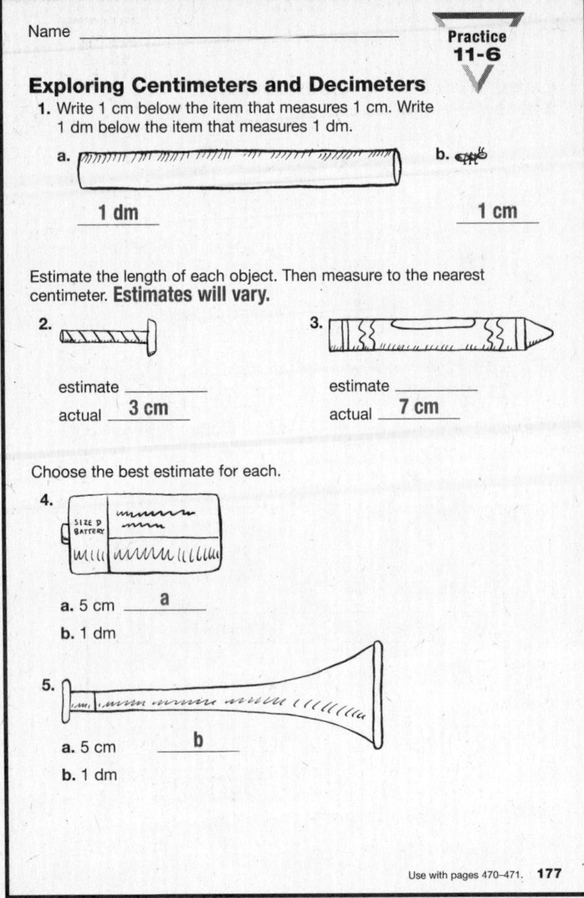

Name ______________________

Practice 11-6

Exploring Centimeters and Decimeters

1. Write 1 cm below the item that measures 1 cm. Write 1 dm below the item that measures 1 dm.

   a. **1 dm** b. **1 cm**

Estimate the length of each object. Then measure to the nearest centimeter. **Estimates will vary.**

2. estimate ________ actual **3 cm**
3. estimate ________ actual **7 cm**

Choose the best estimate for each.

4.
   a. 5 cm **a**
   b. 1 dm
5. a. 5 cm **b**
   b. 1 dm

Name ______________________

Practice 11-7

Meters and Kilometers

Match each with its estimate.

1. length of a hiking trail **b** a. 30 cm
2. width of a frying pan **a** b. 2 kilometers
3. height of a chimney **c** c. 3 m

Write whether you would measure each in cm, m, or km.

4. length of a nail **cm**
5. length of a large table **m**
6. length of a hot dog **cm**
7. height of a mountain **km**
8. length of a van **m**
9. distance of a 20-minute train ride **km**
10. depth of a lake **m**
11. length of the Mississippi River **km**
12. length of a highway bridge **m**

Answer each and explain your answers.

13. Is a 87-cm rug longer or shorter than a 1-meter rug? Explain.
    Shorter; 1 m = 100 cm; 87 cm < 100 cm
14. Is a 300-cm-long sofa longer or shorter than a meter? Explain.
    Longer; 100 cm = 1 m; 300 cm > 100 cm
15. Suppose your mom drove 800 meters to the shopping mall and then drove home again. Did she drive at least one kilometer? Explain.
    Yes; She drove 1,600 meters. 1,000 m = 1 km

Name ______________________

Practice 11-8

Compare Strategies: Use Objects and Draw a Picture

Use any strategy to solve.

1. A bus starts off on its route. At the first stop 18 passengers get on. At the second stop 10 more board, but 2 get off. At the third stop 3 passengers get on and 1 passenger gets off. How many passengers are on board when the bus arrives at the fourth stop? **28**
2. The same bus departed the terminal at 10:00 A.M. It arrived at the first stop 20 minutes later. It was delayed at this stop for 2 minutes. It took another 10 minutes for the bus to arrive at the second stop. At what time did the bus arrive at the second stop? **10:32 A.M.**
3. The same bus arrived at the third stop at 10:45. How much time went by between the time it arrived at the second stop and the time it arrived at the third stop? **13 minutes**
4. Kim, Lisa, Ellen, and Martin have a jump rope contest. The jumper with the fewest misses wins. Martin wins with only 5 misses. Ellen has 3 more misses than Martin. Kim misses twice as many times as Ellen. Lisa has 2 fewer misses than Ellen. Can you give the scores for Ellen, Kim, and Lisa? Who came in second?
   Ellen: 8, Kim: 16, Lisa: 6; Lisa won second place.
5. Some students are making a chart to show how many students in the class were born in each month of the year. There are 22 students in the class. They find out that 1 student was born in January. Three times that many students were born in February. The months of March, April, September and October each had one less birth than the month of February. The rest of the students were born in the summer months. How many students had summer birthdays? **10 students**

Name ______________________

Practice Chapter 11 Section B

Review and Practice

Vocabulary. Choose the best word or words to complete each sentence. Use each word once.

meter	kilometer	centimeter	decimeter

1. A **kilometer** is a metric unit equal to 1,000 meters.
2. A **decimeter** is a metric unit equal to 10 **centimeter**s.
3. A **meter** is a metric unit equal to 100 centimeters.

(Lesson 6) Match each with its estimate.

c 4. 1 m — a. width of an audio cassette tape
b 5. 1 dm — b. length of a pencil
a 6. 1 cm — c. height of your teacher's desk

(Lesson 7) Write whether you would measure each in cm, m, or km.

7. a car trip **km**
8. length of a marathon **km**
9. length of a car **m**
10. width of a book **cm**
11. height of a dog **cm**
12. height of a flag pole **m**

(Lesson 8) Solve. Use any strategy.

13. A shelf at the grocery store had 15 loaves of bread on it. One shopper buys 3 loaves, another buys 5 loaves. The stock person restocks the shelf with 10 more loaves, then 3 more shoppers each buy 2 loaves. How many loaves of bread are on the shelf? **11 loaves**
14. Maxine rode the elevator to the third floor, where she got off. She then climbed up 2 flights of stairs and got back on the elevator. She took the elevator down 3 floors. What floor is she now on? **Second floor**

(Mixed Review) Find each product.

15. $23 \times 5 =$ **115**
16. $45 \times 6 =$ **270**
17. $\$3.14 \times 9 =$ **$28.26**
18. $822 \times 3 =$ **2,466**

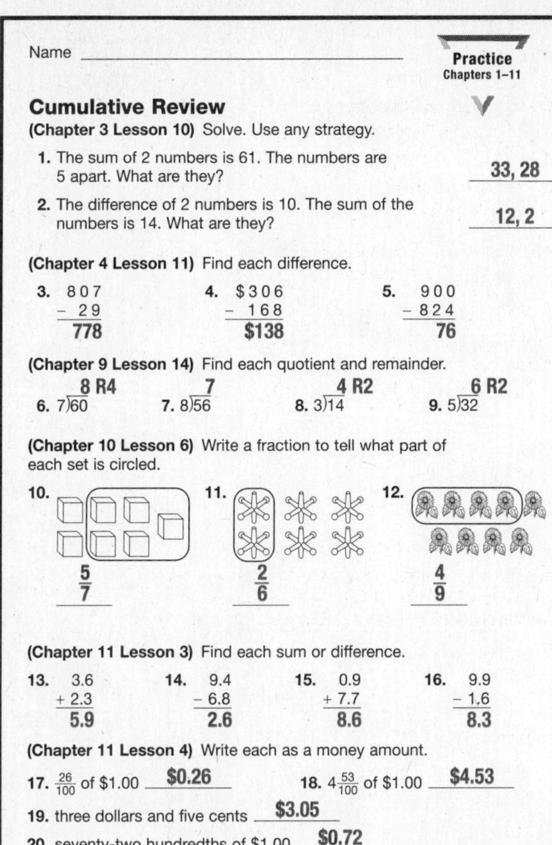

Name ____________________

Practice Chapters 1–11

Cumulative Review

(Chapter 3 Lesson 10) Solve. Use any strategy.

1. The sum of 2 numbers is 61. The numbers are 5 apart. What are they? **33, 28**
2. The difference of 2 numbers is 10. The sum of the numbers is 14. What are they? **12, 2**

(Chapter 4 Lesson 11) Find each difference.

3. $807 - 29 =$ **778**
4. $\$306 - 168 =$ **$138**
5. $900 - 824 =$ **76**

(Chapter 9 Lesson 14) Find each quotient and remainder.

6. $7\overline{)60}$ **8 R4**
7. $8\overline{)56}$ **7**
8. $3\overline{)14}$ **4 R2**
9. $5\overline{)32}$ **6 R2**

(Chapter 10 Lesson 6) Write a fraction to tell what part of each set is circled.

10. **$\frac{5}{7}$**
11. **$\frac{2}{6}$**
12. **$\frac{4}{9}$**

(Chapter 11 Lesson 3) Find each sum or difference.

13. $3.6 + 2.3 =$ **5.9**
14. $9.4 - 6.8 =$ **2.6**
15. $0.9 + 7.7 =$ **8.6**
16. $9.9 - 1.6 =$ **8.3**

(Chapter 11 Lesson 4) Write each as a money amount.

17. $\frac{26}{100}$ of $1.00 **$0.26**
18. $4\frac{53}{100}$ of $1.00 **$4.53**
19. three dollars and five cents **$3.05**
20. seventy-two hundredths of $1.00 **$0.72**

Use with page 481. 181

Name ____________________

Practice 12-1

Exploring Capacity: Customary Units

Complete.

1. **2** cups = 1 pint
2. 4 cups = **2** pints = **1** quart
3. **16** cups = 8 pints = **4** quarts = 1 gallon

Circle the best estimate for each.

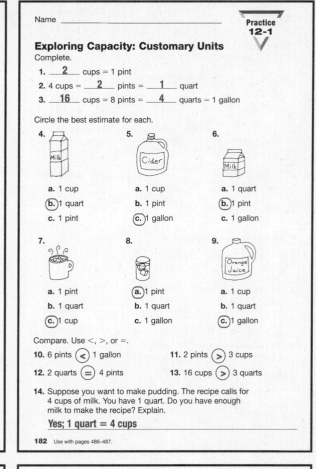

4. a. 1 cup (b.) 1 quart c. 1 pint
5. a. 1 cup b. 1 pint (c.) 1 gallon
6. a. 1 quart (b.) 1 pint c. 1 gallon
7. a. 1 pint b. 1 quart (c.) 1 cup
8. (a.) 1 pint b. 1 quart c. 1 gallon
9. a. 1 cup b. 1 quart (c.) 1 gallon

Compare. Use <, >, or =.

10. 6 pints **(<)** 1 gallon
11. 2 pints **(>)** 3 cups
12. 2 quarts **(=)** 4 pints
13. 16 cups **(>)** 3 quarts
14. Suppose you want to make pudding. The recipe calls for 4 cups of milk. You have 1 quart. Do you have enough milk to make the recipe? Explain.
Yes; 1 quart = 4 cups

182 Use with pages 486–487.

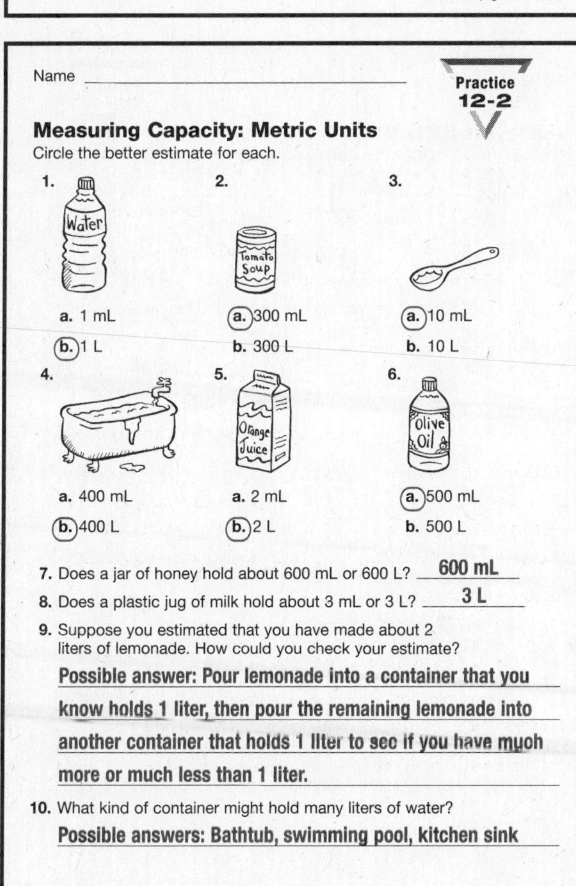

Name ____________________

Practice 12-2

Measuring Capacity: Metric Units

Circle the better estimate for each.

1. a. 1 mL (b.) 1 L
2. (a.) 300 mL b. 300 L
3. (a.) 10 mL b. 10 L
4. a. 400 mL (b.) 400 L
5. a. 2 mL (b.) 2 L
6. (a.) 500 mL b. 500 L
7. Does a jar of honey hold about 600 mL or 600 L? **600 mL**
8. Does a plastic jug of milk hold about 3 mL or 3 L? **3 L**
9. Suppose you estimated that you have made about 2 liters of lemonade. How could you check your estimate?
Possible answer: Pour lemonade into a container that you know holds 1 liter, then pour the remaining lemonade into another container that holds 1 liter to see if you have much more or much less than 1 liter.
10. What kind of container might hold many liters of water?
Possible answers: Bathtub, swimming pool, kitchen sink

Use with pages 488–489. 183

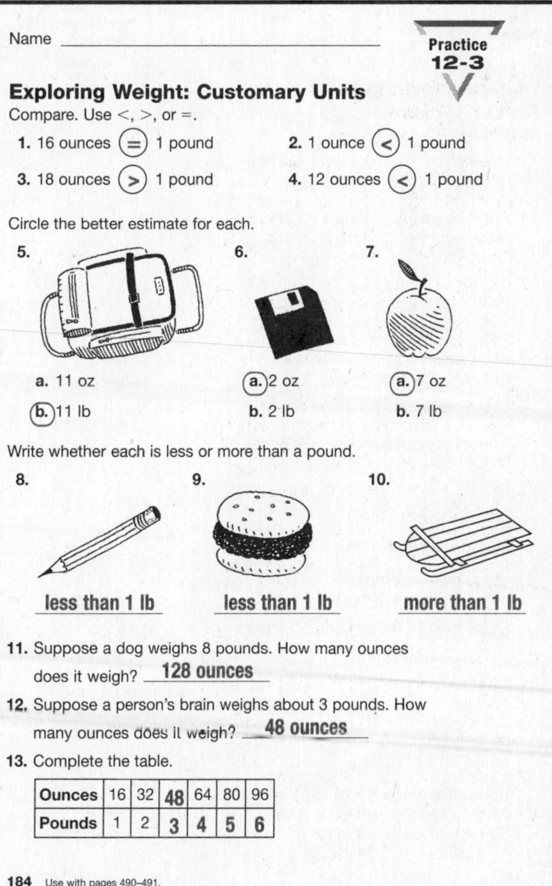

Name ____________________

Practice 12-3

Exploring Weight: Customary Units

Compare. Use <, >, or =.

1. 16 ounces **(=)** 1 pound
2. 1 ounce **(<)** 1 pound
3. 18 ounces **(>)** 1 pound
4. 12 ounces **(<)** 1 pound

Circle the better estimate for each.

5. a. 11 oz (b.) 11 lb
6. (a.) 2 oz b. 2 lb
7. (a.) 7 oz b. 7 lb

Write whether each is less or more than a pound.

8. **less than 1 lb**
9. **less than 1 lb**
10. **more than 1 lb**
11. Suppose a dog weighs 8 pounds. How many ounces does it weigh? **128 ounces**
12. Suppose a person's brain weighs about 3 pounds. How many ounces does it weigh? **48 ounces**
13. Complete the table.

Ounces	16	32	**48**	64	80	96
Pounds	1	2	**3**	**4**	**5**	**6**

184 Use with pages 490–491.

Name ____________________

Practice 12-4

Grams and Kilograms

Circle the better estimate for each.

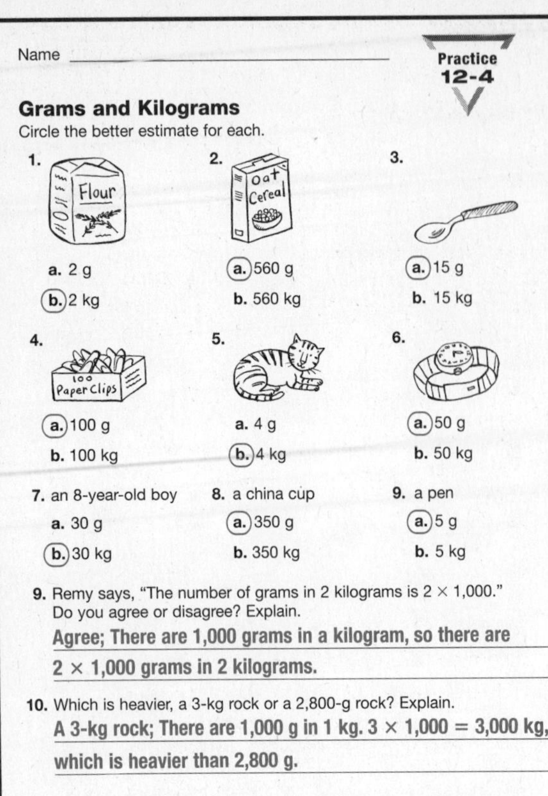

1. a. 2 g — (b.) 2 kg
2. (a.) 560 g — b. 560 kg
3. (a.) 15 g — b. 15 kg
4. (a.) 100 g — b. 100 kg
5. a. 4 g — (b.) 4 kg
6. (a.) 50 g — b. 50 kg
7. an 8-year-old boy — a. 30 g — (b.) 30 kg
8. a china cup — (a.) 350 g — b. 350 kg
9. a pen — (a.) 5 g — b. 5 kg

9. Remy says, "The number of grams in 2 kilograms is 2 × 1,000." Do you agree or disagree? Explain.

Agree; There are 1,000 grams in a kilogram, so there are 2 × 1,000 grams in 2 kilograms.

10. Which is heavier, a 3-kg rock or a 2,800-g rock? Explain.

A 3-kg rock; There are 1,000 g in 1 kg. 3 × 1,000 = 3,000 kg, which is heavier than 2,800 g.

Name ____________________

Practice 12-5

Temperature

Write the temperature using °C or °F.

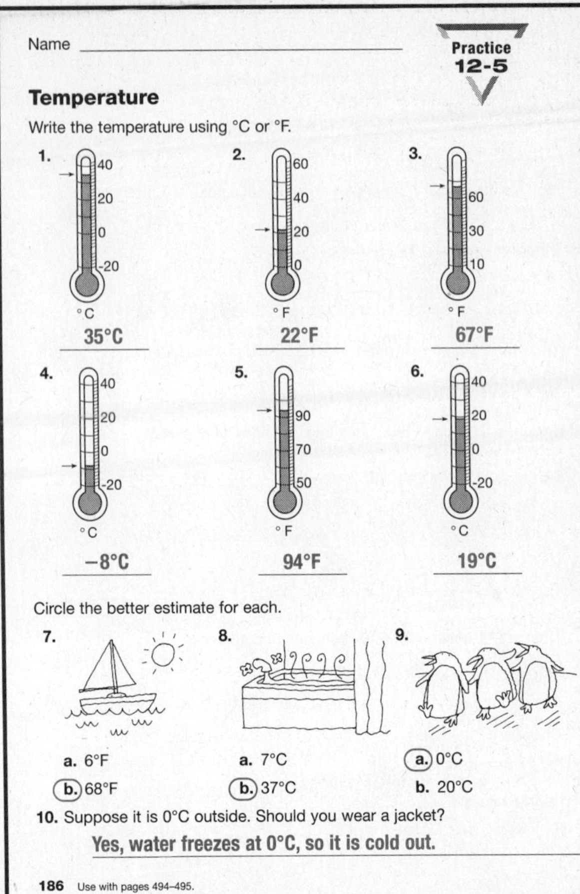

1. **35°C**
2. **22°F**
3. **67°F**
4. **−8°C**
5. **94°F**
6. **19°C**

Circle the better estimate for each.

7. a. 6°F — (b.) 68°F
8. a. 7°C — (b.) 37°C
9. (a.) 0°C — b. 20°C

10. Suppose it is 0°C outside. Should you wear a jacket?

Yes, water freezes at 0°C, so it is cold out.

Name ____________________

Practice 12-6

Decision Making

You are going on a backpacking trip. This is what you plan to take.

Item	Weight
backpack	3 lb
3 sweaters	1 lb each
1 canteen of water	2 lb 8 oz
2 pairs of pants	8 oz each
2 mess kits	8 oz each
3 flashlights	1 lb each
1 camera	2 lb
1 tape player	1 lb
4 cassette tapes	2 oz each
socks, t-shirts, etc.	2 lb

1. What will the total weight of your backpack be when you pack all of these items?

19 lb

2. If you needed to make your pack 2 lb lighter, which items would you remove? Why?

Possible answers: Camera, because it might get broken; 2 flashlights, because I only need one

3. If you had room in your pack for 3 lb more, what would you include? (Estimate the weight of the item if it is not on the list.)

Possible answers: 2 hardcover books, $1\frac{1}{2}$ lb each; More cassette tapes; More clothes

Name ____________________

Practice Chapter 12 Section A

Review and Practice

(Lessons 1 and 2) Circle the best estimate for each.

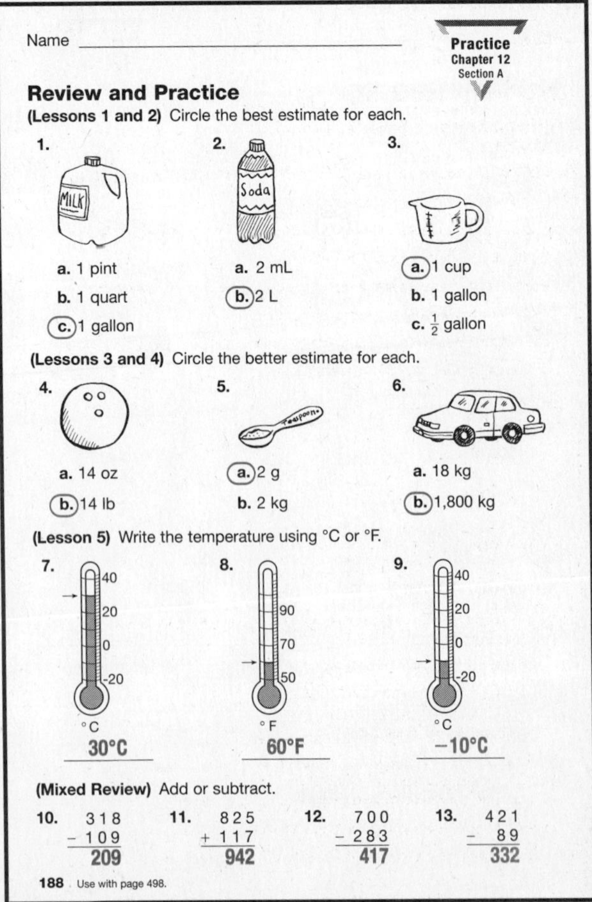

1. a. 1 pint — b. 1 quart — (c.) 1 gallon
2. a. 2 mL — (b.) 2 L
3. (a.) 1 cup — b. 1 gallon — c. $\frac{1}{2}$ gallon

(Lessons 3 and 4) Circle the better estimate for each.

4. a. 14 oz — (b.) 14 lb
5. (a.) 2 g — b. 2 kg
6. a. 18 kg — (b.) 1,800 kg

(Lesson 5) Write the temperature using °C or °F.

7. **30°C**
8. **60°F**
9. **−10°C**

(Mixed Review) Add or subtract.

10. 318 − 109 = **209**
11. 825 + 117 = **942**
12. 700 − 283 = **417**
13. 421 − 89 = **332**

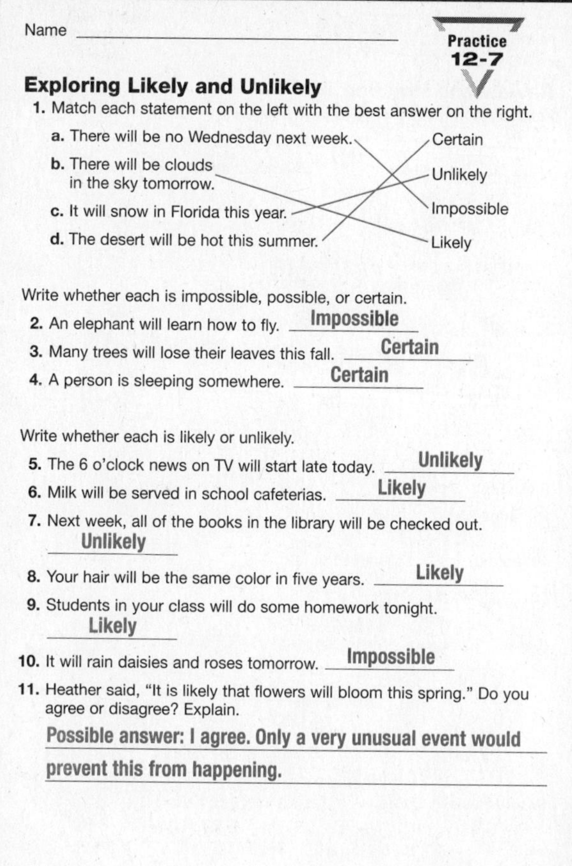

Name ______________________

Practice 12-7

Exploring Likely and Unlikely

1. Match each statement on the left with the best answer on the right.

   a. There will be no Wednesday next week. — Certain

   b. There will be clouds in the sky tomorrow. — Unlikely

   c. It will snow in Florida this year. — Impossible

   d. The desert will be hot this summer. — Likely

Write whether each is impossible, possible, or certain.

2. An elephant will learn how to fly. **Impossible**
3. Many trees will lose their leaves this fall. **Certain**
4. A person is sleeping somewhere. **Certain**

Write whether each is likely or unlikely.

5. The 6 o'clock news on TV will start late today. **Unlikely**
6. Milk will be served in school cafeterias. **Likely**
7. Next week, all of the books in the library will be checked out. **Unlikely**
8. Your hair will be the same color in five years. **Likely**
9. Students in your class will do some homework tonight. **Likely**
10. It will rain daisies and roses tomorrow. **Impossible**
11. Heather said, "It is likely that flowers will bloom this spring." Do you agree or disagree? Explain.
    Possible answer: I agree. Only a very unusual event would prevent this from happening.

Use with pages 500–501. 189

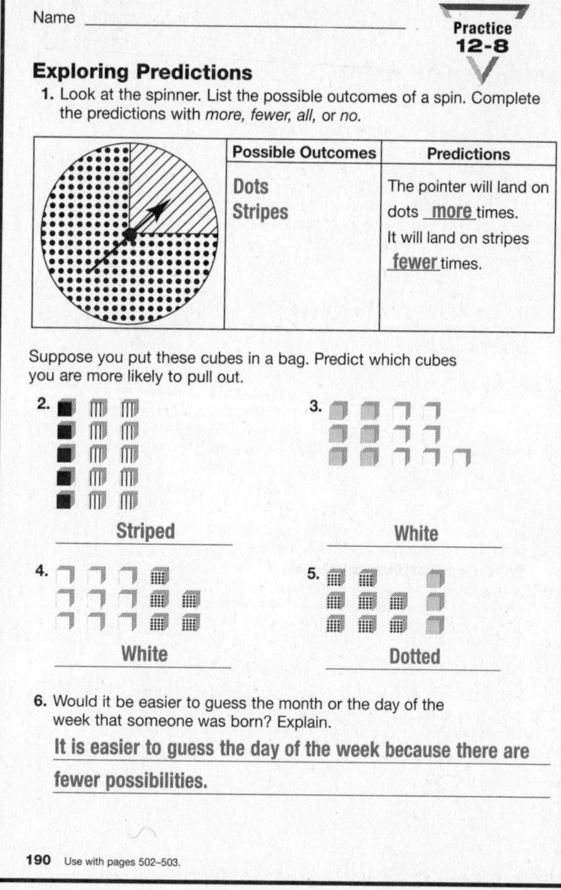

Name ______________________

Practice 12-8

Exploring Predictions

1. Look at the spinner. List the possible outcomes of a spin. Complete the predictions with *more, fewer, all,* or *no.*

	Possible Outcomes	Predictions
	Dots **Stripes**	The pointer will land on dots **more** times. It will land on stripes **fewer** times.

Suppose you put these cubes in a bag. Predict which cubes you are more likely to pull out.

2. **Striped**
3. **White**
4. **White**
5. **Dotted**

6. Would it be easier to guess the month or the day of the week that someone was born? Explain.
   It is easier to guess the day of the week because there are fewer possibilities.

190 Use with pages 502–503.

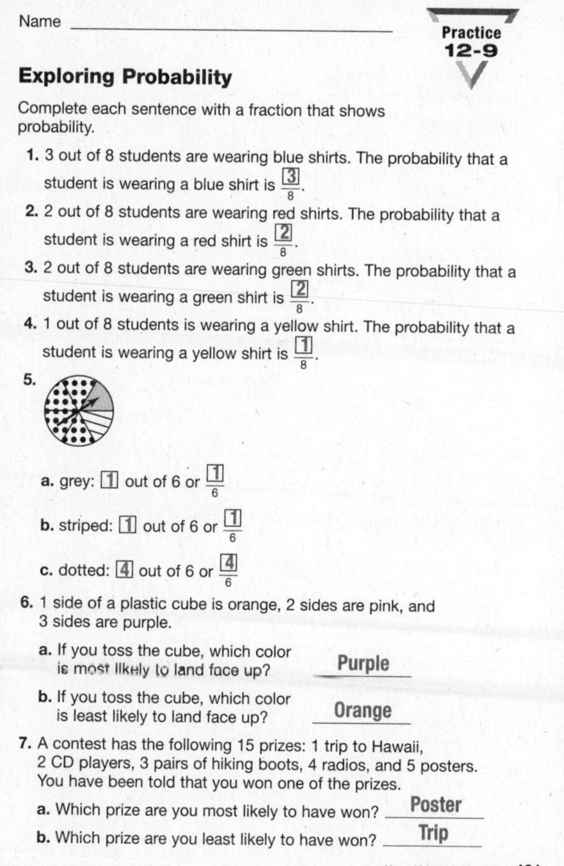

Name ______________________

Practice 12-9

Exploring Probability

Complete each sentence with a fraction that shows probability.

1. 3 out of 8 students are wearing blue shirts. The probability that a student is wearing a blue shirt is $\frac{3}{8}$.
2. 2 out of 8 students are wearing red shirts. The probability that a student is wearing a red shirt is $\frac{2}{8}$.
3. 2 out of 8 students are wearing green shirts. The probability that a student is wearing a green shirt is $\frac{2}{8}$.
4. 1 out of 8 students is wearing a yellow shirt. The probability that a student is wearing a yellow shirt is $\frac{1}{8}$.
5. a. grey: 1 out of 6 or $\frac{1}{6}$

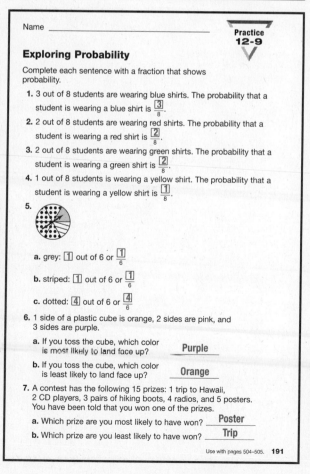

   b. striped: 1 out of 6 or $\frac{1}{6}$

   c. dotted: 4 out of 6 or $\frac{4}{6}$
6. 1 side of a plastic cube is orange, 2 sides are pink, and 3 sides are purple.

   a. If you toss the cube, which color is most likely to land face up? **Purple**

   b. If you toss the cube, which color is least likely to land face up? **Orange**
7. A contest has the following 15 prizes: 1 trip to Hawaii, 2 CD players, 3 pairs of hiking boots, 4 radios, and 5 posters. You have been told that you won one of the prizes.

   a. Which prize are you most likely to have won? **Poster**

   b. Which prize are you least likely to have won? **Trip**

Use with pages 504–505. 191

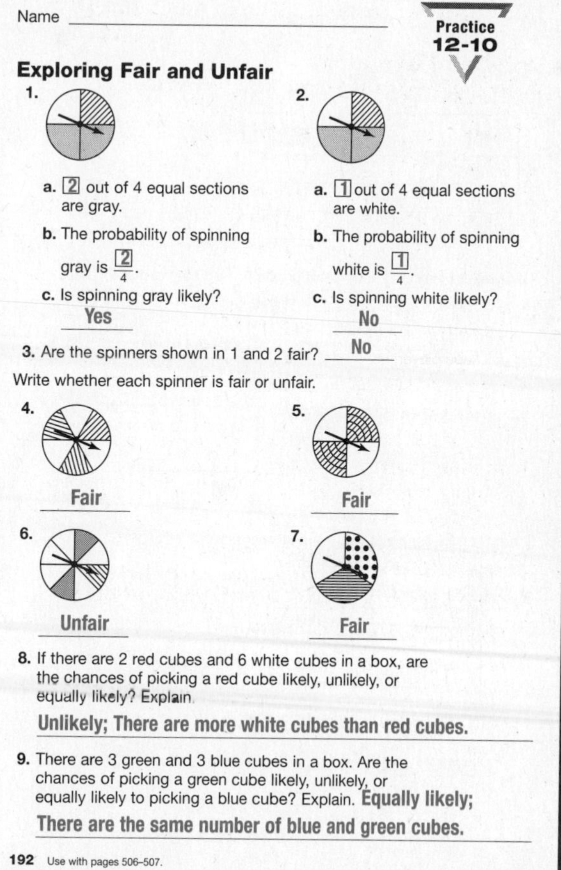

Name ______________________

Practice 12-10

Exploring Fair and Unfair

1. a. 2 out of 4 equal sections are gray.

   b. The probability of spinning gray is $\frac{2}{4}$.

   c. Is spinning gray likely? **Yes**

2. a. 1 out of 4 equal sections are white.

   b. The probability of spinning white is $\frac{1}{4}$.

   c. Is spinning white likely? **No**

3. Are the spinners shown in 1 and 2 fair? **No**

Write whether each spinner is fair or unfair.

4. **Fair**
5. **Fair**
6. **Unfair**
7. **Fair**
8. If there are 2 red cubes and 6 white cubes in a box, are the chances of picking a red cube likely, unlikely, or equally likely? Explain.
   Unlikely; There are more white cubes than red cubes.
9. There are 3 green and 3 blue cubes in a box. Are the chances of picking a green cube likely, unlikely, or equally likely to picking a blue cube? Explain. **Equally likely; There are the same number of blue and green cubes.**

192 Use with pages 506–507.

Name ______________________

Practice 12-11

Analyze Strategies: Work Backward

Work backward or use any strategy to solve each problem.

1. Kim must be at the airport at 8:00 A.M. She needs 45 minutes to shower, dress, and eat breakfast. She needs 1 hour to drive to the airport. She wants to allow an extra 30 minutes for traffic. She needs 8 hours and 45 minutes of sleep the night before her trip. What time should she go to sleep?

9:00 P.M.

2. Jody said, "I am thinking of a number. If I add 24 to the number, then subtract 6, then add 12, and then multiply by 2, I end up with 84." What number did Jody start with? **12**

3. Skyler has a large piece of blue fabric. She wants to make table napkins out of it. If each napkin requires 1 square foot of fabric, how many napkins can she make from the fabric? Use the drawing to help.

6 feet by 6 feet

54 napkins

4. Jason used the exercise machines at the gym. He worked on 2 machines for his arms. He skipped 5 arm exercises that he usually did because each of these machines was busy. Then he worked on his legs, using 6 machines. How many machines does Jason usually use?

13 machines

5. Derek used small rocks to border the garden. He used $\frac{1}{2}$ of the rocks to border the roses. Then he used 31 rocks to border the tulips and 25 to border the daffodils. He had 24 rocks left over. How many rocks did Derek start with?

160 rocks

Name ______________________

Practice Chapter 12 Section B

Review and Practice

Vocabulary Match each with its definition.

c	**1.** certain	**a.** able to happen
a	**2.** possible	**b.** a guess about what will happen
d	**3.** likely	**c.** sure to happen
b	**4.** prediction	**d.** probably will happen

(Lesson 8) Suppose you put these letters in a bag. Predict which letter you are more likely to pull out.

5.

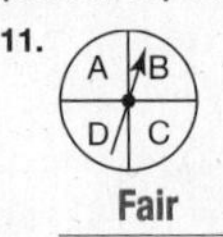

A

6.

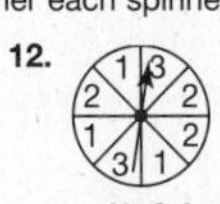

B

7.

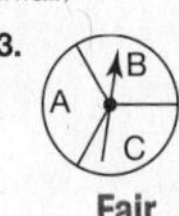

T

(Lesson 9) Complete.

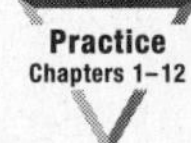

8. striped: **2** out of 5 or $\frac{2}{5}$.

9. dotted: **2** out of 5 or $\frac{2}{5}$.

10. white: **1** out of 5 or $\frac{1}{5}$.

(Lesson 10) Write whether each spinner is fair or unfair.

11. **Fair**

12. **Unfair**

13. **Fair**

(Mixed Review) Divide.

14. $3\overline{)19}$ **6 R1**

15. $5\overline{)49}$ **9 R4**

16. $8\overline{)47}$ **5 R7**

17. $4\overline{)26}$ **6 R2**

Name ______________________

Practice Chapters 1–12

Cumulative Review

(Chapter 8 Lesson 2) Complete the chart.

	Shape	Number of Sides	Number of Corners
1.	triangle	**3**	**3**
2.	circle	**0**	**0**
3.	rectangle	**4**	**4**

(Chapter 9 Lesson 9) Find each product using mental math.

4. 42 × 5 = **210**

5. 21 × 6 = **126**

(Chapter 10 Lesson 12) Measure the length to the nearest $\frac{1}{4}$ inch.

6. **3 in.**

(Chapter 11 Lesson 6) Use a ruler to measure the perimeter to the nearest centimeter.

7. **16 cm**

(Chapter 12 Lesson 5) Write the temperature. Use °C or °F.

8.

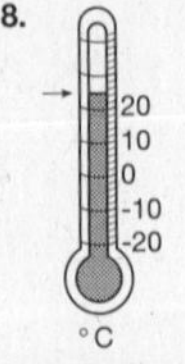

25°C

9.

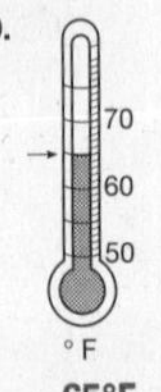

65°F

10.

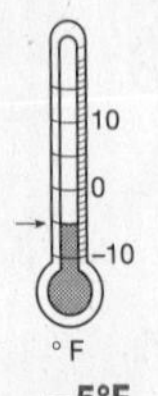

−5°F